# NUMERICAL INTEGRATION

A BLAISDELL BOOK IN COMPUTER SCIENCE

# NUMERICAL INTEGRATION

*Philip J. Davis*

BROWN UNIVERSITY

*Philip Rabinowitz*

WEIZMANN INSTITUTE

BLAISDELL PUBLISHING COMPANY

*A Division of Ginn and Company*

WALTHAM, MASSACHUSETTS · TORONTO · LONDON

*To*

E. R. and H. F. D.

# PREFACE

A casual glance at the logbook of a computation laboratory will reveal that a significant fraction of machine time is spent in the computation of definite integrals. These integrals are sought sometimes for their own sake and other times as an intermediate step in a more extensive computation. It is appropriate, therefore, that a book be devoted to this subject even though its scope is rather narrow.

This is one of a series of books devoted to the exposition of numerical analysis. The object of these books is to present individual topics in numerical analysis in such a way that they will be useful in the classroom as well as in the computation laboratory.

Numerical integration has been on the mathematical horizon since antiquity. This subject is sufficiently simple that many people have been able to contribute to it, and it is sufficiently important that many others have wanted to contribute. Over the centuries the number of research papers in this field has been absolutely enormous. Far from reducing the production of such papers, the electronic computer has actually stimulated much new work in the last twenty years, both by bringing increasingly difficult problems within the range of the possible and by emphasizing new points of view.

In writing this book, we have tried to keep our feet on the ground and our head in the clouds: By ground we imply utility in day-to-day computation and know-how of the computer laboratory; by clouds, theoretical topics that underlie numerical integration. The prerequisite for this book is a course in advanced calculus. It would also be helpful, though not strictly necessary, if the reader had an introductory course in numerical analysis so that he will be familiar with the motivation and the goals of computing. There are several places where some mathematics beyond calculus is used, but they are relatively few. The book is not wholly self-contained; nor has it been possible to include proofs for all statements made. Where these gaps occur, references

v

to other texts or to original articles have been given. For standard material in the theory of interpolation, approximation, and orthogonal polynomials, frequent reference has been made to "Interpolation and Approximation" by P. J. Davis, Blaisdell Publishing Company, New York, 1963.

The amount of material covered, relative to the amount available, is small. We have had to make deliberate choices on practically every page; hopefully we have presented the important things. While we have regretted our omissions time and again, we have not brooded over them. To some extent our bibliography makes up for these omissions.

We wish to thank the Weizmann Institute of Science for partial support granted to Philip Rabinowitz during his sabbatical year.

We would like to thank the Society for Industrial and Applied Mathematics (SIAM), for allowing us to reproduce, in our Appendix, the paper by M. Abramowitz, "On the Practical Evaluation of Integrals," which appeared in the Journal of this Society, vol. 2, 1954.

Our thanks also to Elsie Cerutti for carrying out a number of computations, and to Drs. Henry C. Thacker and John W. Wrench, Jr. for a number of fine suggestions.

Finally, the writing of this book would not have been possible were it not for the Office of Naval Research Contract Nonr 562(36) with the Division of Applied Mathematics at Brown University. Many benefits have been reaped from the liberal research policies of the ONR.

P.J.D.<br>P.R.

Providence, R. I.

# CONTENTS

CHAPTER 1   INTRODUCTION                                                  1

1.1    Why numerical integration?                                      1
1.2    Formal differentiation and integration on computers            2
1.3    Numerical integration and its appeal in mathematics            3
1.4    Limitations of numerical integration                           3
1.5    The Riemann integral                                           4
1.6    Improper integrals                                             6
1.7    The Riemann integral in higher dimensions                      7
1.8    More general integrals                                         9
1.9    The smoothness of functions and approximate
       integration                                                   10
1.10   Weight functions                                              11
1.11   Some useful formulas                                          11


CHAPTER 2   APPROXIMATE INTEGRATION
            OVER A FINITE INTERVAL                                    15

2.1    Primitive rules                                               15
2.2    Simpson's rule                                                19
2.3    Nonequally spaced abscissas                                   22
2.4    Compound rules                                                24
2.5    Integration formulas of interpolatory type                   27
2.6    Integration formulas of open type                            32
2.7    Integration rules of Gauss type                               33
2.8    Integration rules, using derivative data                     52
2.9    Integration of periodic functions                            53
2.10   Integration of rapidly oscillatory functions                 59

2.11     Contour integrals                                          69
2.12     Improper integrals                                         71
2.13     Indefinite integration                                     80


CHAPTER 3     APPROXIMATE INTEGRATION OVER
              INFINITE INTERVALS                                    89

3.1      Change of variable                                         89
3.2      Proceeding to the limit                                    90
3.3      Truncation of the infinite interval                        91
3.4      Primitive rules for the infinite interval                  91
3.5      Formulas of interpolatory type                             94
3.6      Gaussian formulas for the infinite interval                95
3.7      Convergence of formulas of Gauss type for singly
         and doubly infinite intervals                              97
3.8      Oscillatory integrands                                     99


CHAPTER 4     ERROR ANALYSIS                                        102

4.1      Types of error                                             102
4.2      Roundoff error for a fixed integration rule                103
4.3      Truncation error through Peano's theorem                   108
4.4      Special devices                                            112
4.5      Error estimates through differences                        113
4.6      Error estimates through the theory of analytic functions   115
4.7      Error estimates through functional analysis                120
4.8      Errors for integrands with low continuity                  122


CHAPTER 5     APPROXIMATE INTEGRATION IN TWO
              OR MORE DIMENSIONS                                    125

5.1      Introduction                                               125
5.2      Some elementary multiple integrals over
         standard regions                                           126
5.3      Change of order of integration                             127

| | | |
|---|---|---|
| 5.4 | Change of variables | 127 |
| 5.5 | Decomposition into elementary regions | 129 |
| 5.6 | Cartesian products and product rules | 130 |
| 5.7 | Rules exact for monomials | 135 |
| 5.8 | Compound rules | 141 |
| 5.9 | Multiple integration by sampling | 142 |

| | | | |
|---|---|---|---|
| CHAPTER 6 | | AUTOMATIC INTEGRATION | 159 |
| | 6.1 | The goals of automatic integration | 159 |
| | 6.2 | Some automatic integrators | 162 |
| | 6.3 | Romberg integration | 166 |
| | 6.4 | Automatic integration, using Tschebyscheff polynomials | 171 |
| | 6.5 | Automatic integration in several variables | 172 |
| | 6.6 | Concluding remarks | 173 |

| | | |
|---|---|---|
| APPENDIX 1 | *On the Practical Evaluation of Integrals*, Milton Abramowitz | 175 |
| APPENDIX 2 | Some FORTRAN Programs | 191 |
| APPENDIX 3 | Bibliography of ALGOL Procedures | 200 |
| APPENDIX 4 | Bibliography of Tables | 202 |
| APPENDIX 5 | Bibliography of Books and Articles | 205 |
| | INDEX | 227 |

# CHAPTER 1

# INTRODUCTION

## 1.1 Why Numerical Integration?

Numerical integration is the study of how the numerical value of an integral can be found. The beginnings of this subject are to be sought in antiquity. A fine example of ancient numerical integration, but one that is entirely in the spirit of the present volume, is the Greek quadrature of the circle by means of inscribed and circumscribed regular polygons. This process led Archimedes to an upper and lower bound for the value of $\pi$. Over the centuries, particularly since the sixteenth century, many methods of numerical integration have been devised.† These include the use of the fundamental theorem of integral calculus, infinite series, functional relationships, differential equations, and integral transforms. Finally, and this is of prime importance in this volume, there is the method of *approximate integration*, wherein an integral is approximated by a linear combination of the values of the integrand:

$$\int_a^b f(x)\, dx \approx w_1 f(x_1) + w_2 f(x_2) + \cdots + w_n f(x_n),$$

$$-\infty \leqslant a \leqslant x \leqslant b \leqslant +\infty. \quad (1.1.1)$$

In equation (1.1.1), $x_1, x_2, \ldots, x_n$ are $n$ points or abscissas usually chosen so as to lie in the interval of integration, and the numbers $w_1, w_2, \ldots, w_n$ are $n$ "weights" accompanying these points. Occasionally, values of the derivatives of the integrand appear on the right-hand side of (1.1.1), which is frequently called a *rule of approximate integration*. The terms *mechanical or approximate quadrature* are also employed for this type of numerical process.

† For a brief history of the older portions of our subject, see Moors and Runge and Willers.

1

With an abundance of quite general and sophisticated methods for obtaining values of integrals, one may properly ask why such primitive approximations as those provided by (1.1.1) should be developed and utilized. The answer is very simple: The mathematically sophisticated methods don't always work, and even if they do work, it may not be advantageous to use them. Take, for example, the method embodied in the fundamental theorem of integral calculus. With this method

$$\int_a^b f(x)\, dx = F(b) - F(a), \tag{1.1.2}$$

where $F(x)$ is an indefinite integral (an antiderivative) of $f(x)$. If the indefinite integral is readily available and sufficiently simple, (1.1.2) can provide a most expeditious computation. But, as is well known, the process of integration often leads to new transcendental functions. Thus, the simple integration $\int dx/x$ leads to the logarithm, which is not an algebraic function, whereas the integration $\int e^{-x^2}\, dx$ leads to a function that cannot be expressed in finite terms by combinations of algebraic, logarithmic, or exponential operations. Even if the indefinite integral is an elementary function and can be obtained without undue expenditure of labor, it may be sufficiently complicated for one to pause before applying (1.1.2). Take, for example,

$$\int_0^x \frac{dt}{1 + t^4} = \frac{1}{8}\sqrt{2}\log\frac{x^2 + \sqrt{2}\,x + 1}{x^2 - \sqrt{2}\,x + 1} + \frac{1}{4}\sqrt{2}\tan^{-1}\frac{\sqrt{2}\,x}{1 - x^2}. \tag{1.1.3}$$

The number of computations that must be carried out with this "exact" formula is substantial. Notice that to obtain an answer through (1.1.3) we must compute logarithms and inverse tangents—which can be done only with a certain degree of approximation. Methods which appear on the surface to be exact become approximate when reduced to a numerical process.

Yet another reason for developing rules of approximate integration is that, in many instances, we are confronted with the problem of integrating *experimental data*. In such cases, theoretical devices may be wholly inapplicable.

**References.**   Moors [1, Chap. 8], Runge and Willers [1].

### 1.2   Formal Differentiation and Integration on Computers

The reader should be apprised of computer programs designed to perform indefinite integration. For an example see Slagle (reference below). These programs appear to be more interesting from the point of view of simulating intelligence than from that of numerical analysis. On the other hand, certain problems in quantum mechanics have recently been solved by extensive symbolic manipulation on a computer. A molecular wave-form calculation may require the evaluation of several thousand integrals and may employ hundreds of different formulas. It is claimed that highly accurate results can be obtained in this way. Finally, formal differentiation programs could facilitate the use of approximate integration formulas involving higher derivatives of the integrand.

**References.** Fletcher and Reeves [1], Schiff, Lifson, Pekeris, and Rabinowitz [1], Slagle [1], Wactlar and Barnett [1].

### 1.3  Numerical Integration and Its Appeal in Mathematics

Despite (or perhaps because of) the simple nature of the problem and the practical value of its methods, numerical integration has been of great interest to the pure mathematician. The most superficial glance at its history will reveal that many masters of mathematics have contributed to this field; Archimedes, Kepler, Huygens, Newton, Euler, Gauss, Jacobi, Tschebyscheff, Markoff, Féjer, Pólya, and Szegö are among them.

Practical problems have a long history of suggesting subtle problems and deep methods of pure theory. In quite recent years, we have applied, for example, equidistributed sequences (which are part of Diophantine Approximation Theory) to problems of numerical integration in higher dimensional regions. Methods of functional analysis have just begun to play a role and promise much that is interesting. Numerical integration has a deeply theoretical side, which has been widely developed, but we shall have only a taste of this in the present work.

### 1.4  Limitations of Numerical Integration

The skilled programmer should be acquainted with various analytical techniques for handling integrals. Although it would take us too far afield to discuss analytical methods in this book, they are of great importance. In the Appendix we have reproduced an article by M. Abramowitz that will provide an introduction to these methods. The programmer should also be aware of the multitude of integrals whose values have been tabulated and should consider the possibility of reducing his integral to one already known. A tabulation of values of fundamental integrals can be found in the NBS Handbook of Mathematical Functions [1]. Careful compilations of definite and indefinite integrals include Ryshik and Gradstein [1], Gröbner and Hofreiter [1], and Erdélyi *et al.* [1], [2].

As we have seen, numerical integration is utilized when analytical techniques fail. Used sensibly and with proper controls, numerical integration can provide satisfactory answers. When used in a blind fashion—and the availability of sophisticated computer programs makes it a temptation to operate blindly—numerical integration may lead to serious errors.

*Whenever possible, a problem should be analyzed and put into a proper form before it is run on a computer.* An analysis is necessary to establish confidence in the alleged results. But analysis may also be valuable in that it can often establish early in the game ways of carrying out a computation which will save time. *One good thought may be worth a hundred hours on the computer.*

In examples that are given in the various sections, we shall attempt to point out some of the difficulties encountered in numerical integration.

**Reference.**   Chai and Wertz [1].

### 1.5   The Riemann Integral

We shall be dealing entirely with functions which are integrable in the sense of Riemann. In the case of functions of one variable, this concept can be developed as follows. Suppose that $y = f(x)$ is a bounded function on the finite interval $[a, b]$. Partition the interval $[a, b]$ into $n$ subintervals by the points

$$a = x_0 < x_1 < x_2 < \cdots < x_n = b.$$

Let $\xi_i$ be any point in the $i$th subinterval: $x_{i-1} \leqslant \xi_i \leqslant x_i$, and form the sum

$$\sum_{i=1}^{n} f(\xi_i)(x_i - x_{i-1}). \tag{1.5.1}$$

Sums of this sort are called *Riemann sums*. Let the maximum length of the subintervals be denoted by $\Delta$: $\Delta = \max_i(x_i - x_{i-1})$, and consider a sequence of sums of type (1.5.1), $S_1, S_2, \ldots$, whose corresponding maximum subintervals $\Delta_1, \Delta_2, \ldots$ approach 0: $\lim_{m \to \infty} \Delta_m = 0$. If, for *any* sequence of this type and corresponding to any choice of $\xi_i$, the sequences $\{S_m\}$ have a *common* limit $S$, then $f(x)$ is said to have the *Riemann integral S* over $[a, b]$:

$$S = \int_a^b f(x)\, dx. \tag{1.5.2}$$

A necessary and sufficient condition that a bounded function $f(x)$ have a Riemann integral is that $f(x)$ be *continuous almost everywhere*. In particular, if $f(x)$ is continuous on $[a, b]$, it has a Riemann integral. Also, if $f(x)$ is bounded on $[a, b]$ and continuous except for a finite number of points of discontinuity, it has a Riemann integral.

The following properties of the Riemann integral are fundamental. It is assumed that $f$ and $g$ are bounded and Riemann-integrable on $[a, b]$.

$$\int_a^b f(x)\, dx = 0,$$ (1.5.3)

$$\int_a^b f(x)\, dx = -\int_b^a f(x)\, dx,$$ (1.5.4)

$$\int_a^b f(x)\, dx + \int_b^c f(x)\, dx = \int_a^c f(x)\, dx,$$ (1.5.5)

$$\int_a^b cf(x)\, dx = c\int_a^b f(x)\, dx,$$ (1.5.6)

$$\int_a^b (f(x) + g(x))\, dx = \int_a^b f(x)\, dx + \int_a^b g(x)\, dx.$$ (1.5.7)

If $f(x) \leqslant g(x)$ almost everywhere on $[a, b]$, then

$$\int_a^b f(x)\, dx \leqslant \int_a^b g(x)\, dx.$$ (1.5.8)

In particular, if $f(x) \geqslant 0$ on $[a, b]$, then $\int_a^b f(x)\, dx \geqslant 0$.

If $f$ is a bounded Riemann-integrable function on $[a, b]$, then so is $|f|$, and

$$\left| \int_a^b f(x)\, dx \right| \leqslant \int_a^b |f(x)|\, dx.$$ (1.5.9)

### Generalized Mean-Value Theorem

Let $f(x)$ and $g(x)$ be continuous on $a \leqslant x \leqslant b$. Let $g(x) \geqslant 0$ for $a \leqslant x \leqslant b$. Then there exists a value $\xi$ ($a < \xi < b$) such that

$$\int_a^b f(x)g(x)\, dx = f(\xi) \int_a^b g(x)\, dx.$$ (1.5.10)

### First Mean-Value Theorem

Let $f(x)$ be continuous on $a \leqslant x \leqslant b$. Then there exists a value $\xi$ ($a < \xi < b$) such that

$$\int_a^b f(x)\, dx = (b - a)f(\xi).$$ (1.5.11)

If

$$m \leqslant f(x) \leqslant M \qquad \text{for} \quad a \leqslant x \leqslant b,$$ (1.5.12)

then

$$m(b - a) \leqslant \int_a^b f(x)\, dx \leqslant M(b - a). \tag{1.5.13}$$

THE FUNDAMENTAL THEOREM OF INTEGRAL CALCULUS. *If $F(x)$ is differentiable on $[a, b]$ and if $F'(x)$ is Riemann-integrable there, then*

$$\int_a^b F'(x)\, dx = F(b) - F(a). \tag{1.5.14}$$

A formulation that is sufficient for our purposes is: If $f(x)$ is continuous on $a \leqslant x \leqslant b$ and if $F(x)$ is any indefinite integral of $f(x)$, then

$$\int_a^b f(x)\, dx = F(b) - F(a). \tag{1.5.15}$$

*Integration by Parts*

$$\int_a^b f(x)g'(x)\, dx = f(b)g(b) - f(a)g(a) - \int_a^b f'(x)g(x)\, dx. \tag{1.5.16}$$

It is sufficient to assume that $f(x)$ and $g(x)$ are continuously differentiable on $a \leqslant x \leqslant b$.

A special Riemann sum arises when $[a, b]$ is subdivided into $n$ equal parts and $\xi_i$ is taken at the right-hand end point of its subinterval:

$$S_n = h \sum_{k=1}^{n} f(a + kh), \qquad \text{where} \quad h = \frac{b - a}{n}. \tag{1.5.17}$$

If $\xi_i$ is taken at the left-hand end point of its subinterval, we obtain

$$S_n = h \sum_{k=0}^{n-1} f(a + kh). \tag{1.5.18}$$

**References.** Franklin [1, p. 194], Goldberg [1, Chap. 7], Hobson [1, Chap. 6].

### 1.6 Improper Integrals

Integrals whose range or integrand is unbounded are known as *improper integrals*. Such integrals are defined as the limits of certain proper integrals.

1. *Integrals over $[0, \infty]$*

DEFINITION

$$\int_0^\infty f(x)\, dx = \lim_{r \to \infty} \int_0^r f(x)\, dx$$

whenever the latter limit exists. A similar definition is used for $\int_a^\infty f(x)\,dx$ and for $\int_{-\infty}^a f(x)\,dx$.

2. *Integrals over* $[-\infty, \infty]$

Here two definitions are employed.

DEFINITION A

$$\int_{-\infty}^\infty f(x)\,dx = \int_{-\infty}^0 f(x)\,dx + \int_0^\infty f(x)\,dx.$$

This is the commonly employed definition.

DEFINITION B

$$\int_{-\infty}^\infty f(x)\,dx = \lim_{r \to \infty} \int_{-r}^r f(x)\,dx.$$

This is known as the *Cauchy Principal Value of the integral*, frequently designated by $P \int_{-\infty}^\infty f(x)\,dx$.

Whenever both limits exist, the limiting values in A and B will be identical, but the limit in B may exist in cases where that in A does not.

3. *Unbounded integrands*

Assume that $f(x)$ is defined on $(a, b]$ and is unbounded in the neighborhood of $x = a$.

DEFINITION

$$\int_a^b f(x)\,dx = \lim_{r \to a+} \int_a^b f(x)\,dx$$

whenever the latter limit exists. A similar definition applies to integrands that are unbounded in the neighborhood of the upper limit of integration.

Suppose that $a < c < b$ and $f(x)$ is unbounded in the vicinity of $x = c$. The *Cauchy Principal Value* of the integral, $P \int_a^b f(x)\,dx$, is defined by the limit

$$P \int_a^b f(x)\,dx = \lim_{r \to 0+} \left[ \int_a^{c-r} f(x)\,dx + \int_{c+r}^b f(x)\,dx \right].$$

## 1.7   The Riemann Integral in Higher Dimensions

We shall give here the definition of the Riemann integral in the case of two dimensions. Extensions are readily made to the higher dimensional cases.

Let $R$ designate the rectangle $a \leqslant x \leqslant b$, $c \leqslant y \leqslant d$. Let the edges be partitioned: $a = x_0 < x_1 < \cdots < x_n = b$, $c = y_0 < y_1 < \cdots < y_m = d$. Designate the subrectangle $x_i \leqslant x \leqslant x_{i+1}$, $y_j \leqslant y \leqslant y_{j+1}$ by $R_{ij}$ and in each $R_{ij}$ choose a point $p_{ij}$. If $G$ is a grid that partitions $R$ into rectangles $R_{ij}$, then $d(G)$ will designate the maximum diagonal length of the $R_{ij}$. The following definition is now made.

The double integral $\iint_R f(x, y)\, dx\, dy$ exists and has the value $I$ if and only if, given an $\varepsilon > 0$, we can find a value $\delta > 0$ such that

$$\left| I - \sum_{i,j} f(p_{ij})(x_{i+1} - x_i)(y_{j+1} - y_j) \right| \leqslant \varepsilon \qquad (1.7.1)$$

for any grid $G$ with $d(G) \leqslant \delta$ and for any choice of points $p_{ij}$.

Sums of the form $\sum f(p_{ij})(x_{i+1} - x_i)(y_{j+1} - y_j)$ are called *two-dimensional Riemann sums*.

If $f(x, y)$ is continuous on $R$, then $\iint_R f(x, y)\, dx\, dy$ exists. More generally, it exists if $f(x, y)$ is bounded and is continuous in $R$ with the possible exception of a set of points of zero area.

To handle double integrals over bounded regions $B$ that are not rectangular, the following idea is used. Select a rectangle $R$ that contains $B$. Extend $f(x, y)$ from $B$ to $R$ by defining $f(x, y) = 0$ whenever $(x, y) \notin B$. Finally, define $\iint_B f(x, y)\, dx\, dy = \iint_R f(x, y)\, dx\, dy$.

If $B$ is a bounded set in the plane having an area,† and if $f(x, y)$ is bounded on $B$ and continuous at all interior points of $B$, then $\iint_B f(x, y)\, dx\, dy$ exists. Its value is independent of the rectangle $R$ selected to contain $B$.

The following properties of double integrals are fundamental. Let $f(x, y)$ and $g(x, y)$ be continuous and bounded in a bounded region $B$ that has area. Then

$$\iint_B dx\, dy = \text{area of } B, \qquad (1.7.2)$$

$$\iint_B f\, dx\, dy + \iint_B g\, dx\, dy = \iint_B (f + g)\, dx\, dy, \qquad (1.7.3)$$

$$\iint_B cf\, dx\, dy = c \iint_B f\, dx\, dy, \qquad (1.7.4)$$

$$\left| \iint_B f\, dx\, dy \right| \leqslant \iint_B |f|\, dx\, dy. \qquad (1.7.5)$$

† Some two-dimensional point sets have no area, but this fine point is of no consequence in numerical work.

If $f(x, y) \geqslant 0$ for $(x, y) \in B$, then

$$\iint_B f \, dx \, dy \geqslant 0. \tag{1.7.6}$$

If $B = B_1 \cup B_2$, and if the common part of $B_1$ and $B_2$ has zero area, then

$$\iint_B f \, dx \, dy = \iint_{B_1} f \, dx \, dy + \iint_{B_2} f \, dx \, dy. \tag{1.7.7}$$

*Fubini's Theorem*

$$\int_a^b \int_c^d f(x, y) \, dx \, dy = \int_a^b \left( \int_c^d f(x, y) \, dy \right) dx$$
$$= \int_c^d \left( \int_a^b f(x, y) \, dx \right) dy. \tag{1.7.8}$$

*Reduction to an Iterated Integral*

Let $\phi(x)$ and $\psi(x)$ be continuous on $a \leqslant x \leqslant b$ and suppose that $\phi(x) \leqslant \psi(x)$ there. Designate by $B$ the region bounded by $x = a$, $x = b$, $y = \phi(x)$, and $y = \psi(x)$. Then, if $f(x, y)$ is continuous in $B$,

$$\iint_B f(x, y) \, dx \, dy = \int_a^b dx \int_{\phi(x)}^{\psi(x)} f(x, y) \, dy. \tag{1.7.9}$$

*Mean-Value Theorem*

Let $B$ be a bounded, open, connected set in the plane. Suppose that $f(x, y)$, $g(x, y)$ are continuous and bounded in $B$ and suppose, further, that $g(x, y) \geqslant 0$ in $B$. Then there is a point $(\xi, \eta)$ in $B$ such that

$$\iint_B f(x, y) g(x, y) \, dx \, dy = f(\xi, \eta) \iint_B g(x, y) \, dx \, dy. \tag{1.7.10}$$

**Reference.**   Buck [1, Chap. 3].

## 1.8   More General Integrals

The reader who is familiar with more general theories of integration such as that of the Lebesgue integral should observe that the present program is not suitable for the computation of such integrals. We are dealing with approximation of the form

$$\int_a^b f(x) \, dx \approx \sum_{i=1}^n w_i f(x_i) \tag{1.8.1}$$

and ultimately (as $n \to \infty$) with the possibility of having

$$\int_a^b f(x)\, dx = \lim_{n \to \infty} \sum_{i=1}^n w_{in} f(x_{in}). \qquad (1.8.2)$$

We know that such an equation can hold for all Riemann-integrable functions if, for example, we use Riemann sums for the right-hand side. Now, if the functional values of $f$ are changed arbitrarily on the set of points $\{x_{in}\}$ ($i = 1, 2, \ldots, n; n = 1, 2, \ldots$), which is a set of measure zero, then the value of $\int_a^b f(x)\, dx$ as a Lebesgue integral does not change. However, the value of the right-hand side of (1.8.2) will change. This means that computational schemes such as (1.8.2) are not appropriate. For a proper theory of such approximations one must employ as elementary data numbers that are already integrals of the function in question, for example, the moments $\int_a^b x^n f(x)\, dx$ or Fourier coefficients $\int_a^b e^{inx} f(x)\, dx$.

## 1.9   The Smoothness of Functions and Approximate Integration

It is a general phenomenon pervading all of the theory of interpolation and approximation that the quality of the approximation resulting from common methods depends on the degree of smoothness of the function operated upon. The smoother the function, the closer the approximation, and the more rapid the convergence of a sequence of approximations. The concepts that make "degree of smoothness" more precise are those of continuity, the number of continuous derivatives, their magnitude, analyticity, and extent of analyticity in the complex plane.

Starting at a low level and moving in the direction of increased smoothness, we have

(a) Functions that are bounded and Riemann-integrable over the interval $[a, b]$ (Class $R\,[a, b]$).
(b) Functions that are piecewise continuous over the interval in question.
(c) Functions that are continuous over the interval $[a, b]$ (Class $C\,[a, b]$).
(d) Functions that have a continuous first derivative on the interval $[a, b]$ (Class $C^1\,[a, b]$).
(e) Functions that have a continuous $n$th derivative on the interval $[a, b]$ (Class $C^n\,[a, b]$).
(f) Functions that are analytic in a region $B$ containing the interval in its interior (Class $A\,(B)$).
(g) Functions that are entire, that is, have a Taylor expansion convergent in $|z| < \infty$.
(h) Functions that are polynomials of degree $\leqslant n$ (Class $\mathscr{P}_n$).

Though approximation theory makes good use of several other classes of functions, for example, functions of bounded variation, functions satisfying a Lipschitz condition, and functions that are infinitely differentiable, the above classes are the principal ones employed in this volume.

### 1.10   Weight Functions

It is frequently convenient to consider an integral of the form $\int w(x)f(x)\,dx$ instead of the simple integral $\int f(x)\,dx$. Here $w(x)$ is *usually* (but not always) *assumed to be nonnegative* over the interval and *fixed* throughout the discussion. The function $f(x)$, however, may vary. The function $w(x)$ is called a *weight function*, and it is frequently normalized so that

$$\int_a^b w(x)\,dx = 1. \tag{1.10.1}$$

The integral $\int_a^b w(x)f(x)\,dx$ can be interpreted as a weighted average of $f(x)$.

It will be assumed throughout this book that the integrand $w(x)f(x)$ is Riemann-integrable, properly or improperly, and that

$$\int_a^b w(x)\,dx < \infty. \tag{1.10.2}$$

The condition (1.10.2) means that we allow only integrable singularities as, for example,

$$\int_0^1 \frac{f(x)}{\sqrt{x}}\,dx,$$

where $f(x)$ is bounded in the neighborhood of zero.

### 1.11   Some Useful Formulas

We list here some other frequently used formulas.

1.   *Change of Variable in a Single Integral*

Let $g'(u)$ be continuous in the interval $c \leqslant u \leqslant d$, and let $g(c) = a$ and $g(d) = b$. Let $f(x)$ be continuous at all points $x = g(u)$ for $c \leqslant u \leqslant d$. Then

$$\int_a^b f(x)\,dx = \int_c^d f(g(u))g'(u)\,du. \tag{1.11.1}$$

## 2. *Transformation of Multiple Integrals*

Under the transformation

$$x = \phi(u, v), \qquad y = \psi(u, v),$$

we have

$$\iint_B f(x, y)\, dx\, dy = \iint_{B'} f(\phi(u, v), \psi(u, v))\, |J(u, v)|\, du\, dv, \qquad (1.11.2)$$

where

$$J(u, v) = \begin{vmatrix} \dfrac{\partial \phi}{\partial u} & \dfrac{\partial \phi}{\partial v} \\[2mm] \dfrac{\partial \psi}{\partial u} & \dfrac{\partial \psi}{\partial v} \end{vmatrix}. \qquad (1.11.3)$$

Under the transformation

$$x = \phi(u, v, w),$$
$$y = \psi(u, v, w),$$
$$z = \chi(u, v, w),$$

we have

$$\iiint_V f(x, y, z)\, dx\, dy\, dz$$

$$= \iiint_{V'} f[\phi(u, v, w), \psi(u, v, w), \chi(u, v, w)]\, |J(u, v, w)|\, du\, dv\, dw, \qquad (1.11.4)$$

where

$$J(u, v, w) = \begin{vmatrix} \dfrac{\partial \phi}{\partial u} & \dfrac{\partial \phi}{\partial v} & \dfrac{\partial \phi}{\partial w} \\[2mm] \dfrac{\partial \psi}{\partial u} & \dfrac{\partial \psi}{\partial v} & \dfrac{\partial \psi}{\partial w} \\[2mm] \dfrac{\partial \chi}{\partial u} & \dfrac{\partial \chi}{\partial v} & \dfrac{\partial \chi}{\partial w} \end{vmatrix}.$$

Sufficient conditions for the validity of these transformations are (1) The regions $B$ and $B'$ (or $V$ and $V'$) correspond to one another in a one to one manner, (2) the functions $\phi$, $\psi$, $\chi$ have continuous first partial derivatives in $B'$ or $V'$, and (3) the Jacobian $J \neq 0$ in the region. Similar formulas hold for integrals in higher dimensions.

3. *Jacobians for various transformations*

Polar coordinates in the plane

$$x = r \cos \phi, \qquad J(r, \phi) = r.$$
$$y = r \sin \phi,$$

Cylindrical coordinates in 3-space

$$x = r \cos \phi,$$
$$y = r \sin \phi, \qquad J(r, \phi, z) = r.$$
$$z = z,$$

Spherical coordinates in 3-space

$$x = r \sin \phi \cos \theta,$$
$$y = r \sin \phi \sin \theta, \qquad J(r, \phi, \theta) = r^2 \sin \phi.$$
$$z = r \cos \phi,$$

General Spherical Coordinates

$$x_1 = r \sin \theta_1 \sin \theta_2 \cdots \sin \theta_{n-2} \sin \theta_{n-1},$$
$$x_2 = r \sin \theta_1 \sin \theta_2 \cdots \sin \theta_{n-2} \cos \theta_{n-1},$$
$$x_3 = r \sin \theta_1 \sin \theta_2 \cdots \cos \theta_{n-2},$$
$$\vdots$$
$$x_{n-1} = r \sin \theta_1 \cos \theta_2,$$
$$x_n = r \cos \theta_1,$$
$$J = r^{n-1} \sin^{n-2} \theta_1 \cdots \sin \theta_{n-2}.$$

**Reference.**   Buck [1, Chap. 6].

4. *Lagrange Interpolation Formula*

Let $x_0 < x_1 < x_2 \cdots < x_n$ be $n + 1$ distinct points, and let there be given $n + 1$ arbitrary numbers $v_0, v_1, \ldots, v_n$. Then there exists a unique polynomial $p_n(x)$, of class $\mathscr{P}_n$, such that

$$p_n(x_i) = v_i \qquad i = 0, 1, \ldots, n. \tag{1.11.6}$$

The polynomial $p_n(x)$ can be given the following explicit representation. Define $n + 1$ *fundamental polynomials* $\ell_i(x)$:

$$\ell_i(x) = \frac{(x - x_0)\cdots(x - x_{i-1})(x - x_{i+1})\cdots(x - x_n)}{(x_i - x_0)\cdots(x_i - x_{i-1})(x_i - x_{i+1})\cdots(x_i - x_n)}, \qquad i = 0, 1, \ldots, n. \tag{1.11.7}$$

For these polynomials

$$\ell_i(x_j) = \delta_{ij} = \begin{cases} 0 & \text{if } i \neq j, \\ 1 & \text{if } i = j. \end{cases} \tag{1.11.8}$$

Then

$$p_n(x) = \sum_{i=0}^{n} v_i \ell_i(x). \tag{1.11.9}$$

The fundamental polynomials may also be written in the form

$$\ell_i(x) = \frac{w(x)}{(x - x_i)w'(x_i)}, \tag{1.11.10}$$

where

$$w(x) = (x - x_0)(x - x_1) \cdots (x - x_n). \tag{1.11.11}$$

When we wish to interpolate to a function $f(x)$, the polynomial

$$p_n(f; x) = \sum_{i=0}^{n} f(x_i) \frac{w(x)}{(x - x_i)w'(x_i)} \tag{1.11.12}$$

is the unique member of $\mathscr{P}_n$ for which

$$p_n(f; x_i) = f(x_i), \qquad i = 0, 1, \ldots, n. \tag{1.11.13}$$

**Reference.** Davis [6, pp. 33–34].

5. *Iterated Indefinite Integrals*

$$\int_a^x dt_n \int_a^{t_n} dt_{n-1} \cdots \int_a^{t_3} dt_2 \int_a^{t_2} f(t_1) \, dt_1$$

$$= \frac{1}{(n-1)!} \int_a^x (x - t)^{n-1} f(t) \, dt = \frac{(x - a)^n}{(n-1)!} \int_0^1 t^{n-1} f(x - (x - a)t) \, dt.$$

# CHAPTER 2

# APPROXIMATE INTEGRATION OVER A FINITE INTERVAL

## 2.1 Primitive Rules

By a *primitive rule* of approximate numerical integration we mean either a Riemann sum of the form

$$R_n(f) = R_n = h \sum_{k=1}^{n} f(a + kh), \qquad h = \frac{b-a}{n}, \tag{2.1.1}$$

$$R_n(f) = R_n = h \sum_{k=0}^{n-1} f(a + kh), \tag{2.1.2}$$

$$M_n(f) = M_n = h \sum_{k=0}^{n-1} f(a + (k + \tfrac{1}{2})h) \qquad \text{(the *midpoint* rule)}, \tag{2.1.3}$$

or the *trapezoidal rule*

$$T_n(f) = T_n$$
$$= h \left[ \frac{f(a)}{2} + f(a + h) + f(a + 2h) + \cdots + f(a + (n-1)h) + \frac{f(b)}{2} \right]. \tag{2.1.4}$$

The Riemann sums are simple averages of the function. Note also that the trapezoidal rule is the average of the "right-hand" and the "left-hand" Riemann sums (2.1.1) and (2.1.2). The convergence to the integral of primitive sums is not rapid (exceptions must be made in the case of certain periodic functions) and is governed by the following estimates of error.

DEFINITION. *Let* $f(x)$ *be continuous in* $[a, b]$. *Then the modulus of continuity* $w(\delta)$ *of* $f(x)$ *is defined by*

$$w(\delta) = \max_{|x_1 - x_2| \leq \delta} |f(x_1) - f(x_2)|, \qquad a \leq x_1, x_2 \leq b. \tag{2.1.5}$$

In other words, the inequality $|x_1 - x_2| \leqslant \delta$ implies that $|f(x_1) - f(x_2)| \leqslant w(\delta)$. As the interval $\delta$ becomes smaller, the variation of $f$ becomes smaller, so that $\lim_{\delta \to 0} w(\delta) = 0$.

**Reference.** Davis [6, p. 7].

THEOREM. *Let $f(x)$ be continuous in $[a, b]$. Then*

$$\left| \int_a^b f(x)\, dx - h \sum_{k=1}^n f(a + kh) \right| \leqslant (b - a)w\left(\frac{b - a}{n}\right). \qquad (2.1.6)$$

*Proof*

$$\int_a^b f(x)\, dx - h \sum_{k=1}^n f(a + kh) = \sum_{k=1}^n \int_{a+(k-1)h}^{a+kh} (f(x) - f(a + kh))\, dx.$$

Now, $|f(x) - f(a + kh)| \leqslant w(h)$ for $a + (k - 1)h \leqslant x \leqslant a + kh$. Hence

$$\left| \int_{a+(k-1)h}^{a+kh} (f(x) - f(a + kh))\, dx \right| \leqslant hw(h).$$

Therefore, by adding $n$ of these inequalities, we obtain

$$\left| \int_a^b f(x) - h \sum_{k=1}^n f(a + kh) \right| \leqslant nhw(h) = (b - a)w\left(\frac{b - a}{n}\right).$$

A similar estimate holds for the Riemann sum (2.1.2). These estimates tell us that for continuous functions the sums (2.1.1) or (2.1.2) approach the integral $\int_a^b f(x)\, dx$ with a rapidity which is *at worst* the rapidity of $w[(b - a)/n]$ approaching 0.

More precise error estimates can be given when restrictions are made on the smoothness of the integrand. We have, for example, the following.

THEOREM. *Let*

$$E_n(f) = E_n = \int_a^b f(x)\, dx - h \sum_{k=1}^n f(a + kh). \qquad (2.1.7)$$

*If $f'(x)$ exists and is bounded in $[a, b]$, then*

$$\tfrac{1}{2}h^2 \sum_{k=1}^n m_k \leqslant - E_n \leqslant \tfrac{1}{2}h^2 \sum_{k=1}^n M_k, \qquad (2.1.8)$$

*where*

$$\begin{aligned} m_k &= \inf f'(x), \\ M_k &= \sup f'(x), \end{aligned} \qquad a + (k - 1)h \leqslant x \leqslant a + kh. \qquad (2.1.9)$$

*If it is further assumed that $f'(x)$ is integrable over $[a, b]$, then we have*

$$\lim_{n \to \infty} nE_n = \frac{b - a}{2} [f(a) - f(b)]. \qquad (2.1.10)$$

For such functions, therefore, if we assume that $f(a) \neq f(b)$, the error in the Riemann sum goes to 0 precisely as $1/n$.

**Reference.** Pólya and Szegö [1, Vol. I, pp. 37, 195].

The trapezoidal and midpoint rules are exact for linear functions and converge at least as fast as $n^{-2}$, if we assume that the integrand has a continuous second derivative.

THEOREM.  *Let $f(x) \in C^2[a, b]$. Then*

$$\int_a^b f(x)\, dx - h \left[ \frac{f(a)}{2} + f(a + h) + \cdots + f(a + (n - 1)h) + \frac{f(b)}{2} \right]$$

$$= -\frac{(b - a)^3}{12n^2} f''(\xi), \qquad a < \xi < b, \qquad (2.1.11)$$

$$\int_a^b f(x)\, dx - h \sum_{k=0}^{n-1} f\left( a + \frac{2k + 1}{2} h \right) = \frac{(b - a)^3}{24n^2} f''(\xi), \qquad a < \xi < b. \qquad (2.1.12)$$

**Reference.** See Section 4.3.

**Example.** *Riemann Sums.* The high-speed computing machine offers the possibility of carrying out numerical integration by means of primitive formulas, using large values of $n$. We present three such computations. In each case we have computed

$$R_n = \frac{1}{n} \sum_{k=0}^{n-1} f\left(\frac{k}{n}\right) \approx \int_0^1 f(x)\, dx. \qquad (2.1.13)$$

| $n$ | $f(x) = x$ | $f(x) = x^{1/2}$ | $f(x) = \sin \pi x$ |
|---|---|---|---|
| 2 | .2500 0000 | .3535 5334 | .5000 0000 |
| 4 | .3750 0000 | .5182 8297 | .6035 5337 |
| 8 | .4375 0000 | .5956 3020 | .6284 1740 |
| 16 | .4687 5000 | .6323 3112 | .6345 7306 |
| 32 | .4843 7500 | .6499 3387 | .6361 0828 |
| 64 | .4921 8750 | .6584 5814 | .6364 9176 |
| 128 | .4960 9364 | .6626 1916 | .6365 8754 |
| 256 | .4980 4664 | .6646 6308 | .6366 1144 |
| 512 | .4990 2287 | .6656 7123 | .6366 1644 |
| 1024 | .4995 0988 | .6661 6973 | .6366 1790 |
| 2048 | .4997 5292 | .6664 1684 | .6366 1782 |
| 4096 | .4998 7386 | .6665 3536 | .6366 1043 |
| Exact value | .5000 0000 | .6666 6667 | .6366 1977 |

These examples emphasize the very slow rate of convergence of primitive rules. In the first example, the exact error is $1/2n$. For $n = 4096$, the observed error is .000126, whereas the exact error should be .000122. The difference is attributable to roundoff, which, with 4096 addends, has affected the sixth decimal place.

The function $y = x^{1/2}$ does not have a bounded derivative in $[0, 1]$. For this function, $w(\delta) = \delta^{1/2}$, so that by (2.1.6) the error is at worst $n^{-1/2}$. For $n = 4096$, this amounts to .016. The observed error is .00013.

Some further remarks, which apply to the numerical examples in this book, should be made here. In the first place, in order to be in a position to compare the computed value with an exact value, we must take integrals that can be evaluated in an alternative way, for example, through indefinite integrals, transformations, infinite series, tables of special functions, and so on. Although this may give an impression of undesirable simplicity, the examples have in reality been chosen so as to exhibit a variety of behaviors.

In the second place, many of the examples have been "overcomputed." That is, more work has been done than was necessary to obtain the answer to a given number of significant figures. This reflects not only the conscious desire on our part to exhibit the deleterious effects of roundoff but also a frame of mind easily slipped into: Let the machine run a bit longer; it can't hurt.

The examples that are not credited to other authors were computed on the IBM 7070 at the Brown University Computation Laboratory. This computer is a decimal computer which works with eight significant figures. However, the results of arithmetic operations are not rounded correctly to eight figures but are truncated.

Despite the poor convergence properties of the Riemann sums, it must *not* be ruled out as a practical device.† For example, the Riemann sum

$$\sum_{i=1}^{n} f(z_k)(z_i - z_{i-1}) \approx \int_C f(z)\,dz, \qquad z_k \in (z_{i-1}, z_i), \qquad (2.1.14)$$

has been used to obtain integrals over arcs in the complex plane. Riemann sums come into their own when the arcs are hard to handle, that is, when they are given by a complicated parametric representation or merely by data points. Primitive situations may require primitive tools.

Riemann sums have also been used in the computation of certain integrals that come up in the solution of partial differential equations over complicated

---

† No mathematical method should ever be ruled out of consideration from computing practice. Changing machine characteristics and more versatile programming languages have restored to good practice numerous mathematical devices previously considered too cumbersome or uneconomical. Thus, whereas current programming tends to avoid the difference calculus approach to numerical analysis, and this is reflected in the selection of material in this book, we may yet see the difference calculus restored.

domains by means of the method of least squares. They have been applied to integral equations, too.

**References.**   Davis and Rabinowitz [5, pp. 58–60], Pfalz [A1], Rall [1].

**Example.**   Compute $\int_0^1 \sin \pi x \, dx$ by means of the trapezoidal rule.

| No. of intervals | |
| --- | --- |
| 2 | .5000 0000 |
| 4 | .6035 5337 |
| 8 | .6284 1740 |
| 16 | .6345 7306 |
| 32 | .6361 0828 |
| 64 | .6364 9176 |
| 128 | .6365 8754 |
| 256 | .6366 1144 |
| 512 | .6366 1644 |
| 1024 | .6366 1790 |
| 2048 | .6366 1782 |
| 4096 | .6366 1043 |
| 8192 | .6366 0027 |
| Exact value | .6366 1977 2 $= 2\pi^{-1}$. |

Steady improvement in the answer is observed through $n = 1024$. The theoretical error is $f''(\xi)/12n^2$. Since $|f''(x)| \leqslant |\pi^2 \sin \pi x| \leqslant \pi^2$, a theoretical error bound is $\pi^2/12n^2$. At $n = 64$, say, the theoretical error is accordingly $\leqslant \pi^2/12 \cdot 4096 \approx .00020$. The observed error at $n = 64$ is .000128. Beyond $n = 1024$, the quality of the result deteriorates. (See also Section 4.2.)

## 2.2   Simpson's Rule

This rule is by far the most frequently used in obtaining approximate integrals. Our late colleague Milton Abramowitz used to say—somewhat in jest—that 95% of all practical work in numerical analysis boiled down to applications of Simpson's rule and linear interpolation.

THEOREM.   *Let $f(x) \in C^4[a, b]$; then*

$$\int_a^b f(x) \, dx - \frac{b - a}{6}\left[f(a) + 4f\left(\frac{a + b}{2}\right) + f(b)\right]$$

$$= -\frac{(b - a)^5}{2880} f^{(4)}(\xi), \qquad a < \xi < b. \qquad (2.2.1)$$

**Reference.**   Davis [6, p. 75].

The Simpson approximation

$$\int_a^b f(x)\,dx \approx \frac{b-a}{6}\left[f(a) + 4f\left(\frac{a+b}{2}\right) + f(b)\right] \qquad (2.2.2)$$

is therefore exact for all polynomials of degree three or less.

Simpson's rule is most frequently applied in its extended or *compound* form. (Some authors refer to the compound form of a rule as a *composite* rule.) The interval $[a, b]$ is divided into a number of equal subintervals or *panels* and Simpson's rule is applied to each. In order to describe the final result, it is convenient to employ a somewhat different notation than that of (2.2.2).

Let

$$a = x_0 < x_1 < \cdots < x_{2n-1} < x_{2n} = b$$

be a sequence of equally spaced points in $[a, b]$:

$$x_{i+1} - x_i = h, \qquad i = 0, \ldots, 2n - 1. \qquad (2.2.3)$$

Set $f_i = f(x_i)$. Then the compound Simpson's rule is

$$\int_{x_0}^{x_{2n}} f(x)\,dx = \frac{h}{3}\Big[f_0 + 4(f_1 + f_3 + \cdots + f_{2n-1})$$

$$+ 2(f_2 + f_4 + \cdots + f_{2n-2}) + f_{2n}\Big] + E_n. \qquad (2.2.4)$$

The remainder $E_n$ is given by

$$E_n = -\frac{nh^5}{90} f^{(4)}(\xi), \qquad a < \xi < b. \qquad (2.2.5)$$

If $N$ designates the (even) number of subdivisions of $[a, b]$, then $N = 2n$ and $h = (b - a)/N$, so that

$$E_n = -\frac{(b-a)^5}{180N^4} f^{(4)}(\xi), \qquad a < \xi < b. \qquad (2.2.6)$$

For functions that have four continuous derivatives, Simpson's rule (or, really, the compound Simpson's rule) converges to the true value of the integral with rapidity $N^{-4}$ at worst. In practice, therefore, one might expect that the use of ten subintervals would secure about four decimals, and the use of 100 subintervals would secure about eight decimals.

**Example.** Integrate the functions

$$f_1(x) = \frac{1}{1+x}, \quad f_2(x) = \frac{x}{e^x - 1}, \quad f_3(x) = x^{3/2}, \quad f_4(x) = x^{1/2}$$

over [0, 1] by Simpson's rule.

| $n$ | $f_1(x)$ | $f_2(x)$ | $f_3(x)$ | $f_4(x)$ |
|---|---|---|---|---|
| 1 | .6944 4444 | .7774 9413 | .4023 6892 | .6380 7119 |
| 2 | .6932 5395 | .7775 0400 | .4004 3191 | .6565 2627 |
| 4 | .6931 5450 | .7775 0446 | .4000 7723 | .6630 7925 |
| 8 | .6931 4759 | .7775 0450 | .4000 1368 | .6653 9813 |
| 16 | .6931 4708 | .7775 0438 | .4000 0235 | .6662 1804 |
| 32 | .6931 4683 | .7775 0416 | .4000 0033 | .6665 0782 |
| 64 | .6931 4670 | .7775 0411 | .3999 9984 | .6666 1024 |
| 128 | .6931 4664 | .7775 0407 | .3999 9973 | .6666 4641 |
| Exact value | .6931 4718 | .7775 0463 | .4000 0000 | .6666 6667 |

The theoretical error bound may be easily computed for the first function. We select $n = 8$. Then from (2.2.6) we have

$$|E| \leqslant \frac{1}{180 \cdot 16^4} \max_{0 \leqslant x \leqslant 1} |f^{(4)}(x)|.$$

Now $f^{(4)}(x) = 24(1 + x)^{-5}$, so that $\max_{0 \leqslant x \leqslant 1} |f^{(4)}(x)| = 24$. Therefore $|E| \leqslant 24/180 \cdot 16^4 \approx .000002$. The observed error at $n = 8$ is .0000004. Note that after $n = 16$, the accuracy of the answer has deteriorated due to roundoff.

The second function is a Debye function. It has only an apparent singularity at $x = 0$, and we have $\lim_{x \to 0} f_2(x) = 1$. The value 1 was inserted at $x = 0$. Since $f_2(x)$ has derivatives of all orders in [0, 1], it is possible theoretically to use the error estimate (2.2.6), but we would have to compute the fourth derivative of $x/(e^x - 1)$ and estimate its maximum value. This is a troublesome computation; we can avoid it by using the series expansion for $x/(e^x - 1)$. We have

$$f_2(x) = \frac{x}{e^x - 1} = \sum_{n=0}^{\infty} \frac{B_n}{n!} x^n,$$

where $B_n$ is the $n$th Bernoulli number. Hence

$$\left(\frac{x}{e^x - 1}\right)^{(4)} = B_4 + \frac{B_6}{2!} x^2 + \frac{B_8}{4!} x^4 + \cdots$$

and

$$m = \max_{0 \leqslant x \leqslant 1} |f_2^{(4)}(x)| \leqslant B_4 + \frac{B_6}{2!} + \frac{B_8}{4!} + \cdots \leqslant .05.$$

Selecting $n = 2$, we have $|E| \leqslant .05/180 \cdot 4^4 \approx 10^{-6}$. This high accuracy is borne out by comparison with the exact value.

**Reference**   NBS Handbook [1, pp. 804, 998].

The functions $f_3(x)$ and $f_4(x)$ are not in class $C^4$ [0, 1]; therefore (2.2.6) is not applicable to them. The function $f_3$ has only one continuous derivative in [0, 1], whereas $f_4$ lacks even a bounded first derivative. The convergence in the case of $f_4$ is correspondingly slower. An analysis of $f_3$ and $f_4$ may be carried out by use of a method set forth in Section 4.8.

**Example.**   Determine the value of the elliptic integral

$$I = \int_2^3 [(2x^2 + 1)(x^2 - 2)]^{-1/2} \, dx.$$

Using Simpson's rule with an interval of $\frac{1}{10}$ yields $I = .141117$. An alternative computation of this integral can be made from tables of the elliptic integral of the first kind; it yields $I = .141114$.

**Reference.**   NBS Handbook [1, p. 603].


### 2.3   Nonequally Spaced Abscissas

The problem here is to obtain the integral $\int_a^b f(x) \, dx$ when $f(x)$ has been tabulated at nonequally spaced abscissas. This case arises frequently when experimental data are processed but is not likely to arise with functions defined by "formulas."

The following rule, based on overlapping parabolas, is frequently employed. It combines both an integrating and a smoothing feature. Let the abscissas be $a = x_0 < x_1 < \cdots < x_n = b$, and let

$$P_2(x_{i-1}, x_i, x_{i+1}) = a_i x^2 + b_i x + c_i \tag{2.3.1}$$

be the quadratic polynomial that interpolates to $f(x)$ at the three consecutive points $x_{i-1}, x_i, x_{i+1}$ $(i = 1, 2, \ldots, n - 1)$. Then for $i = 1, 2, \ldots, n - 2$ use the approximation

$$\int_{x_i}^{x_{i+1}} f(x) \, dx \approx \frac{1}{2} \int_{x_i}^{x_{i+1}} (P_2(x_{i-1}, x_i, x_{i+1}) + P_2(x_i, x_{i+1}, x_{i+2})) \, dx$$

$$= \frac{a_i + a_{i+1}}{2} \left( \frac{x_{i+1}^3 - x_i^3}{3} \right) + \frac{b_i + b_{i+1}}{2} \left( \frac{x_{i+1}^2 - x_i^2}{2} \right)$$

$$+ \frac{c_i + c_{i+1}}{2} (x_{i+1} - x_i). \tag{2.3.2}$$

Over the first and last intervals no smoothing is done and the approximations

$$\int_{x_0}^{x_1} f(x)\,dx \approx \int_{x_0}^{x_1} P_2(x_0, x_1, x_2)\,dx,$$

$$\int_{x_{n-1}}^{x_n} f(x)\,dx \approx \int_{x_{n-1}}^{x_n} P_2(x_{n-2}, x_{n-1}, x_n)\,dx,$$

(2.3.3)

are used.

When $a$ or $b$ do not occur at one of the given abscissas but, say, $x_i < a < x_{i+1}$, then, if $1 \leqslant i \leqslant n - 2$, we use the approximation

$$\int_a^{x_{i+1}} f(x)\,dx \approx \tfrac{1}{2} \int_a^{x_{i+1}} (P_2(x_{i-1}, x_i, x_{i+1}) + P_2(x_i, x_{i+1}, x_{i+2}))\,dx.$$

(2.3.4)

If $x_0 < a < x_1$ and also if $a < x_0$, we use the approximation

$$\int_a^{x_1} f(x)\,dx \approx \int_a^{x_1} P_2(x_0, x_1, x_2)\,dx. \tag{2.3.5}$$

Similar formulas hold for $x_i < b < x_{i+1}, 1 \leqslant i \leqslant n - 2, x_{n-1} < b < x_n,$ and $x_n < b$. Finally, for $x_{n-1} < a < x_n$ or $x_0 < b < x_1$, we use formulas similar to (2.3.3).

The use of interpolation polynomials of degree higher than two is *not recommended* when dealing with experimental data on unequal abscissas (or on equal abscissas, for that matter), that is, in situations where the accuracy of the data is significantly less than the accuracy of the available arithmetic.

Questions of error in the integration of experimental data cannot be discussed within the mathematical framework of this book. However, in order to have an idea of what can be accomplished with this method, examples are given where elementary functions have been integrated from data at unequal stations.

**References.**    Hennion [A1], Secrest [1].

**Example.**    Values of the four functions $x^{1/2}$, $x^{1/4}$, $x^{1/8}$, $x^{1/16}$ were prescribed at $x = 0, .1, .15, .20, .23, .25, .30, .40, .45, .48, .53, .62, .78, .82, .89, .92,$ and $1.0$ and the functions were integrated over $[0, 1]$ by the method just explained.

|  | $x^{1/2}$ | $x^{1/4}$ | $x^{1/8}$ | $x^{1/16}$ |
|---|---|---|---|---|
| Approximate integral | .6634 2607 | .7883 1842 | .8676 3089 | .9126 5294 |
| Exact value | .6666 6667 | .8000 0000 | .8888 8889 | .9411 7647 |

The infinite derivative at $x = 0$ and the large jump in abscissas from $x = 0$ to $x = .1$ joined forces to produce these indifferent results.

When the point $x = 0$ was omitted, and the integrals computed over [.05, 1] using the remaining 16 points, considerable improvement was obtained.

|  | $x^{1/2}$ | $x^{1/4}$ | $x^{1/8}$ | $x^{1/16}$ |
|---|---|---|---|---|
| Approximate integral | .6593 8498 | .7813 4166 | .8585 3442 | .9022 8430 |
| Exact value | .6592 1311 | .7810 8517 | .8583 2640 | .9021 5293 |

### 2.4 Compound Rules

A rule of integration may be transferred to an arbitrary interval. Suppose that we have the rule

$$R(f) = \sum_{k=1}^{n} w_k f(x_k) \approx \int_0^1 f(x)\, dx, \qquad 0 \leqslant x_k \leqslant 1, \qquad (2.4.1)$$

which is written for the interval [0, 1]. This rule may be transferred to the interval [a, b] as follows. The transformation $y = a + (b - a)x$ maps [0, 1] onto [a, b]. The abscissas $x_k$ become $a + (b - a)x_k$ and the weights $w_k$ become $w_k(b - a)$. Therefore

$$R(f) = (b - a) \sum_{k=1}^{n} w_k f(a + (b - a)x_k) \approx \int_a^b f(x)\, dx. \qquad (2.4.2)$$

We shall call two rules by the same name, provided that their abscissas and weights are related by a linear transformation as above. For example, we shall speak of Simpson's rule over the interval [0, 1] and over [a, b].

A *compound* rule arises when the interval of integration is subdivided and a *fixed* rule of integration is applied to each of the subintervals. The extended trapezoidal and the extended Simpson's rule are examples of compound rules.

DEFINITION. *If R designates a fixed rule of approximate integration utilizing m points, then $n \times R$ will designate the rule of mn points which results from dividing the interval of integration into n equal subintervals and applying R to each of them.*

*Remark.* In many cases of importance, when both end points of the interval are included among the abscissas in the rule R, the number of points in the $n \times R$ rule is less than mn and is in fact $(m - 1)n + 1$.

It is convenient to standardize the rule $R$ so that it applies to the interval $[-1, 1]$:

$$R(f) = \sum_{k=1}^{m} w_k f(t_k) \approx \int_{-1}^{1} f(x)\, dx, \qquad -1 \le t_k \le 1. \qquad (2.4.3)$$

Now, let the interval $[a, b]$ be divided into $n$ equal subintervals by $a = x_0 < x_1 < \cdots < x_{n-1} < x_n = b$. Then $R$ applied to the $i$th subinterval $[x_{i-1}, x_i]$ yields

$$\int_{x_{i-1}}^{x_i} f(x)\, dx \approx \frac{b-a}{2n} \sum_{k=1}^{m} w_k f(y_{ki}), \qquad (2.4.4)$$

where

$$y_{ki} = x_{i-1} + \frac{b-a}{2n}(1 + t_k), \qquad i = 1, 2, \ldots, n. \qquad (2.4.5)$$

Therefore, by the rule $n \times R$ applied to the interval $[a, b]$ we mean

$$(n \times R)(f) = \sum_{i=1}^{n} \frac{b-a}{2n} \sum_{k=1}^{m} w_k f(y_{ki})$$

$$= \frac{b-a}{2n} \sum_{i=1}^{n} \sum_{k=1}^{m} w_k f(y_{ki}) \approx \int_{a}^{b} f(y)\, dy. \qquad (2.4.6)$$

Several theoretical facts should be noted about the effectiveness of a family of compound rules $n \times R$ as $n \to \infty$. In the first place, if the rule $R$ integrates the constant 1 exactly, then $(n \times R)(f)$ will converge to $\int_{a}^{b} f(x)\, dx$.

THEOREM. *Let $R$ be a fixed m-point rule such that $R(1) = \int_{-1}^{1} dx = 2$. Let $n \times R$ designate the compound rule on $[a, b]$ as defined above. Then, if $f(x)$ is a bounded, Riemann-integrable function,*

$$\lim_{n \to \infty} (n \times R)(f) = \int_{a}^{b} f(x)\, dx. \qquad (2.4.7)$$

*Proof.* From (2.4.6) we have, by rearrangement,

$$(n \times R)(f) = \sum_{k=1}^{m} w_k \frac{b-a}{2n} \sum_{i=1}^{n} f(y_{ki}).$$

For each fixed $k$,

$$\frac{b-a}{n} \sum_{i=1}^{n} f(y_{ki})$$

is a Riemann sum and, hence, as $n \to \infty$, it has the limit $\int_a^b f(x)\,dx$. Since $R(1) = 2$, $\sum_{k=1}^m w_k = 2$ and, therefore, (2.4.7) follows.

In the second place, if $R$ is taken as one of the "usual" sort of rules, then, if we assume sufficient smoothness of $f$, $(n \times R)(f)$ will approach $\int_a^b f(x)\,dx$ with arithmetic rapidity.

THEOREM. *Let $R$ be a fixed $m$-point integration rule defined over an interval $[\alpha, \beta]$ and let its error, $E_R$, be given by an expression of the form*

$$E_R(f) = c(\beta - \alpha)^{k+1} f^{(k)}(\xi), \qquad \alpha < \xi < \beta, \tag{2.4.8}$$

*whenever $f \in C^k[\alpha, \beta]$. (The constant $c$ may depend on $R$ but is independent of $\alpha$, $\beta$, and $f$.) Let $n \times R$ be the compound rule formed from $R$ and let $E_{n \times R}$ designate its error. If $f \in C^k[a, b]$, then*

$$\lim_{n \to \infty} n^k E_{n \times R}(f) = c(b - a)^{(k+1)}(f^{(k-1)}(b) - f^{(k-1)}(a)). \tag{2.4.9}$$

*Proof.* Let $E_{i,R}$ designate the error obtained when $f$ is integrated by $R$ over the $i$th subinterval $[x_{i-1}, x_i]$. Then

$$E_{n \times R}(f) = \sum_{i=1}^n E_{i,R}(f) = \sum_{i=1}^n c\left(\frac{b-a}{n}\right)^{k+1} f^{(k)}(\xi_i)$$

$$= c\left(\frac{b-a}{n}\right)^{k+1} \sum_{i=1}^n f^{(k)}(\xi_i), \qquad x_{i-1} < \xi_i < x_i.$$

Since

$$\lim_{n \to \infty} \frac{1}{n} \sum_{i=1}^n f^{(k)}(\xi_i) = \int_a^b f^{(k)}(x)\,dx = f^{(k-1)}(b) - f^{(k-1)}(a),$$

Equation (2.4.9) follows.

**Reference.** Davis [4, p. 55].

**Example.** Let $S$ designate Simpson's rule. Then, by (2.2.1),

$$E_S(f) = -\tfrac{1}{2880}(b - a)^5 f^{(4)}(\xi)$$

and by (2.4.9),

$$\lim_{n \to \infty} n^4 E_{n \times S}(f) = -\tfrac{1}{2880}(b - a)^5(f^{(3)}(b) - f^{(3)}(a)).$$

For function of class $C^4[a, b]$, the family of compound Simpson's rules converges with rapidity of $n^{-4}$.

The more "refined" a rule of approximate integration is, the more certain we must be that it has been applied to a function which is sufficiently smooth. There may be little or no advantage in using a "better" rule for a function that is not smooth.

**Example.** A striking example of this has been given by Salzer and Levine. The function

$$W(x) = \frac{1}{\pi} \sum_{n=1}^{\infty} 2^{-n} \cos (7^n \pi x) \qquad (2.4.10)$$

is a *Weierstrass continuous nondifferentiable function*. The integrals

$$\int_{0}^{1/10} W(x) \, dx, \ \ldots, \int_{4/10}^{5/10} W(x) \, dx$$

were computed by the trapezoidal rule and by Simpson's rule using intervals of 0.001. The following values were obtained:

| Interval | Exact value | Trapezoidal rule | Error | Simpson's rule | Error |
|----------|-------------|------------------|-------|----------------|-------|
| 0 to .1  | .0189 929   | .0189 876        | −.0000 053 | .0190 144 | .0000 215 |
| .1 to .2 | −.0414 565  | −.0414 380       | .0000 185  | −.0414 543 | .0000 022 |
| .2 to .3 | .0308 462   | .0308 443        | −.0000 019 | .0308 514 | .0000 052 |
| .3 to .4 | .0033 770   | .0034 254        | .0000 484  | .0034 027 | .0000 257 |
| .4 to .5 | −.0329 802  | −.0330 067       | −.0000 265 | −.0328 827 | .0000 975 |

These results show no advantage whatsoever in using Simpson's rule.

**Reference.** Salzer and Levine [1].

### 2.5 Integration Formulas of Interpolatory Type

Suppose we want to develop a formula of approximate integration in the form

$$\int_{a}^{b} k(x)f(x) \, dx \approx \sum_{k=0}^{n} w_k f(x_k). \qquad (2.5.1)$$

The points $x_0, x_1, x_2, \ldots, x_n$ are *fixed and distinct numbers* lying between $a$ and $b$ *prescribed in advance*. The function $k(x)$ is a fixed weight function, not necessarily positive. Two ways suggest themselves for the determination of the constants $w_k$.

(1) Interpolate to the function $f(x)$ at the $n + 1$ points $x_0, \ldots, x_n$ by a polynomial of class $\mathscr{P}_n$. Then integrate the interpolating polynomial, and express the result in the form (2.5.1).

(2) Select the constants $w_0, w_1, \ldots, w_n$ so that the error

$$E(f) = \int_{a}^{b} k(x)f(x) \, dx - \sum_{k=0}^{n} w_k f(x_k) \qquad (2.5.2)$$

is zero for $f(x) = 1, x, x^2 \ldots, x^n$. These two programs lead to the same formula, one which is called an approximate integration formula of *interpolatory type*.

THEOREM.   *The two ways of determining $w_0, w_1, \ldots, w_n$, (1) and (2), yield the same numbers.*

*Proof.*   The polynomial of class $\mathscr{P}_n$ that interpolates to $f(x)$ at $x_0, x_1, \ldots, x_n$ is given explicitly by

$$p_n(f; x) = \sum_{j=0}^{n} f(x_j) \frac{w(x)}{w'(x_j)(x - x_j)}, \qquad (2.5.3)$$

where

$$w(x) = (x - x_0)(x - x_1) \cdots (x - x_n). \qquad (2.5.4)$$

Hence the approximate integration formula is

$$\int_a^b k(x)f(x)\, dx \approx \int_a^b k(x)p_n(f; x)\, dx$$

$$= \int_a^b k(x) \sum_{j=0}^{n} f(x_j) \frac{w(x)}{w'(x_j)(x - x_j)}\, dx$$

$$= \sum_{j=0}^{n} w_j f(x_j), \qquad (2.5.5)$$

where

$$w_j = \int_a^b k(x) \frac{w(x)\, dx}{w'(x_j)(x - x_j)}, \qquad j = 0, 1, \ldots, n. \qquad (2.5.6)$$

We must now prove that

$$E(1) = 0, \quad E(x) = 0, \ldots, \quad E(x^n) = 0 \qquad (2.5.7)$$

if and only if the $w_k$ are given by (2.5.6). If $w_k$ are given by (2.5.6), then

$$E(f) = \int_a^b k(x)(f(x) - p_n(f; x))\, dx.$$

But the integrand vanishes identically for $f = 1, x, x^2, \ldots, x^n$, and this leads to (2.5.7). Suppose conversely that (2.5.7) holds. Then

$$w_0 + w_1 + \cdots + w_n = \int_a^b k(x)\, dx = m_0,$$

$$w_0 x_0 + w_1 x_1 + \cdots + w_n x_n = \int_a^b k(x)x\, dx = m_1,$$

$$\vdots$$

$$w_0 x_0^n + w_1 x_1^n + \cdots + w_n x_n^n = \int_a^b k(x)x^n\, dx = m_n. \qquad (2.5.8)$$

The matrix of this system is the Vandermonde matrix $V(x_0, x_1, \ldots, x_n)$, which is nonsingular if the $x_i$ are distinct. Therefore, there is one and only one solution for the $w$'s. But as we have observed, (2.5.6) is a solution; hence, it must coincide with that given by (2.5.7).

The *Newton-Cotes integration formulas* are a notable example of formulas of interpolatory type. The interval $[a, b]$ is divided into $n$ subintervals of equal length at the points

$$a, a + h, a + 2h, \ldots, a + (n - 1)h, a + nh = b, \qquad (2.5.9)$$

where

$$h = \frac{b - a}{n}. \qquad (2.5.10)$$

The weight $k(x) \equiv 1$ is used. Then the integration formula of interpolatory type is given by

$$\int_a^b f(x)\, dx \approx \frac{(b - a)}{n} \sum_{k=0}^{n} B_{nk} f(a + kh), \qquad (2.5.11)$$

where

$$B_{nk} = \frac{n}{b - a} \int_a^b \frac{w(x)\, dx}{(x - a - kh)w'(a + kh)} \qquad (2.5.12)$$

with

$$w(x) = (x - a)(x - a - h) \cdots (x - a - nh). \qquad (2.5.13)$$

It is convenient to express the integrals in (2.5.12) in a somewhat more standard form. We introduce the variable $t$ by means of

$$x = a + th. \qquad (2.5.14)$$

Then

$$\begin{aligned} w(x) &= (th)(th - h) \cdots (th - nh) \\ &= h^{n+1} t(t - 1) \cdots (t - n). \end{aligned} \qquad (2.5.15)$$

Now

$$\begin{aligned} w'(a + kh) &= (a + kh - a)(a + kh - (a + h)) \cdots (a + kh - (a + (k - 1)h)) \\ &\quad \times (a + kh - (a + (k + 1)h)) \cdots (a + kh - (a + nh)) \\ &= (kh)(k - 1)h \cdots (h)(-h) \cdots (k - n)h \\ &= (-1)^{n-k} h^n k! (n - k)!. \end{aligned} \qquad (2.5.16)$$

Therefore

$$B_{nk} = (-1)^{n-k} \frac{nh}{b-a} \int_0^n \frac{h^{n+1}t(t-1)\cdots(t-n)\,dt}{h(t-k)h^n k!\,(n-k)!} \qquad (2.5.17)$$

or

$$B_{nk} = \frac{(-1)^{n-k}}{k!(n-k)!} \int_0^n t(t-1)\cdots(t-k+1)(t-k-1)\cdots(t-n)\,dt. \qquad (2.5.18)$$

The trapezoidal rule, which integrates linear functions exactly, and Simpson's rule, which integrates cubics exactly, are the first two rules in the Newton–Cotes family. The next few rules are listed below. The notation is as follows:

$$a = x_0 < x_1 < \cdots < x_{n-1} < x_n = b, \qquad x_{i+1} - x_i = h = (b-a)/n,$$

$$f(x_i) = f_i.$$

*Simpson's $\frac{3}{8}$ Rule*

$$\int_a^b f(x)\,dx = \frac{3h}{8}(f_0 + 3f_1 + 3f_2 + f_3) + E, \qquad (2.5.19)$$

where

$$E = -\tfrac{3}{80}h^5 f^{(4)}(\xi), \qquad a < \xi < b. \qquad (2.5.20)$$

*Boole's Rule*

$$\int_a^b f(x)\,dx = \frac{2h}{45}(7f_0 + 32f_1 + 12f_2 + 32f_3 + 7f_4) + E, \qquad (2.5.21)$$

where

$$E = -\frac{8h^7}{945}f^{(6)}(\xi), \qquad a < \xi < b. \qquad (2.5.22)$$

*Newton–Cotes 6-Point Rule*

$$\int_a^b f(x)\,dx = \frac{5h}{288}(19f_0 + 75f_1 + 50f_2 + 50f_3 + 75f_4 + 19f_5) + E, \qquad (2.5.23)$$

where

$$E = -\frac{275h^7 f^{(6)}(\xi)}{12096}, \qquad a < \xi < b. \qquad (2.5.24)$$

It is a feature of the Newton–Cotes rules that if the number of points is odd, say $2k - 1$, the error is of the form

$$E = c_k h^{2k+1} f^{(2k)}(\xi). \qquad (2.5.25)$$

If the number of points is even, say $2k$, the error is of the same form:

$$E = d_k h^{2k+1} f^{(2k)}(\xi).$$     (2.5.26)

Exact values of the Newton–Cotes coefficients are available for the first twenty or so rules.

**References.** NBS Handbook [1, pp. 886–887], Kopal [1], Miller [1].

The following question immediately suggests itself: What happens as $n \to \infty$ when the sequence of $n$-point Newton–Cotes rules are applied to an integrand? The answer, surprisingly, is that this process may very well be divergent. In fact, it was shown by Pólya that even though the integrand is analytic on the interval of integration, the process may be divergent. On the other hand, it was shown by Davis that the process is convergent if the integrand is an analytic function that is regular in a sufficiently large region of the complex plane containing the interval of integration. Let us draw the ellipse, $\mathscr{E}$, whose center is at $(a + b)/2$, whose major axis lies on the $x$-axis, and whose semimajor and semiminor axes have length $\frac{5}{8}(b - a)$ and $\frac{3}{8}(b - a)$, respectively. If $f(z)$ is regular in the closure of $\mathscr{E}$, then the Newton–Cotes process over $[a, b]$ will converge to $\int_a^b f(x)\, dx$ as $n \to \infty$. The convergence is of geometric rapidity.

When $n$ is large, the Newton–Cotes $n$-point coefficients are large and are of mixed sign. Since this may lead to large losses of significance by cancellation, a high-order Newton–Cotes rule must be used with caution, and the use of a sequence of Newton–Cotes rules of increasing order has little or nothing to recommend it.

**References.** Davis [3], Krylov [1, pp. 248–249], Pólya [1].

**Example.** The value of the integral $2 \int_0^1 dx/(1 + x^2) = \pi$ was obtained by a sequence of Newton–Cotes rules with 2–21 points. The print-outs were as follows.

| | | | |
|---|---|---|---|
| 2 | 3.0000 000 | 12 | 3.1415 925 |
| 3 | 3.1333 333 | 13 | 3.1415 926 |
| 4 | 3.1384 615 | 14 | 3.1415 920 |
| 5 | 3.1421 176 | 15 | 3.1415 932 |
| 6 | 3.1418 781 | 16 | 3.1415 925 |
| 7 | 3.1415 708 | 17 | 3.1415 962 |
| 8 | 3.1415 789 | 18 | 3.1415 935 |
| 9 | 3.1415 925 | 19 | 3.1415 896 |
| 10 | 3.1415 926 | 20 | 3.1415 920 |
| 11 | 3.1415 925 | 21 | 3.1415 775 |
| | | Exact value | 3.1415 926 |

The function $f(z) = 1/(1 + z^2)$ has singularities only at $a = \pm i$. It is therefore regular in the ellipse $\mathscr{E}$ and, theoretically, convergence to the proper value should take place. The improvement is rapid up to $n = 10$. No progress is made beyond this point.

**Reference.**   Ohringer [1].

### 2.6   Integration Formulas of Open Type

An integration formula

$$\int_a^b f(x)\, dx \approx \sum_{k=1}^n w_k f(x_k), \qquad x_1 < x_2 < \cdots < x_n \qquad (2.6.1)$$

is said to be of *closed type* if the function $f(x)$ is evaluated at the end points of the interval, that is, if $x_1 = a$ and $x_n = b$. An integration formula is said to be of *open type* if both of the end points are omitted from the evaluation. A formula of open type, so to speak, performs an extrapolation of the function to the whole interval and then integrates forward and backward beyond the last known values.

Formulas of open type are of use in the integration of ordinary differential equations. We list several such formulas, sometimes called Steffensen's formulas.

*Two-point Formula*

$$\int_a^b f(x)\, dx = \frac{3h}{2}\left[f(a + h) + f(a + 2h)\right] + \frac{3h^3}{4}f''(\xi),$$

$$h = \frac{b - a}{3}, \quad a < \xi < b. \qquad (2.6.2)$$

*Three-point Formula*

$$\int_a^b f(x)\, dx = \frac{4h}{3}\left[2f(a + h) - f(a + 2h) + 2f(a + 3h)\right] + \frac{14h^5}{45}f^{(4)}(\xi),$$

$$h = \frac{b - a}{4}, \qquad a < \xi < b. \qquad (2.6.3)$$

*Four-point Formula*

$$\int_a^b f(x)\, dx = \frac{5h}{24}\left[11f(a + h) + f(a + 2h) + f(a + 3h) + 11f(a + 4h)\right]$$

$$+ \frac{95h^5}{144}f^{(4)}(\xi), \qquad h = \frac{b - a}{5}, \qquad a < \xi < b, \qquad (2.6.4)$$

In addition to these, there is the

*Midpoint Formula*

$$\int_a^{a+h} f(x)\,dx = hf\left(a + \frac{h}{2}\right) + \frac{1}{24}h^3 f''(\xi), \qquad a < \xi < a + h, \quad (2.6.5)$$

mentioned before. It is the first of a series of formulas of *Maclaurin type*:

$$\int_a^b f(x)\,dx \approx h \sum_{k=1}^n w_{kn} f\left(a + \frac{2k-1}{2}h\right), \qquad h = \frac{b-a}{n}. \quad (2.6.6)$$

If $f$ is convex (or concave) the midpoint formula can be used together with the trapezoidal rule to bound the integral from above and below.

**References.**  Hammer [1], Miller [1], Rubbert [1].

A note of caution must be sounded for the use of formulas of open type. The error estimates given in (2.6.2), (2.6.3), and (2.6.4) are valid provided that the integrands $f(x)$ are, respectively, in classes $C^2[a, b]$, $C^4[a, b]$, and $C^4[a, b]$. When the value of the function at an end point of the interval cannot be computed because of a singularity, the use of such formulas can lead to serious error.

Open formulas are not necessarily restricted to equidistant points. For example, the Gauss formulas are of open type. The Lobatto formulas are closed, while the Radau formulas are half-open (see Sections 2.7 and 2.7.1).

**References.**  Hildebrand [1, p. 88], Kunz [1, p. 148].

### 2.7  *Integration Rules of Gauss Type*

Let $w(x) \geqslant 0$ be a fixed weight function defined on $[a, b,]$. The integral

$$\int_a^b w(x)f(x)g(x)\,dx = (f, g) \qquad (2.7.1)$$

is known as the *inner product* of the functions $f(x)$ and $g(x)$ over the interval $[a, b]$ with respect to the weight $w(x)$. The notation $(f, g)$ is widely used for inner products.

Two functions, $f$ and $g$, are called *orthogonal* over $[a, b]$ with respect to the weight $w(x)$ if

$$(f, g) = \int_a^b w(x)f(x)g(x)\,dx = 0. \qquad (2.7.2)$$

For a given weight $w(x)$, it is possible to define a sequence of polynomials $p_0(x), p_1(x), \ldots$, which are orthogonal and in which $p_n(x)$ is of exact degree $n$:

$$(p_m, p_n) = \int_a^b w(x)p_m(x)p_n(x)\,dx = 0, \qquad m \neq n. \qquad (2.7.3)$$

By multiplying each $p_n(x)$ by an appropriate constant we can produce a set of polynomials, $p_n^*$, which are *orthonormal*:

$$(p_m^*, p_n^*) = \int_a^b w(x)p_m^*(x)p_n^*(x)\, dx = \delta_{mn} = \begin{cases} 0 & \text{if} \quad m \neq n, \\ 1 & \text{if} \quad m = n. \end{cases} \quad (2.7.4)$$

The leading coefficient of $p_n^*$ can be taken as positive:

$$p_n^*(x) = k_n x^n + \cdots, \qquad k_n > 0. \quad (2.7.5)$$

The following special selections $[a, b]$ and $w(x)$ have been used extensively.

(1)  $a = -1$,  $b = 1$,  $w(x) = 1$                    Legendre polynomials

(2)  $a = -1$,  $b = 1$,  $w(x) = (1 - x^2)^{-1/2}$     Tschebyscheff polynomials (of the first kind)

(3)  $a = -1$,  $b = 1$,  $w(x) = (1 - x^2)^{1/2}$      Tschebyscheff polynomials (of the second kind)

(4)  $a = -1$,  $b = 1$,  $w(x) = (1 - x)^\alpha(1 + x)^\beta$   Jacobi polynomials
                                  $\alpha, \beta > -1$

(5)  $a = 0$,   $b = \infty$,  $w(x) = e^{-x}$          Laguerre polynomials

(6)  $a = 0$,   $b = \infty$,  $w(x) = x^\alpha e^{-x}$  $\alpha > -1$   Associated Laguerre polynomials

(7)  $a = -\infty$,  $b = \infty$,  $w(x) = e^{-x^2}$   Hermite polynomials

It should be observed that the polynomials under (1), (2), and (3) are special cases of (4).

THEOREM.  *The zeros of (real) orthogonal polynomials are real, simple, and located in the interior of $[a, b]$.*

THEOREM.  *The orthonormal polynomials $p_n^*(x)$ satisfy a three-term recurrence relationship.*

$$p_n^*(x) = (a_n x + b_n)p_{n-1}^*(x) - c_n p_{n-2}^*(x), \qquad n = 2, 3, \ldots . \quad (2.7.6)$$

The following recurrence is particularly convenient for systematic computation.

$$p_{-1}(x) = 0,$$

$$p_0(x) = 1,$$

$$\vdots$$

$$p_{n+1}(x) = xp_n^*(x) - (xp_n^*, p_n^*)p_n^*(x) - (p_n, p_n)^{1/2}p_{n-1}^*(x),$$

$$p_n^*(x) = p_n(x)/(p_n, p_n)^{1/2}, \qquad n = 0, 1, 2, \ldots .$$

**References.** Davis [6, pp. 167–168, 234–255], NBS Handbook [1, Chap. 22].

If $n$ distinct points $x_1, \ldots, x_n$ of the interval $[a, b]$ are specified in advance, then we know that we can find coefficients $w_1, w_2, \ldots, w_n$ such that the rule

$$\int_a^b w(x) f(x)\, dx \approx \sum_{k=1}^n w_k f(x_k)$$

will be exact for all polynomials of class $\mathscr{P}_{n-1}$. If we treat both the $x$'s and the $w$'s as $2n$ unknowns, and determine them carefully, perhaps we can arrange matters so that the rule will be exact for polynomials of class $\mathscr{P}_{2n-1}$, that is, for all linear combinations of the $2n$ powers $1, x, x^2, \ldots, x^{2n-1}$. This is possible, and the solution is intimately related to the orthogonal polynomials generated by the weight function $w(x)$.

THEOREM. *Let $w(x) \geqslant 0$ be a weight function defined on $[a, b]$ with corresponding orthonormal polynomials $p_n^*(x)$. Let the zeros of $p_n^*(x)$ be*

$$a < x_1 < x_2 < \cdots < x_n < b.$$

*Then we can find positive constants $w_1, w_2, \ldots, w_n$ such that*

$$\int_a^b w(x) p(x)\, dx = \sum_{k=1}^n w_k p(x_k) \tag{2.7.7}$$

*whenever $p(x)$ is a polynomial of class $\mathscr{P}_{2n-1}$.*

*The weights $w_j$ have the explicit representation*

$$w_j = -\frac{k_{n+1}}{k_n} \frac{1}{p_{n+1}^*(x_j) p_n^{*\prime}(x_j)}. \tag{2.7.8}$$

When abscissas and weights have been determined as in this theorem, we say that the resulting integration rule is of *Gauss type*. We shall frequently refer to the $n$-point Gauss rule with the weight $w(x) \equiv 1$ by the symbol $G_n$.

The error incurred in Gaussian integration is governed by the following estimate.

THEOREM. *Let $w(x), x_1, \ldots, x_n, w_1, \ldots, w_n$ be as in the previous theorem. Then, if $f(x) \in C^{2n}[a, b]$,*

$$E_n(f) = \int_a^b w(x) f(x)\, dx - \sum_{k=1}^n w_k f(x_k)$$

$$= \frac{f^{(2n)}(\xi)}{(2n)! k_n^2}, \qquad a < \xi < b. \tag{2.7.9}$$

COROLLARY. *In the case of the Jacobi weight*

$$w(x) = (1 - x)^\alpha (1 + x)^\beta, \qquad \alpha > -1, \qquad \beta > -1,$$

*over the interval* $[-1, 1]$, *the error is given by*

$$E_n(f) = \frac{2^{2n+\alpha+\beta+1}\Gamma(n+\alpha+1)\Gamma(n+\beta+1)\Gamma(n+\alpha+\beta+1)n!}{\Gamma(2n+\alpha+\beta+1)\Gamma(2n+\alpha+\beta+2)(2n)!}$$

$$\times f^{(2n)}(\xi), \qquad -1 < \xi < 1. \qquad (2.7.10)$$

COROLLARY. *In the case of the weight* $w(x) \equiv 1$ *over* $[-1, 1]$ (*that is,* $\alpha = 0$, $\beta = 0$) *the error is given by*

$$E_n(f) = \frac{2^{2n+1}(n!)^4}{(2n+1)[(2n)!]^3} f^{(2n)}(\xi), \qquad -1 < \xi < 1. \qquad (2.7.11)$$

*Over the interval* $[a, b]$ *and for the weight* $w(x) \equiv 1$, *the error is given by*

$$E_n(f) = \frac{(b-a)^{2n+1}(n!)^4}{(2n+1)[(2n)!]^3} f^{(2n)}(\xi), \qquad a < \xi < b. \qquad (2.7.12)$$

**Reference.** Davis [6, pp. 343–344], Stroud and Secrest [2].

**Example**

| Rule | $\int_0^1 f(x)\,dx$ | $\int_0^1 x^{1/2}\,dx$ | $\int_0^1 x^{3/2}\,dx$ | $\int_0^1 \dfrac{2\,dx}{2+\sin 10\pi x}$ |
|---|---|---|---|---|
| $G_2$ | .2261 0880 | .6738 8730 | .3987 7398 | 1.0312 8090 |
| $G_3$ | .3092 5766 | .6691 7960 | .3998 1240 | 1.0217 8810 |
| $G_4$ | .3461 1571 | .6678 2760 | .3999 5037 | 1.1978 1310 |
| $G_{10}$ | .3302 4749 | .6667 5595 | .3999 9931 | 1.1614 6310 |
| $G_{16}$ | .2949 6114 | .6666 8950 | .3999 9988 | 1.1980 6070 |
| $G_{32}$ | .3120 5246 | .6666 6885 | .4000 0086 | 1.1521 3885 |
| $G_{48}$ | .3071 4028 | | | |
| Exact value | .3068 5282 | .6666 6667 | .4000 0000 | 1.1547 0054 |

$G_2$ = Gauss 2-point formula; $G_3$, 3-point; etc.

$(f(x) = (x + 2)^{-1}, \quad 0 \leqslant x \leqslant e - 2; \quad f(x) = 0, \quad e - 2 \leqslant x \leqslant 1.)$

| Rule | $\int_0^1 \dfrac{dx}{1+x^4}$ | $\int_0^1 \dfrac{dx}{1+x}$ | $\int_0^1 \dfrac{dx}{1+e^x}$ | $\int_0^1 \dfrac{x\,dx}{e^x-1}$ |
|---|---|---|---|---|
| $G_2$ | .8595 2250 | .6923 0770 | .3799 0886 | .7775 1165 |
| $G_3$ | .8675 1845 | .6931 2165 | .3798 8529 | .7775 0450 |
| $G_4$ | .8669 5565 | .6931 4640 | .3798 8548 | .7775 0460 |
| $G_{10}$ | .8669 7285 | .6931 4710 | .3798 8547 | .7775 0450 |
| $G_{16}$ | .8669 7280 | .6931 4705 | .3798 8545 | .7775 0440 |
| $G_{32}$ | .8669 7075 | .6931 4755 | .3798 8550 | .7775 0455 |
| Exact value | .8669 7298 7 | .6931 4718 | .3798 8549 | .7775 0463 |

$G_2$ = Gauss 2-point formula; $G_3$, 3-point; etc.

These examples, reading from left to right, are in order of increasing smoothness of integrand in the sense explained in Section 1.9. The function in the first column is piecewise continuous. It is in $R$ [0, 1] but not in $C$ [0, 1]. The function $x^{1/2}$, which has a singularity at $x = 0$, is in $C$ [0, 1] but is not in $C^1$ [0, 1]. The function $x^{3/2}$, which also has a singularity at $x = 0$, is in $C^1$ [0, 1] but is not in $C^2$ [0, 1].

The function $2/(2 + \sin 10\pi x)$ is analytic on [0, 1] but has a singularity at $x = -(.05 + .0418i)$. The function $(1 + x^4)^{-1}$ has four singularities on $|x| = 1$ while $(1 + x)^{-1}$ has one singularity on $|x| = 1$. The function $(1 + e^x)^{-1}$ has a singularity at $x = \pi i$. The function $x(e^x - 1)^{-1}$ has an apparent singularity at $x = 0$ but, in reality, is an entire function with no singularities in the finite part of the complex plane.

Notice that the rapidity of convergence increases as we move from the left-hand columns to the right. The results to the far left are quite poor. Of course, the piecewise continuous function should be integrated in two parts. Our point here is merely to exhibit the quality of the convergence. The difficulties in integrating a rapidly oscillating function such as $(2 + \sin 10\pi x)^{-1}$ are apparent from the figures. When good accuracy is obtained early, as with $x/(e^x - 1)$, roundoff sets in to vitiate the value of the later computations.

### 2.7.1  Integration Formulas of Gauss Type with Preassigned Abscissas

Next we consider integration formulas of Gauss type with a certain number of preassigned abscissas. By this we mean a formula of the type

$$\int_a^b w(x) f(x)\, dx \approx \sum_{k=1}^m a_k f(y_k) + \sum_{k=1}^n w_k f(x_k), \qquad (2.7.1.1)$$

where the abscissas $y_k$ are fixed and prescribed in advance and where the $m + 2n$ constants $a_k$, $w_k$, and $x_k$ are to be determined so that the rule is exact for polynomials of the highest possible degree (that is, $m + 2n - 1$). We introduce the polynomials

$$r(x) = (x - y_1)(x - y_2) \cdots (x - y_m),$$

$$s(x) = (x - x_1)(x - x_2) \cdots (x - x_n). \qquad (2.7.1.2)$$

THEOREM. *The rule* (2.7.1.1) *is exact for all polynomials that are of degree* $\leqslant m + 2n - 1$ *if and only if*

(a) *it is exact for all polynomials of degree* $\leqslant m + n - 1$,

(b) $\int_a^b w(x) r(x) s(x) p(x)\, dx = 0$

*for every polynomial* $p(x)$ *of degree* $\leqslant n - 1$.

*Proof.* The necessity of (a) is trivial. Let $p(x)$ have degree $\leqslant n - 1$. Then $t(x) = r(x)s(x)p(x)$ is a polynomial of degree $\leqslant m + 2n - 1$. Hence, if (2.7.1.1) is exact for such polynomials, then

$$\int_a^b w(x)t(x)\,dx = \sum_{k=1}^m a_k t(y_k) + \sum_{k=1}^n w_k t(x_k).$$

But $t(y_k) = 0$ $(k = 1, 2, \ldots, m)$ and $t(x_k) = 0$ $(k = 1, 2, \ldots, n)$. Thus the necessity of (b) follows.

Suppose, conversely, that (a) and (b) hold. Let $t(x)$ be a polynomial of degree $\leqslant m + 2n - 1$. Then it can be written in the form $t(x) = r(x)s(x)q(x) + v(x)$, where $q(x)$ is a polynomial of degree $\leqslant n - 1$ and $v(x)$ is a polynomial of degree $\leqslant m + n - 1$. Note that $t(y_k) = v(y_k)$ $(k = 1, 2, \ldots, m)$ and $t(x_k) = v(x_k)$ $(k = 1, 2, \ldots, n)$. Then

$$\int_a^b w(x)t(x)\,dx = \int_a^b w(x)[r(x)s(x)q(x) + v(x)]\,dx$$

$$= \int_a^b w(x)v(x)\,dx,$$

inasmuch as the first part vanishes, by (b). But, by (a),

$$\int_a^b w(x)v(x)\,dx = \sum_{k=1}^m a_k v(y_k) + \sum_{k=1}^n w_k v(x_k)$$

$$= \sum_{k=1}^m a_k t(y_k) + \sum_{k=1}^n w_k t(x_k).$$

This proves the sufficiency.

In order to proceed numerically, it is clear that we must determine $s(x) = (x - x_1)\cdots(x - x_n)$ as one of a family of polynomials that are orthogonal on $[a, b]$ with respect to the weight $w(x)r(x)$. Toward this end, a theorem of Christoffel is of importance.

THEOREM. *Let $p_n(x), n = 0, 1, \ldots$ be orthonormal polynomials on $[a, b]$ with respect to the weight $w(x) \geqslant 0$. Let $r(x) = (x - y_1)(x - y_2)\cdots(x - y_m) \geqslant 0$ on $[a, b]$ and suppose that the $y_i$ are distinct. Suppose that $q_n(x), n = 0, 1, \ldots$ are orthogonal polynomials over $[a, b]$ with respect to $w(x)r(x)$. Then*

$$r(x)q_n(x) = \begin{vmatrix} p_n(x) & p_{n+1}(x) & \cdots & p_{n+m}(x) \\ p_n(y_1) & p_{n+1}(y_1) & \cdots & p_{n+m}(y_1) \\ \vdots & & & \vdots \\ p_n(y_m) & p_{n+1}(y_m) & \cdots & p_{n+m}(y_m) \end{vmatrix}. \qquad (2.7.1.3)$$

*Proof.* It is clear that the right-hand side of (2.7.1.3) is in $\mathscr{P}_{n+m}$. Moreover, it vanishes for $x = y_1, x = y_2, \ldots, x = y_m$ (equal rows in the determinant). Hence, it can be written in the form $r(x)q_n(x)$, where $q_n(x) \in \mathscr{P}_n$. We show next that $q_n(x)$ is orthogonal to all members of class $\mathscr{P}_{n-1}$ with respect to the weight $w(x)r(x)$. Let $q(x) \in \mathscr{P}_{n-1}$. Then, since $r(x)q_n(x)$ is obviously a certain linear combination of $p_n(x), \ldots, p_{n+m}(x)$,

$$r(x)q_n(x) = c_1 p_n(x) + \cdots + c_{m+1} p_{n+m}(x).$$

Therefore we have

$$\int_a^b w(x)r(x)q_n(x)q(x)\,dx = \int_a^b w(x)[c_1 p_n(x) + \cdots + c_{m+1} p_{n+m}(x)]q(x)\,dx = 0,$$

$$(2.7.1.4)$$

in view of the fact that each orthonormal polynomial is orthogonal to polynomials of lower degree.

Finally, we show that the degree of $q_n(x)$ is precisely $n$. This will follow if we show that the coefficient of $p_{n+m}(x)$ does not vanish. Now, this coefficient is

$$c_{m+1} = \begin{vmatrix} p_n(y_1) & p_{n+1}(y_1) & \cdots & p_{n+m-1}(y_1) \\ \vdots & & & \vdots \\ p_n(y_m) & p_{n+1}(y_m) & \cdots & p_{n+m-1}(y_m) \end{vmatrix}. \qquad (2.7.1.5)$$

If $c_{m+1} = 0$, we could find constants $d_1, d_2, \ldots, d_m$, not all zero, such that the polynomial

$$s(x) = d_1 p_n(x) + d_2 p_{n+1}(x) + \cdots + d_m p_{n+m-1}(x) \qquad (2.7.1.6)$$

would vanish at $x = y_1, x = y_2, \ldots, x = y_m$. The polynomial $s(x)$ would therefore be of the form $s(x) = r(x)t(x)$, where $t(x) \in \mathscr{P}_{n-1}$. Furthermore $s(x)$ is obviously orthogonal to all elements of $\mathscr{P}_{n-1}$. Hence

$$0 = \int_a^b w(x)s(x)t(x)\,dx = \int_a^b w(x)r(x)t^2(x)\,dx.$$

Therefore $t(x) \equiv 0$, and this contradicts the fact that the $d_i$ do not all vanish.

The two most common rules of Gauss type with preassigned abscissas have the preassigned abscissas at the end points of the interval. The weight $w(x) \equiv 1$ is used. These rules are called Radau and Lobatto integration. The specific formulas are as follows.

THEOREM (*Radau integration*). *Let* $f(x) \in C^{2n-1}[-1, 1]$. *Then*

$$\int_{-1}^{+1} f(x)\,dx = \frac{2}{n^2}f(-1) + \sum_{j=1}^{n-1} w_j f(x_j) + E, \qquad (2.7.1.7)$$

*where $x_j$ is the jth zero of*

$$\frac{P_{n-1}(x) + P_n(x)}{x - 1}, \qquad P(x) = Legendre\ polynomial, \qquad (2.7.1.8)$$

*where*

$$w_j = \frac{1}{n^2} \frac{1 - x_j}{[P_{n-1}(x_j)]^2} = \frac{1}{1 - x_j} \frac{1}{[P'_{n-1}(x_j)]^2}, \qquad (2.7.1.9)$$

*and where*

$$E = E(f) = \frac{2^{2n-1} n}{[(2n-1)!]^3} [(n-1)!]^4 f^{(2n-1)}(\xi), \qquad -1 < \xi < 1. \quad (2.7.1.10)$$

THEOREM (*Lobatto integration*).   *Let $f(x) \in C^{2n-2}[-1, 1]$. Then*

$$\int_{-1}^{+1} f(x)\,dx = \frac{2}{n(n-1)} [f(1) + f(-1)] + \sum_{j=2}^{n-1} w_j f(x_j) + E, \qquad (2.7.1.11)$$

*where $x_j$ is the $(j-1)$th zero of $P'_{n-1}(x)$, $P(x) = Legendre\ polynomial$.*

*Here*

$$w_j = \frac{2}{n(n-1)[P_{n-1}(x_j)]^2}, \qquad x_j \neq \pm 1, \qquad (2.7.1.12)$$

*and*

$$E = E(f) = \frac{-n(n-1)^3 2^{2n-1} [(n-2)!]^4}{(2n-1)[(2n-2)!]^3} f^{(2n-2)}(\xi), \qquad -1 < \xi < 1.$$
$$(2.7.1.13)$$

The approximate integration formulas of Radau and Lobatto are of use in the following situations.

(1) $f(\pm 1) = 0$ or any other known value.

(2) $f(x)$ displays peculiar behavior at $x = \pm 1$ such as an apparent singularity.

(3) If an $(n \times L)$-rule is set up (L = Lobatto), the functional values and weights at the end of the $(k-1)$th panel coincide with those at the beginning of the $k$th panel; hence, the number of functional evaluations is reduced.

(4) The Radau formula is useful for solving the ordinary differential equation

$$y' = f(x, y) \qquad (2.7.1.14)$$

as follows:

$$y(1) = y(-1) + \int_{-1}^{1} f(x, y)\,dx$$
$$(2.7.1.15)$$
$$\approx y(-1) + \frac{2}{n^2} f(-1, y(-1)) + \sum_{i=1}^{n-1} w_i f(x_i, y(x_i)).$$

**Example**

| Rule | $\int_0^1 x^{1/2}\,dx$ | $\int_0^1 x^{3/2}\,dx$ | $\int_0^1 dx/(1+x)$ | $\int_0^1 dx/(1+x^4)$ | $\int_0^1 dx/(1+e^x)$ | $\int_0^1 x\,dx/(e^x-1)$ | $\int_0^1 \dfrac{2\,dx}{2+\sin 10\pi x}$ |
|---|---|---|---|---|---|---|---|
| $L_4$ | .6568 2575 | .4003 5216 | .6931 8175 | .8662 6090 | .3798 8573 | .7775 0460 | 1.1072 996 |
| $L_{10}$ | .6661 9835 | .4000 0197 | .6931 4715 | .8669 7295 | .3798 8546 | .7775 0445 | 1.1911 951 |
| $R_6$ | .6648 1856 | .4000 2406 | .6931 4056 | .8669 7524 | .3798 8349 | .7775 0077 | 1.3259 693 |
| $\bar{R}_6$ | .6671 5144 | .3999 7720 | .6931 4938 | .8669 7911 | .3798 8712 | .7775 0741 | .8791 6927 |
| Exact value | .6666 6667 | .4000 0000 | .6931 4718 | .8669 72987 | .3798 8549 | .7775 0463 | 1.1547 0054 |

*Note:* $L_4$ = Lobatto 4-point formula,   $R_6$ = Radau 6-point left-hand formula,
$L_{10}$ = Lobatto 10-point formula,   $\bar{R}_6$ = Radau 6-point right-hand formula.

Here the $x_i$ are the Radau abscissas and the $w_i$ are the corresponding weights. If the values $f(x_i, y(x_i))$ are computed by some standard method, then the above approximation will "improve" the value of $y(1)$. See also Gates for further applications to differential equations.

**References.** Gates [1], Henrici [1, pp. 101–102], Hildebrand [1, Chap. 8], Kopal [1, Chap. 7], Michels [1], Rabinowitz [1], Shohat [1], Szegö [1, pp. 29–30].

Gauss-type integration formulas involving derivatives,

$$\int_a^b f(x)\,dx \approx \sum_{k=1}^m \sum_{j=1}^{n_k} A_{kj} f^{(j)}(a_k), \qquad -\infty < a < b < \infty, \qquad (2.7.1.16)$$

have also been developed.

**References.** Popoviciu [1], Stancu and Stroud [1], Stroud and Stancu [1], L. Tchakaloff [1].

### 2.7.2 The Algebraic Approach to the Gauss Integration Formulas

Let $w(x) \geq 0$. It is desired to find the $2n$ values $w_1, w_2, \ldots, w_n, x_1, x_2, \ldots, x_n$ such that

$$\int_a^b w(x)f(x)\,dx = \sum_{i=1}^n w_i f(x_i) \qquad (2.7.2.1)$$

for $f(x) = 1, x, x^2, \ldots, x^{2n-1}$. Writing out each of these conditions, and using the abbreviation $\int_a^b w(x)x^j\,dx = m_j$, we obtain the system below.

$$
\begin{aligned}
m_0 &= w_1 + w_2 + \cdots + w_n, \\
m_1 &= w_1 x_1 + w_2 x_2 + \cdots + w_n x_n, \\
m_2 &= w_1 x_1^2 + w_2 x_2^2 + \cdots + w_n x_n^2, \\
&\vdots \\
m_{2n-1} &= w_1 x_1^{2n-1} + w_2 x_2^{2n-1} + \cdots + w_n x_n^{2n-1}.
\end{aligned}
\qquad (2.7.2.2)
$$

We define

$$p(x) = (x - x_1)(x - x_2)\cdots(x - x_n) = \sum_{k=0}^n c_k x^k, \qquad c_n = 1. \qquad (2.7.2.3)$$

Now we have the following:

$$
\begin{aligned}
m_0 c_0 &= w_1 c_0 + w_2 c_0 + \cdots + w_n c_0, \\
m_1 c_1 &= w_1 c_1 x_1 + w_2 c_1 x_2 + \cdots + w_n c_1 x_n, \\
m_2 c_2 &= w_1 c_2 x_1^2 + w_2 c_2 x_2^2 + \cdots + w_n c_2 x_n^2, \\
&\vdots \\
m_n c_n &= w_1 c_n x_1^n + w_2 c_n x_2^n + \cdots + w_n c_n x_n^n.
\end{aligned}
\qquad (2.7.2.4)
$$

Hence

$$m_0 c_0 + m_1 c_1 + m_2 c_2 + \cdots + m_n c_n = w_1(c_0 + c_1 x_1 + \cdots + c_n x_1^n)$$
$$+ w_2(c_0 + c_1 x_2 + \cdots + c_n x_2^n)$$
$$+ \cdots + w_n(c_0 + c_1 x_n + \cdots + c_n x_n^n).$$

Since a typical parenthesis is $\sum_{k=0}^n c_k x_i^k = p(x_i) = 0$, we have

$$m_0 c_0 + m_1 c_1 + \cdots + m_n c_n = 0.$$

Treating the 2nd, 3rd, ..., $(n + 1)$th equations of (2.7.2.2) in the same way, we obtain $m_1 c_0 + m_2 c_1 + \cdots + m_{n+1} c_n = 0$. Proceeding similarly, we obtain the system (since $c_n = 1$) of $n$ equations in the quantities $c_0, \ldots, c_{n-1}$:

$$m_0 c_0 + m_1 c_1 + \cdots + m_{n-1} c_{n-1} = -m_n,$$
$$m_1 c_0 + m_2 c_1 + \cdots + m_n c_{n-1} = -m_{n+1},$$
$$m_2 c_0 + m_3 c_1 + \cdots + m_{n+1} c_{n-1} = -m_{n+2}, \qquad (2.7.2.5)$$
$$\vdots$$
$$m_{n-1} c_0 + m_n c_1 + \cdots + m_{2n-2} c_{n-1} = -m_{2n-1}.$$

The determinant of this system is

$$d = |m_{i+j}| = \left| \int_a^b w(x) x^i \cdot x^j \, dx \right|,$$

which is the Gram determinant of the functions $1, x, x^2, \ldots, x^{n-1}$. In view of the fact that these functions are linearly independent, it follows that $d \neq 0$ (see, for example, Davis [6, p. 178]). Hence, the system (2.7.2.5) may be solved uniquely for the constants $c_0, \ldots, c_{n-1}$. From (2.7.2.3) we may therefore solve for the abscissas $x_1, \ldots, x_n$ [which, as we know, will be real, simple, and located in $(a, b)$]. Having determined the abscissas, we may find the weights from (2.7.2.2).

A modification of this device may be used to obtain formulas of Gauss type with one or more fixed points. For example, let us find the $2n - 1$ values $w_1, w_2, \ldots, w_n, x_2, x_3, \ldots, x_n$ such that

$$\int_a^b w(x) f(x) = w_1 f(x_1) + \sum_{k=2}^n w_k f(x_k) \qquad (2.7.2.6)$$

is valid for $f(x) = 1, x, x^2, \ldots, x^{2n-2}$. It is assumed that $x_1$ is a *fixed* number satisfying $x_1 \geqslant b$ or $x_1 \leqslant a$.

The defining equations are now

$$m_k = w_1 x_1^k + \sum_{i=2}^n w_i x_i^k, \qquad k = 0, 1, \ldots, 2n - 2. \qquad (2.7.2.7)$$

By subtracting appropriate multiples of Equations (2.7.2.7) from one another, we therefore obtain

$$\mu_k = m_{k+1} - x_1 m_k = \sum_{i=2}^{n} w_i(x_i - x_1)x_i^k, \qquad k = 0, 1, \ldots, 2n - 3. \quad (2.7.2.8)$$

If we now set

$$p(x) = (x - x_2)(x - x_3) \cdots (x - x_n) = \sum_{k=0}^{n-1} c_k x^k \qquad (2.7.2.9)$$

and proceed as before, we have

$$\sum_{k=0}^{n-1} c_k \mu_{k+j} = \sum_{i=2}^{n} w_i(x_i - x_1)p(x_i) = 0, \qquad j = 0, 1, \ldots, n - 2. \quad (2.7.2.10)$$

The determinant of this system $d = |\mu_{k+j}|$ is

$$\det \left| \int_a^b w(x)(x^{k+j+1} - x_1 x^{k+j}) \, dx \right| = \det \left| \int_a^b w(x)(x - x_1)x^k \cdot x^j \, dx \right|.$$

This is the Gram determinant of the powers $1, x, x^2, \ldots$ with respect to the semidefinite weighting function $w(x)(x - x_1)$. Hence, the determinant does not vanish. The system (2.7.2.10) may therefore be solved, and we can proceed as before. This method of determining Gauss integration formulas is not advocated for numerical work inasmuch as the relevant matrices are often ill-conditioned.

**Reference.**   Hildebrand [1, pp. 351–353].

### 2.7.3   Determination of Gaussian Integration Formulas Through Orthogonal Polynomials

A good way of determining numerically the Gauss-type integration formulas is through the three-term recurrence formula for orthogonal polynomials. The zeros of the polynomials are real and simple, and can be calculated expeditiously via Newton–Raphson iteration. In numerous instances, for example in the case of the Jacobi weight function $(1 - x)^\alpha \times (1 + x)^\beta$, the three-term recurrence is known explicitly. To see how this method works, let us consider the classical Gauss case ($\alpha = \beta = 0$). The Legendre polynomials, $P_n(x)$, are orthogonal over $[-1, 1]$ and satisfy the recurrence

$$P_0(x) = 1,$$
$$P_1(x) = x, \qquad\qquad\qquad\qquad\qquad\qquad (2.7.3.1)$$
$$nP_n(x) = (2n - 1)xP_{n-1}(x) - (n - 1)P_{n-2}(x), \qquad n \geqslant 2.$$

The zeros of $P_n(x)$, $x_{kn}$, are given approximately by

$$x_{kn} \approx x_{kn}^{(0)} = \cos \theta_{kn}, \qquad k = 1, 2, \ldots, n,$$

where

$$\frac{j_k}{\left[\left(n + \frac{1}{2}\right)^2 + \frac{c}{4}\right]^{1/2}} < \theta_{kn} < \frac{j_k}{n + \frac{1}{2}}, \qquad k = 1, 2, \ldots, n. \quad (2.7.3.3)$$

Here $j_k$ are the successive zeros of the Bessel function $J_0(x)$, and $c = 1 - (2/\pi)^2$. A sequence of approximations to each zero, $x_{kn}^{(i)}$, is defined by the Newton iteration scheme

$$x_{kn}^{(i+1)} = x_{kn}^{(i)} - \frac{P_n(x_{kn}^{(i)})}{P_n'(x_{kn}^{(i)})}, \qquad i = 0, 1, 2, \ldots. \quad (2.7.3.4)$$

The derivative $P_n'(x)$ may be computed through the orthogonal polynomials themselves:

$$(1 - x^2)P_n'(x) = n[P_{n-1}(x) - xP_n(x)]. \quad (2.7.3.5)$$

If $P_n^*(x)$ are the *normalized* Legendre polynomials, that is if $\int_{-1}^{1} \left( (P_n^*(x))^2 \right) dx = 1$, and if

$$P_n^*(x) = k_n x^n + \cdots, \quad (2.7.3.6)$$

then the Gaussian weights, $w_{kn}$, are given by

$$w_{kn} = -\frac{k_{n+1}}{k_n} \frac{1}{P_{n+1}^*(x_{kn})P_n^{*'}(x_{kn})}. \quad (2.7.3.7)$$

The alternative formula

$$w_{kn} = \frac{2(1 - x_{kn}^2)}{[nP_{n-1}(x_{kn})]^2} \quad (2.7.3.8)$$

may be used.

A refinement of the Newton scheme may also be used conveniently. We can use, instead of (2.7.3.4), the iteration

$$x_{kn}^{(i+1)} = x_{kn}^{(i)} - \frac{P_n(x_{kn}^{(i)})}{P_n'(x_{kn}^{(i)})}\left(1 + \frac{P_n(x_{kn}^{(i)})}{P_n'(x_{kn}^{(i)})} \frac{P_n''(x_{kn}^{(i)})}{2P_n'(x_{kn}^{(i)})}\right), \quad (2.7.3.9)$$

which is more rapidly (in fact, cubically) convergent. In view of the fact that orthogonal polynomials satisfy a second-order linear differential equation, the values of $P_n''$ are available as linear combinations of $P_n$ and $P_n'$.

**References.** Davis [6, pp. 246–253], Davis and Rabinowitz [3], [4], Hofsommer [1], Shao, Chen, and Frank [2], Szegö [1], Wynn [1].

For weight functions, $w(x)$, whose related theory of orthogonal polynomials is not well developed, there are several difficulties that must be met. In the first place, while there is a three-term recurrence formula for all sets of orthogonal polynomials, its form may not be known in advance and might have to be calculated step by step. A convenient way of doing this is as follows, in which we shall use the inner product notation $(f, g) = \int_a^b w(x)f(x)g(x)\,dx$. We write the orthogonal polynomials as

$$p_n(x) = A_n x^n + \cdots, \qquad n = 0, 1, \ldots, \qquad (2.7.3.10)$$

where the constants $A_0, A_1, \ldots$ may be selected to suit our convenience. The selection $A_0 = 1$, $A_n = 2^{n-1}$, $n \geqslant 1$, for example, corresponds to the Tschebyscheff polynomials $T_n(x)$ under the normalization $T_n(1) = 1$ and is probably a good choice for computation. Then we have

$$p_0(x) = A_0, \qquad p_1(x) = A_1\left(x - \frac{(xp_0, p_0)}{(p_0, p_0)}\right),$$

$$p_n(x) = \frac{A_n}{A_{n-1}}\left(x - \frac{xp_{n-1}, p_{n-1}}{(p_{n-1}, p_{n-1})}\right) p_{n-1}(x)$$

$$-\frac{A_n A_{n-2}}{A_{n-1}^2}\frac{(p_{n-1}, p_{n-1})}{(p_{n-2}, p_{n-2})} p_{n-2}(x), \qquad n = 2, 3, \ldots. \qquad (2.7.3.11)$$

The inner products that occur in this recursion may all be evaluated as linear combinations of the basic quantities

$$(x^i, x^j) = (x^{i+j}, 1) = \int_a^b w(x)x^{i+j}\,dx = m_{i+j}.$$

These are the moments of the weight function $w(x)$. It may be that the moments $m_i$ are evaluable in closed form. This is the case with

$$\int_0^1 \left(\log\frac{1}{x}\right)x^n\,dx = \frac{1}{(n+1)^2}.$$

But if $w(x)$ is sufficiently complicated, for example if

$$m_n = \int_0^1 \frac{x^n}{\sqrt{x} + e^x}\,dx,$$

then special analysis or a numerical "boot strap" operation may be required to determine these basic numbers with sufficient accuracy.

Another complication is that unusual weights $w(x)$ may induce an unknown or an unusual asymptotic distribution of zeros of the orthogonal polynomials in $[a, b]$. It may require an initial scanning of the interval to locate the zeros crudely and, hence, in such a case the bisection routine for the solution of polynomial equations may be appropriate. One can also take advantage of the "separation" property of the zeros of successive orthogonal polynomials.

**THEOREM.** *Let $a < x_1 < x_2 < \cdots < x_n < b$ be the zeros of the orthogonal polynomial $p_n(x)$. Then in each interval $(a, x_1)$, $(x_1, x_2)$, $\ldots$, $(x_{n-1}, x_n)$, $(x_n, b)$ there is precisely one zero of the orthogonal polynomial $p_{n+1}(x)$.*

*Proof.* If $p_n^*(x) = k_n x^n + \cdots$, $(k_n > 0)$ are the orthonormalized polynomials, then by the Christoffel–Darboux formula we obtain

$$\sum_{k=0}^{n} (p_k^*(x))^2 = \frac{k_n}{k_{n+1}} (p_{n+1}^{*\prime}(x)p_n^*(x) - p_n^{*\prime}(x)p_{n+1}^*(x)). \qquad (2.7.3.12)$$

This implies that

$$p_{n+1}'(x)p_n(x) - p_n'(x)p_{n+1}(x) > 0. \qquad (2.7.3.13)$$

It follows from (2.7.3.13) that if $x_i$ and $x_{i+1}$ are two adjacent zeros of $p_n(x)$, then

$$p_n'(x_i)p_{n+1}(x_i) < 0,$$
$$p_n'(x_{i+1})p_{n+1}(x_{i+1}) < 0. \qquad (2.7.3.14)$$

Since the zeros of $p_n$ are simple, $p_n'(x_i)$ and $p_n'(x_{i+1})$ must have opposite signs and from (2.3.3.14), therefore, $p_{n+1}(x_i)$ and $p_{n+1}(x_{i+1})$ must have opposite signs. Thus $p_{n+1}(x)$ must have at least one zero between $x_i$ and $x_{i+1}$. This accounts for at least $n - 1$ zeros of $p_{n+1}(x)$.

Now, $p_n'(x_n) > 0$ and hence from (2.7.3.14), $p_{n+1}(x_n) < 0$. Since $p_{n+1}(b) > 0$, there must be a zero of $p_{n+1}(x)$ between $x_n$ and $b$. A similar argument shows that there must be a zero of $p_{n+1}(x)$ between $a$ and $x_1$. Thus, each of the $n + 1$ intervals $(a, x_1)$, $(x_1, x_2)$, $\ldots$, $(x_{n-1}, x_n)$, $(x_n, b)$ has at least one zero and, hence, precisely one zero of $p_{n+1}(x)$.

**References.** Davis [6, pp. 238–239], Szegö [1, p. 46].

*2.7.4   Determination of Gaussian Integration Formulas Through the Use of Continued Fractions*

It is also possible to obtain Gaussian integration formulas beginning with a knowledge of the coefficients in the continued fraction expansion of the transform

$$\int_a^b \frac{w(x)}{z - x} dx = \frac{1|}{|z} - \frac{q_1|}{|1} - \frac{e_1|}{|z} - \frac{q_1|}{|1} - \frac{e_2|}{|z} - \cdots. \qquad (2.7.4.1)$$

Let $R_n(z)/S_n(z)$ be the successive convergents of this continued fraction. Then $S_n(z)$ are the polynomials orthogonal on $[a, b]$ with respect to $w(x)$. The poles of these convergents are therefore the abscissas $x_{kn}$ of the Gauss integration rule of order $n$. Moreover

$$\frac{R_n(z)}{S_n(z)} = \text{const} \sum_{k=1}^{n} \frac{w_{kn}}{z - x_{kn}}. \tag{2.7.4.2}$$

When a modified $Q$-$D$ algorithm is applied to these convergents, it yields the abscissas and weights. We cannot enter into the details here. Thacher reports numerical instability for $\int_0^\infty x^{-1/2} e^{-x} f(x) \, dx$, using this method.

**References.**   Rutishauser [1, A1], Szegö [1, pp. 54–57].


### 2.7.5   Convergence of Gaussian Rules

The Gaussian rules $G_n$ have the remarkable property that as $n \to \infty$, $G_n(f)$ converges to $\int f \, dx$ for a very extensive class of functions.

THEOREM.   *Let $f(x) \in C[-1, 1]$, and suppose that*

$$E_{G_n}(f) = \int_{-1}^{1} f(x) \, dx - G_n(f).$$

*Then*

$$\lim_{n \to \infty} E_{G_n}(f) = 0. \tag{2.7.5.1}$$

*Proof.*   Let an $\varepsilon > 0$ be given. Then by the Weierstrass approximation theorem (see, for example, Davis [6, p. 107]) we can find a polynomial $p_m(x)$ such that $|f(x) - p_m(x)| \leqslant \varepsilon$ for $-1 \leqslant x \leqslant 1$. Now we know that

$$E_{G_n}(f) = E_{G_n}(p_m) + E_{G_n}(f - p_m).$$

Since $p_m$ is a polynomial, then for all $n$ such that $m \leqslant 2n - 1$, we have $E_{G_n}(p_m) = 0$. Hence, for all $n$ sufficiently large, we obtain

$$|E_{G_n}(f)| = |E_{G_n}(f - p_m)|$$

$$= \left| \int_{-1}^{+1} (f - p_m) \, dx - \sum_{k=1}^{n} w_{nk} \big( f(x_{nk}) - p_m(x_{nk}) \big) \right|$$

$$\leqslant \int_{-1}^{+1} |f(x) - p_m(x)| \, dx + \sum_{k=1}^{n} w_{nk} |f(x_{nk}) - p_m(x_{nk})|$$

$$\leqslant \varepsilon \int_{-1}^{+1} dx + \varepsilon \sum_{k=1}^{n} w_{nk} = 4\varepsilon.$$

However, it is possible to prove still more: if $f$ is a bounded Riemann-integrable function on $[-1, 1]$, that is, if $f \in R[-1, 1]$, then $\lim\limits_{n \to \infty} E_{G_n}(f) = 0$ is also valid. To prove this we need several lemmas.

LEMMA. *Let $f(x) \in R[a, b]$. Then, given $\varepsilon > 0$, we can find two piecewise continuous functions $s(x)$ and $S(x)$ such that*

$$s(x) \leqslant f(x) \leqslant S(x), \qquad (2.7.5.2)$$

$$\int_a^b (S(x) - s(x)) \, dx \leqslant \varepsilon. \qquad (2.7.5.3)$$

*Proof.* Introduce a partition $a = x_0 < x_1 < \cdots < x_n = b$. Now set $M_k = \sup_{x_{k-1} \leqslant x \leqslant x_k} f(x)$, $m_k = \inf_{x_{k-1} \leqslant x \leqslant x_k} f(x)$, and form

$$U = \sum_{k=1}^n M_k(x_k - x_{k-1}), \qquad L = \sum_{k=1}^n m_k(x_k - x_{k-1}).$$

By the definition of the Riemann integral we can take a partition so fine that $U - L \leqslant \varepsilon$. Then define

$$\begin{aligned}
S(x) &= M_k \quad \text{for} \quad x_{k-1} \leqslant x < x_k, \quad k = 1, 2, \ldots, n; \\
S(b) &= M_n.
\end{aligned} \qquad (2.7.5.4)$$

Define $s(x)$ similarly with $m_k$. Now, $\int_a^b S(x) \, dx = U$ and $\int_a^b s(x) \, dx = L$. Hence, $\int_a^b (S(x) - s(x)) \, dx \leqslant \varepsilon$.

We shall next prove that $G_n(f)$ converges to the "proper" answer when $f$ is a simple piecewise constant function.

LEMMA. *Let $-1 < a < b < 1$ and set*

$$\begin{aligned}
f(x) &= 0, \quad -1 \leqslant x < a, \\
f(x) &= 1, \quad a \leqslant x < b, \\
f(x) &= 0, \quad b \leqslant x \leqslant 1.
\end{aligned} \qquad (2.7.5.5)$$

*Then $\lim\limits_{n \to \infty} E_{G_n}(f) = 0$.*

*Proof.* Take an $\varepsilon$ so small that $-1 < a - \varepsilon, b + \varepsilon < 1$, and $a + \varepsilon < b - \varepsilon$. Construct two continuous functions $\phi$ and $\psi$ (depending on $\varepsilon$) as follows.

$$\begin{aligned}
\phi(x) &= 0, \quad -1 \leqslant x \leqslant a - \varepsilon, \\
\phi(x) &= \text{linear}, \quad a - \varepsilon \leqslant x \leqslant a, \\
\phi(x) &= 1, \quad a \leqslant x \leqslant b, \\
\phi(x) &= \text{linear}, \quad b \leqslant x \leqslant b + \varepsilon, \\
\phi(x) &= 0, \quad b + \varepsilon \leqslant x \leqslant 1.
\end{aligned} \qquad (2.7.5.6)$$

$$\psi(x) = 0, \qquad -1 \leqslant x \leqslant a,$$
$$\psi(x) = \text{linear}, \qquad a \leqslant x \leqslant a + \varepsilon,$$
$$\psi(x) = 1, \qquad a + \varepsilon \leqslant x \leqslant b - \varepsilon, \qquad (2.7.5.7)$$
$$\psi(x) = \text{linear}, \qquad b - \varepsilon \leqslant x \leqslant b,$$
$$\psi(x) = 0, \qquad b \leqslant x \leqslant 1.$$

Then we have $\phi(x) \geqslant f(x) \geqslant \psi(x)$. Since the Gauss rule $G_n$ has positive weights, then

$$G_n(\phi) \geqslant G_n(f) \geqslant G_n(\psi).$$

In this inequality, allow $n \to \infty$. Since $\phi$ and $\psi$ are continuous, we have

$$\int_{-1}^{1} \phi(x)\, dx \geqslant \lim_{n \to \infty} \sup G_n(f) \geqslant \lim_{n \to \infty} \inf G_n(f) \geqslant \int_{-1}^{1} \psi(x)\, dx.$$

But

$$\int_{-1}^{1} \phi(x)\, dx = b - a + \varepsilon \qquad \text{and} \qquad \int_{-1}^{1} \psi(x)\, dx = b - a - \varepsilon.$$

Therefore, since $\varepsilon$ may be chosen arbitrarily small, it follows that

$$\lim_{n \to \infty} G_n(f) = b - a = \int_{-1}^{1} f(x)\, dx.$$

COROLLARY.  If $f(x)$ is piecewise constant on $[-1, 1]$, then

$$\lim_{n \to \infty} E_{G_n}(f) = 0 \qquad \text{or} \qquad \lim_{n \to \infty} G_n(f) = \int_{-1}^{1} f(x)\, dx. \qquad (2.7.5.8)$$

Proof.  Every piecewise constant function is a finite linear combination of the simple sort of function just investigated.

THEOREM.  Let $f(x) \in R[-1, 1]$. Then

$$\lim_{n \to \infty} E_{G_n}(f) = 0. \qquad (2.7.5.9)$$

Proof.  Given $\varepsilon$. Construct piecewise constant functions $s(x)$ and $S(x)$ as in the first lemma. Since $s(x) \leqslant f(x) \leqslant S(x)$, we have

$$\int_{-1}^{1} s(x)\, dx \leqslant \int_{-1}^{1} f(x)\, dx \leqslant \int_{-1}^{1} S(x)\, dx$$

and $G_n(s) \leqslant G_n(f) \leqslant G_n(S)$. Allow $n \to \infty$; then by the corollary, we know that

$$G_n(s) \to \int_{-1}^{1} s(x)\, dx \qquad \text{and} \qquad G_n(S) \to \int_{-1}^{1} S(x)\, dx.$$

Therefore

$$\int_{-1}^{1} s(x)\, dx \leqslant \liminf_{n \to \infty} G_n(f) \leqslant \limsup_{n \to \infty} G_n(f) \leqslant \int_{-1}^{1} S(x)\, dx.$$

Hence

$$\int_{-1}^{1} f(x)\, dx - \varepsilon \leqslant \liminf_{n \to \infty} G_n(f) \leqslant \limsup_{n \to \infty} G_n(f) \leqslant \int_{-1}^{1} f(x)\, dx + \varepsilon.$$

Since $\varepsilon$ is arbitrary, it follows that

$$\lim_{n \to \infty} G_n(f) = \int_{-1}^{1} f(x)\, dx.$$

It should be observed that a similar theorem holds for integrals of the form $\int_a^b w(x) f(x)\, dx$, where $-\infty < a < b < \infty$.

A theorem of great generality which deals with the convergence of a family of rules is due to Pólya.

THEOREM. *Let*

$$L_n(f) = \sum_{k=1}^{n} w_{nk} f(x_{nk}), \qquad a \leqslant x_{nk} \leqslant b.$$

*Then*

$$\lim_{n \to \infty} L_n(f) = \int_a^b f(x)\, dx \qquad \text{for all} \quad f \in C[a, b] \qquad (2.7.5.10)$$

*if and only if*

$$\lim_{n \to \infty} L_n(x^k) = \int_a^b x^k\, dx, \qquad k = 0, 1, \cdots \qquad (2.7.5.11)$$

*and*

$$\sum_{k=1}^{n} |w_{nk}| \leqslant M, \qquad n = 1, 2, \ldots \qquad (2.7.5.12)$$

*for some constant M.*

If the weights $w_{nk}$ are positive (as they are in the Gauss case), then (2.7.5.11) implies (2.7.5.12). For, in this case,

$$\sum_{k=1}^{n} |w_{nk}| = \sum_{k=1}^{n} w_{nk} = L_n(1)$$

and $L_n(1)$ is bounded since $L_n(1) \to b - a$. If the integration formula is of interpolatory type and the weights are positive, then (2.7.5.11) and, hence, (2.7.5.10) will be fulfilled.

We should note that a family of approximate integration formulas,

$$L_n(f) = \sum_{k=1}^{n} w_{nk} f(x_{nk}), \qquad a \leqslant x_{nk} \leqslant b, \qquad (2.7.5.13)$$

which converges for all functions of class $C[a, b]$, will not automatically converge for all functions of class $R[a, b]$. This fact is brought out by the selection of weights and abscissas

$$x_{nj} = \frac{j-1}{n}, \qquad j = 1, 2, \ldots, n,$$

$$w_{n1} = 1,$$

$$w_{n2} = -1, \qquad\qquad\qquad (2.7.5.14)$$

$$w_{nj} = \frac{1}{n}, \qquad j = 3, 4, \ldots, n.$$

This family of rules integrates all continuous functions in $[0, 1]$ properly in the limit but fails to integrate the function

$$f(0) = 1,$$

$$f(x) = 0, \qquad 0 < x \leqslant 1.$$

**References.**  Davis [6, pp. 353–355], Féjer [1], Pólya [1].


## 2.8  Integration Rules, Using Derivative Data

In this book, the emphasis has been on approximate rules of integration that involve functional values. However, it is possible to derive approximate rules that make use of other sorts of functional information. For example, from the Euler–Maclaurin summation formula (see Section 2.9), we have

$$\int_{a}^{b} f(x)\, dx = \frac{h}{2}\left[f(a) + f(b)\right] + \frac{h^2}{12}\left[f'(a) - f'(b)\right]$$

$$+ \frac{h^5}{720} f^{(4)}(\xi), \qquad a < \xi < b, \qquad h = b - a. \qquad (2.8.1)$$

This rule makes use of the derivative values at $a$ and $b$ in addition to the values of the function itself. In cases where derivative information is readily available, for example with functions that satisfy a differential equation, such rules may be used to advantage.

One should note also that in compounding such rules the weights of the first derivative at the interior points cancel and hence we need evaluate the derivatives only at the end points of the interval to achieve a substantial increase in accuracy. Thus, the trapezoidal rule with "end correction" is

$$\int_a^b f(x)\,dx = h\left[\frac{f(a)}{2} + f(a + h) + f(a + 2h) + \cdots + f(a + (n - 1)h) + \frac{f(b)}{2}\right]$$

$$+ \frac{h^2}{12}[f'(a) - f'(b)] + E, \qquad h = \frac{b - a}{n}, \qquad (2.8.2)$$

where

$$E = \frac{\theta}{720} h^4(b - a) \max_{a \leqslant x \leqslant b} f^{(4)}(x), \qquad -1 \leqslant \theta \leqslant 1. \qquad (2.8.3)$$

There are similar rules of Simpson's and of Gauss type.

**Reference.** Kowalewski [1, p. 130].

Derivative rules are disadvantageous if derivatives are not easily computed, and they are less "automatic" in that more pen and pencil work is involved in setting them up. For these reasons, we shall merely provide a few references.

**References.** Flinn [1], Hammer and Wicke [1], Lambert and Mitchell [1], Lanczos [2], Lotkin [1], Sack [1], Salzer [1], Schoenberg [1], Squire [1].

## 2.9  Integration of Periodic Functions

Under certain conditions, the trapezoidal rule gives surprisingly good results when it is applied to *periodic* functions, much better in fact than what might have been predicted from the error estimate (2.1.11). We begin our discussion of this possibility by first developing the Euler–Maclaurin formula. This formula may be regarded as an extension of the trapezoidal rule.

The following identity is easily verified by integration by parts:

$$\tfrac{1}{2}[f(k) + f(k + 1)] = \int_k^{k+1} f(x)\,dx + \int_k^{k+1} (x - [x] - \tfrac{1}{2})f'(x)\,dx. \qquad (2.9.1)$$

Here

$$[x] = \text{largest integer} \leqslant x.$$

We set

$$P_1(x) = x - [x] - \tfrac{1}{2}. \qquad (2.9.2)$$

The function $P_1(x)$ is a piecewise linear, periodic function with period 1. Writing Equation (2.9.1) with $k = 0, 1, \ldots, n - 1$, and adding, we obtain

$$\frac{1}{2}f(0) + f(1) + \cdots + f(n - 1) + \frac{1}{2}f(n) = \int_0^n f(x)\,dx + \int_0^n P_1(x)f'(x)\,dx. \qquad (2.9.3)$$

Notice that the left-hand side of (2.9.3) is a trapezoidal sum.
The function $P_1(x)$ has the Fourier expansion

$$P_1(x) = - \sum_{n=1}^{\infty} \frac{\sin 2\pi nx}{\pi n}. \tag{2.9.4}$$

We integrate this series formally and set, by way of definition,

$$P_2(x) = \sum_{n=1}^{\infty} \frac{\cos 2\pi nx}{(2\pi n)^2}. \tag{2.9.5}$$

Repeating this, we have

$$P_3(x) = \sum_{n=1}^{\infty} \frac{2 \sin 2\pi nx}{(2\pi n)^3}. \tag{2.9.6}$$

In general, for $j = 2, 3, \ldots$,

$$P_{2j}(x) = (-1)^{j-1} \sum_{n=1}^{\infty} \frac{2 \cos 2\pi nx}{(2\pi n)^{2j}},$$

$$\tag{2.9.7}$$

$$P_{2j+1}(x) = (-1)^{j-1} \sum_{n=1}^{\infty} \frac{2 \sin 2\pi nx}{(2\pi n)^{2j+1}}.$$

The following properties of $P_n(x)$ should be noted: $P_n(x)$ is a piecewise polynomial of degree $n$, and it is a periodic function of period 1. Moreover

$$P'_{n+1}(x) = P_n(x), \tag{2.9.8}$$

$$P_{2j+1}(0) = P_{2j+1}(1) = 0, \qquad j = 1, 2, \ldots, \tag{2.9.9}$$

$$P_{2j}(0) = P_{2j}(1) = (-1)^{j-1} \sum_{n=1}^{\infty} \frac{2}{(2n\pi)^{2j}} = \frac{B_{2j}}{(2j)!}, \qquad j > 1. \tag{2.9.10}$$

The constants $B_{2j}$ are the *Bernoulli numbers* and have the values

$$B_2 = \tfrac{1}{6}, \qquad B_4 = -\tfrac{1}{30}, \qquad B_6 = \tfrac{1}{42}, \qquad B_8 = -\tfrac{1}{30}, \ldots. \tag{2.9.11}$$

Further integration by parts yields

$$\int_0^n P_1(x)f'(x)\,dx = P_2(x)f'(x)\Big|_0^n - \int_0^n P_2(x)f''(x)\,dx$$

$$= \frac{B_2}{2!}[f'(n) - f'(0)] - \int_0^n P_2(x)f''(x)\,dx \tag{2.9.12}$$

and

$$\int_0^n P_2(x)f''(x)\,dx = P_3(x)f''(x)\Big|_0^n - \int_0^n P_3(x)f'''(x)\,dx$$

$$= - \int_0^n P_3(x)f'''(x)\,dx. \tag{2.9.13}$$

This process of integration by parts can be carried out again and again and, if Equations (2.9.3), (2.9.12), (2.9.13) and similarly developed equations are combined, we obtain

$$\frac{1}{2} f(0) + f(1) + \cdots + f(n-1) + \frac{1}{2} f(n)$$

$$= \int_0^n f(x)\, dx + \frac{B_2}{2!} [f'(n) - f'(0)] + \frac{B_4}{4!} [f'''(n) - f'''(0)]$$

$$+ \cdots + \frac{B_{2k}}{(2k)!} [f^{(2k-1)}(n) - f^{(2k-1)}(0)]$$

$$+ \int_0^n P_{2k+1}(x) f^{(2k+1)}(x)\, dx. \tag{2.9.14}$$

This establishes the Euler–Maclaurin summation formula, which follows.

**THEOREM.**  *Let* $f(x) \in C^{2k+1}[0, n]$; *then formula (2.9.14) is valid.*

**COROLLARY.**  *Let* $g(x) \in C^{2k+1}[a, b]$. *Set* $h = (b - a)/n$. *Then*

$$h\left[\frac{1}{2} g(a) + g(a + h) + g(a + 2h) + \cdots + g(a + (n-1)h) + \frac{1}{2} g(b)\right]$$

$$= \int_a^b g(x)\, dx + \frac{B_2}{2!} h^2[g'(b) - g'(a)] + \frac{B_4}{4!} h^4(g'''(b) - g'''(a)]$$

$$+ \cdots + \frac{B_{2k}}{(2k)!} h^{2k}[g^{(2k-1)}(b) - g^{(2k-1)}(a)]$$

$$+ h^{2k+1} \int_a^b P_{2k+1}\left(n\, \frac{x-a}{b-a}\right) g^{(2k+1)}(x)\, dx. \tag{2.9.15}$$

*Proof.*  Apply the Euler–Maclaurin summation to $g(a + hx)$.

Formula (2.9.15) is convenient because it refers to a fixed interval.

**THEOREM.**  *Let*  $g(x) \in C^{(2k+1)}[a, b]$,  $g'(a) = g'(b)$,  $g'''(a) = g'''(b), \ldots,$ $g^{(2k-1)}(a) = g^{(2k-1)}(b)$, *and let* $|g^{(2k+1)}(x)| \leqslant M$ *for* $a \leqslant x \leqslant b$. *If* $T_n$ *designates the trapezoidal sum, that is, if*

$$T_n(g) = h[\tfrac{1}{2} g(a) + g(a + h) + \cdots + g(a + (n-1)h) + \tfrac{1}{2} g(b)],$$

$$h = (b - a)/n,$$

*then*

$$\left| \int_a^b g(x)\, dx - T_n(g) \right| \leqslant \frac{C}{n^{2k+1}}. \tag{2.9.16}$$

*The constant C is independent of n and may be taken as*

$$C = M(b - a)^{2k+2} 2^{-2k} \pi^{-2k-1} \zeta(2k + 1),$$

*where $\zeta(k) = \sum_{j=1}^{\infty} j^{-k}$ is the Riemann zeta function.*

*Proof.* Under the above hypothesis we have, from (2.9.15),

$$\int_a^b g(x) \, dx - T_n(g) = -h^{2k+1} \int_a^b P_{2k+1}\left(n \frac{x-a}{b-a}\right) g^{(2k+1)}(x) \, dx.$$

Hence

$$\left| \int_a^b g(x) \, dx - T_n(g) \right| \leqslant h^{2k+1} \int_a^b \left| P_{2k+1}\left(n \frac{x-a}{b-a}\right) \right| |g^{(2k+1)}(x)| \, dx.$$

Now

$$P_{2k+1}(t) = (-1)^{k-1} \sum_{j=1}^{\infty} 2 \frac{\sin 2\pi j t}{(2\pi j)^{2k+1}}.$$

Hence

$$|P_{2k+1}(t)| \leqslant \sum_{j=1}^{\infty} \frac{2}{(2\pi j)^{2k+1}} = 2^{-2k} \pi^{-2k-1} \zeta(2k + 1). \tag{2.9.17}$$

Combining these inequalities, we obtain the stated result.

The conditions of this theorem are fulfilled, for example, when $g(x)$ is a periodic function of a high degree of smoothness in $(-\infty, \infty)$.

COROLLARY.   *Let $g(x)$ have period $2\pi$ and be of class $C^{2k+1}[-\infty, \infty]$. Then*

$$\left| \int_0^{2\pi} g(x) \, dx - T_n(g) \right| \leqslant \frac{C}{n^{2k+1}}. \tag{2.9.18}$$

*Proof.*   In this case, $g'(0) = g'(2\pi), \ldots, g^{(2k-1)}(0) = g^{(2k-1)}(2\pi)$.

If $g(x)$ is a periodic function, $g(a) = g(b)$ and, hence, the trapezoidal rule becomes

$$T_n(g) = \frac{b-a}{n} [g(a) + g(a + h) + \cdots + g(a + (n - 1)h)],$$

which is a *simple average* of the functional values at equally spaced points.

If we set $b - a = p$ and

$$E_{T_n}(f) = \frac{p}{n} \sum_{k=0}^{n-1} f\left(\frac{k}{n} p\right) - \int_0^p f(x) \, dx, \tag{2.9.19}$$

it is easily verified that

$$E_{T_n}\left(\exp \frac{2\pi i j x}{p}\right) = \begin{cases} p, & j \neq 0, \ n \mid j, \\ 0, & \text{otherwise,} \end{cases} \quad i = \sqrt{-1}. \tag{2.9.20}$$

This means that the trapezoidal rule $T_n$ is exact for the $2n$ periodic functions 1, $\sin x, \cos x, \ldots, \sin (n - 1)x, \cos (n - 1)x, \sin nx$. A further consequence of (2.9.20) is that if a periodic function $f(x)$ has the Fourier expansion

$$f(x) = \tfrac{1}{2}\alpha_0 + \sum_{n=1}^{\infty} \alpha_n \cos \frac{2\pi nx}{p} + \beta_n \sin \frac{2\pi nx}{p}, \qquad (2.9.21)$$

then, assuming the series converges uniformly, it follows that

$$E_{T_n}(f(x)) = p \sum_{k=1}^{\infty} \alpha_{kn} = p(\alpha_n + \alpha_{2n} + \alpha_{3n} + \cdots). \qquad (2.9.22)$$

This is *Poisson's summation formula*, frequently written in the form

$$\int_0^p f(x)\, dx = h\{\tfrac{1}{2}[f(0) + f(p)] + \sum_{k=1}^{n-1} f(kh)\} - 2\sum_{k=1}^{\infty} g\left(\frac{2k\pi}{h}\right), \qquad (2.9.23)$$

$$h = \frac{p}{n}, \qquad g(t) = \int_0^p f(x) \cos xt\, dx.$$

For generalizations of the Euler–Maclaurin formula which are valid for functions with certain types of singularity, see the work of Navot.

**References.**   Davis [4], Fettis [2], Hämmerlin [1], Kowalewski [1, Chap. 3], Lohmann [1], Navot [1], [2], [3], Walsh and Sewell [1].

**Example.**   The function $(1 + \sigma \sin 2j\pi x)^{-1}$ has period 1 and, if $|\sigma| < 1$, has derivatives of all orders on $-\infty < x < \infty$. Hence, the convergence of the trapezoidal rule should be better than $n^{-k}$ for *all* integers $k$.

| No. of points | $(1 + \tfrac{1}{2} \sin 2\pi x)^{-1}$ | $(1 + \tfrac{1}{2} \sin 10\,\pi x)^{-1}$ |
|---|---|---|
| 2 | .9999 9995 | .9999 9980 |
| 4 | 1.1666 6660 | 1.1666 6650 |
| 8 | 1.1547 6180 | 1.1547 6180 |
| 16 | 1.1547 0050 | 1.1547 0050 |
| 32 | 1.1547 0040 | 1.1547 0040 |
| 64 | 1.1547 0030 | 1.1547 0020 |
| 128 | 1.1547 0010 | 1.1547 0010 |
| 256 | 1.1546 9960 | 1.1546 9950 |
| 512 | 1.1546 9880 | 1.1546 9840 |
| 1024 | 1.1546 9790 | 1.1546 9760 |
| 2048 | 1.1546 9440 | 1.1546 9400 |
| 4096 | 1.1546 8600 | 1.1546 8240 |
| Exact value | 1.1547 0054 | 1.1547 0054 |

As predicted, the convergence is very rapid; seven decimals are achieved when $n = 16$. Thereafter, the quality of the results deteriorates due to roundoff. This emphasizes the fact that when a high-precision rule is employed, care must be taken not to use too fine a mesh or the noise level in the output will rise. Note that the oscillation of $\sin 10\pi x$ is not sufficiently rapid to induce any significant difference in the numerical integration.

It is interesting to compare the results of $(1 + \frac{1}{2} \sin 10\pi x)^{-1}$ integrated by the trapezoidal rule and integrated by the Gauss rule. With 16 points, the trapezoidal rule is greatly superior.

**Example.** For rapid convergence with the trapezoidal rule it is not necessary to have a periodic function; it is sufficient to have one for which $f'(a) = f'(b)$, $f'''(a) = f'''(b)$, and so on. The function $f(x) = \exp[x^2(1 - x)^2]$ has this behavior over $[0, 1]$. Here are the results of determining $\int_0^1 \exp[x^2(1 - x)^2]\,dx$ by the trapezoidal rule.

| $n$ | Trapezoidal rule |
|---|---|
| 2 | 1.0322 472 |
| 4 | 1.0340 143 |
| 8 | 1.0341 329 |
| 16 | 1.0341 405 |
| 32 | 1.0341 409 |
| 64 | 1.0341 407 |
| 128 | 1.0341 407 |
| 256 | 1.0341 401 |
| 512 | 1.0341 389 |
| 1024 | 1.0341 379 |
| Exact value | 1.0341 4105 |

Eight figures are achieved at $n = 32$.

**Example** (Imhof). Another example of this kind is provided by the integral

$$J_k(t) = \frac{1}{\pi} \int_0^\pi \cos(t \sin x - kx)\,dx.$$

$J_k(t)$ is the *Bessel function.*  The values below are for $k = 1$, $t = 8$.

| $n$ | Trapezoidal rule | Simpson's rule |
|---|---|---|
| 6 | .2123 144 | .1673 824 |
| 8 | .2343 632 | .2991 192 |
| 16 | .2346 363 | .2347 274 |
| Exact value | .2346 3634 7 | |

**Reference.** Imhof [1].

Approximate integration can lead to useful functional approximations. Here is an example that also involves the Bessel functions. It is known that

$$J_k(z) = \frac{(i)^k}{\pi} \int_0^\pi \exp[iz \cos t] \cos kt \, dt. \qquad (2.9.24)$$

In the case $k = 0$, we apply the trapezoidal rule with $h = \pi/6$. This leads to

$$J_0(z) \approx \frac{1}{6} \left\{ \frac{1}{2} \exp[iz] + \exp\left[iz \cos\left(\frac{\pi}{6}\right)\right] + \exp\left[iz \cos\left(\frac{\pi}{3}\right)\right] + \exp\left[iz \cos\left(\frac{\pi}{2}\right)\right] \right.$$

$$\left. + \exp\left[iz \cos\left(\frac{2\pi}{3}\right)\right] + \exp\left[iz \cos\left(\frac{5\pi}{6}\right)\right] + \frac{1}{2} \exp[-iz] \right\}$$

$$= \frac{1}{6} \left[ \cos z + 2 \cos\left(\frac{\sqrt{3}}{2} z\right) + 2 \cos\left(\frac{z}{2}\right) + 1 \right]. \qquad (2.9.25)$$

Over the range $0 \leqslant z \leqslant 2$, this approximation is found to be accurate to within $10^{-8}$.

**References.** Fettis [1], Luke [4].


## 2.10   *Integration of Rapidly Oscillatory Functions*

By a *rapidly oscillatory integrand* we mean one with numerous (more than 10) local maxima and minima over the range of integration.

The principal examples of rapidly oscillatory integrands occur in various transforms. There is the *Fourier transform*:

$$\int_a^b f(x) \cos nx \, dx, \qquad \int_a^b f(x) \sin nx \, dx$$

or in complex form,

$$\int_a^b f(x) e^{isx} \, dx.$$

There is the *Fourier–Bessel transform*

$$\int_0^1 f(x) x J_n(\gamma_m x) \, dx,$$

where $0 < \gamma_1 < \gamma_2 < \cdots$ are the zeros of the Bessel function $J_n(x)$.

What is usually desired is not the value of an isolated integral, but a whole family of such integrals where the oscillations increase. We may take the general form to be

$$I(t) = \int_a^b f(x)K(x, t)\, dx, \qquad -\infty \leqslant a < b \leqslant \infty, \qquad (2.10.1)$$

where $K(x, t)$ is an oscillatory kernel and $f(x)$ is the "nonoscillatory" part.

Numerical integration of oscillatory integrands is beset with difficulties peculiar to it. For example, consider the determination of

$$\int_0^{2\pi} f(x) \cos tx\, dx.$$

As $t \to \infty$, the graph of $f(x) \cos tx$ will consist of plus areas and minus areas of nearly equal size and the resulting cancellation of area is attended by a loss of significance. Furthermore, as $t \to \infty$, the function $f(x) \cos tx$ looks less and less like a polynomial of low degree, and this suggests that special methods should be developed.

Fourier integrals may occasionally be treated by means of repeated integration by parts.

THEOREM.   *Let $f(x) \in C^n[a, b]$. Then*

$$I(s) = \int_a^b e^{isx} f(x)\, dx = e^{isb} \sum_{k=0}^{n-1} i^{k-1} f^{(k)}(b) s^{-k-1}$$

$$-e^{isa} \sum_{k=0}^{n-1} i^{k-1} f^{(k)}(a) s^{-k-1} + (-is)^{-n} \int_a^b e^{isx} f^{(n)}(x)\, dx. \qquad (2.10.2)$$

*Proof.*   Integrate the remainder by parts $n$ times.

COROLLARY.   This theorem is true when $a = -\infty$, $b = \infty$ (or both), provided that $f^{(k)}(x) \to 0$ as $x \to -\infty$ (or $x \to \infty$) for each $k = 0, 1, \ldots, n - 1$ and provided that

$$\int_a^b |f^{(n)}(x)|\, dx < \infty. \qquad (2.10.3)$$

This theorem provides an asymptotic expansion of $I(s)$ in negative powers of $s$. It may be useful numerically when the parameter is large.

**Example.**   $I_n = \int_0^\pi e^{x^2} \cos nx\, dx$. Integration by parts three times yields

$$I_n = \frac{(-1)^n}{n^2} 2\pi e^{\pi^2} + \frac{2}{n^3} \int_0^\pi (xe^{x^2})'' \sin nx\, dx.$$

Since the integral on the right approaches 0 as $n \to \infty$, we have

$$I_n = \frac{(-1)^n}{n^2} 2\pi e^{n^2} + \frac{2\varepsilon_n}{n^3}$$

with $\lim_{n \to \infty} \varepsilon_n = 0$.

Generalizations can be obtained in which $f(x)$ is allowed to possess singularities at $x = a$ or $x = b$.

**Reference.**   Erdélyi [1].

### 2.10.1   Integration Between the Zeros

In this very simple method, the zeros of the integrand are located: $a \leqslant x_1 < x_2 < \cdots < x_p \leqslant b$ and each subintegral $\int_{x_i}^{x_{i+1}}$ is evaluated by a rule. It is advantageous to use a rule that employs the values of the integrand at the end points of the integration interval. Since the integrand is zero at these points, more accuracy is obtained without additional computation. A Lobatto rule would seem particularly good for this purpose.

Let us write

$$\int_0^{2\pi} f(x) \sin nx \, dx = \sum_{k=0}^{2n-1} \int_{k\pi/n}^{(k+1)\pi/n} f(x) \sin nx \, dx. \qquad (2.10.1.1)$$

In each of the integrals in the right-hand sum, the integrand vanishes at the end points. Hence

$$\int_{k\pi/n}^{(k+1)\pi/n} f(x) \sin nx \, dx$$

may be expeditiously computed by use of a Lobatto rule. For example, a 5-point Lobatto rule (2 end points and 3 interval points) can be carried out with 3 functional evaluations per interval. A similar reduction can be made for the integral $\int_0^{2\pi} f(x) \cos nx \, dx$. An alternative development has been worked out by Price for finite Fourier integrals. Let us consider, for example,

$$I(k) = \int_0^\pi g(t) \sin kt \, dt = \frac{1}{k} \int_0^{k\pi} g\left(\frac{u}{k}\right) \sin u \, du. \qquad (2.10.1.2)$$

If $k$ is an integer, we have

$$I(k) = \frac{1}{k} \sum_{j=1}^k \int_{(j-1)\pi}^{j\pi} g\left(\frac{u}{k}\right) \sin u \, du. \qquad (2.10.1.3)$$

This throws the burden onto integrals of the form $\int_{k\pi}^{(k+1)\pi} f(y) \sin y \, dy$, for which the following formula of interpolatory type can be obtained.

$$\int_{k\pi}^{(k+1)\pi} f(y) \sin y \, dy = H_1[f(k\pi) + f((k+1)\pi)]$$

$$+ H_2[f((k + \tfrac{1}{4})\pi) + f((k + \tfrac{3}{4})\pi)] + 2H_3 f((k + \tfrac{1}{2})\pi)$$

$$+ (-1)^k .01002 f^{(4)}(\xi), \qquad k\pi < \xi < (k+1)\pi;$$

$$H_1 = (-1)^k \left[ 1 + \frac{2}{\pi} - \frac{16}{\pi^2} \right] \approx (-1)^k .0154\,8084, \qquad (2.10.1.4)$$

$$H_2 = (-1)^k \left[ \frac{8}{\pi} \left( \frac{4}{\pi} - 1 \right) \right] \approx (-1)^k .6957\,9877,$$

$$H_3 = (-1)^k \left[ \frac{2}{\pi} \left( 3 - \frac{8}{\pi} \right) \right] \approx (-1)^k .2887\,2038.$$

**Reference.**   Price [1].

Note that this formula requires the evaluation only of $f$ at the given abscissas and does not require any computation of $\sin x$.

2.10.2   *Use of Approximation: Filon's Method for Finite Fourier Integrals*

Suppose that we can write

$$f(x) = a_1\phi_1(x) + a_2\phi_2(x) + \cdots + a_n\phi_n(x) + \varepsilon(x), \qquad a \leqslant x \leqslant b, \quad (2.10.2.1)$$

where $\varepsilon(x)$ is small over $a \leqslant x \leqslant b$ and where the transforms

$$\psi_k(t) = \int_a^b \phi_k(x)K(t, x) \, dx, \qquad k = 1, 2, \ldots, n \qquad (2.10.2.2)$$

can be computed explicitly in elementary terms. (This will be the case, for example, where $\phi_k(x) = x^k$ and $K(x, t) = e^{itx}$.) Then

$$I(t) = \int_a^b f(x)K(x, t) \, dx = \sum_{k=1}^{n} a_k\psi_k(t) + \int_a^b \varepsilon(x)K(x, t) \, dx$$

$$\approx \sum_{k=1}^{n} a_k\psi_k(t). \qquad (2.10.2.3)$$

This program was worked out by Filon, who approximates $f(x)$ by parabolic arcs.

Consider the integral

$$I(k) = \int_a^b f(t) \cos kt \, dt. \tag{2.10.2.4}$$

In Filon's method, the interval $[a, b]$ is divided into $2N$ subintervals of equal length $h$:

$$h = \frac{b - a}{2N}. \tag{2.10.2.5}$$

Over each double subinterval, $f(t)$ is approximated by a parabola obtained by interpolation to $f(t)$ at the mesh points. For parabolic $f(t)$, the Fourier integrals can be computed explicitly by integration by parts. This program leads to the following rules of approximate integration. Let

$$C_{2n} = \tfrac{1}{2}f(a) \cos ka + f(a + 2h) \cos k(a + 2h)$$

$$+ f(a + 4h) \cos k(a + 4h) + \cdots + \tfrac{1}{2}f(b) \cos kb, \tag{2.10.2.6}$$

$$C_{2n-1} = f(a + h) \cos k(a + h) + f(a + 3h) \cos k(a + 3h)$$

$$+ \cdots + f(b - h) \cos k(b - h). \tag{2.10.2.7}$$

Similarly, define $S_{2n}$ and $S_{2n-1}$ as the corresponding sums formed from $f(t) \sin kt$. Further, let

$$\theta = kh = \frac{k(b - a)}{2N}, \tag{2.10.2.8}$$

and

$$\alpha = \alpha(\theta) = \frac{\theta^2 + \theta \sin \theta \cos \theta - 2 \sin^2 \theta}{\theta^3},$$

$$\beta = \beta(\theta) = \frac{2[\theta(1 + \cos^2 \theta) - 2 \sin \theta \cos \theta]}{\theta^3}, \tag{2.10.2.9}$$

$$\gamma = \gamma(\theta) = \frac{4(\sin \theta - \theta \cos \theta)}{\theta^3}.$$

Then

$$\int_a^b f(t) \cos kt \, dt \approx h\{\alpha[f(b) \sin kb - f(a) \sin ka] + \beta C_{2n} + \gamma C_{2n-1}\},$$

$$\tag{2.10.2.10}$$

$$\int_a^b f(t) \sin kt \, dt \approx h\{-\alpha[f(b) \cos kb - f(a) \cos ka] + \beta S_{2n} + \gamma S_{2n-1}\}.$$

It should be noted that for small $\theta$, the functions $\alpha$, $\beta$ and $\gamma$ have the Taylor expansions

$$\alpha(\theta) = \tfrac{2}{45}\,\theta^3 - \tfrac{2}{315}\,\theta^5 + \tfrac{2}{4725}\,\theta^7 + \cdots,$$

$$\beta(\theta) = \tfrac{2}{3} + \tfrac{2}{15}\,\theta^2 + \tfrac{4}{105}\,\theta^4 + \tfrac{2}{567}\,\theta^6 + \cdots, \qquad (2.10.2.11)$$

$$\gamma(\theta) = \tfrac{4}{3} - \tfrac{2}{15}\,\theta^2 + \tfrac{1}{210}\,\theta^4 - \tfrac{1}{11.340}\,\theta^6 + \cdots.$$

Thus for $\theta = 0$, Filon's rule reduces to an $N \times S$ rule.

It is advisable in numerical work to keep the parameter $\theta$ smaller than 1. This means that for large values of $k$, we are compelled to take small values of $h$.

The remainder in Filon's sine formula is given by

$$E = \frac{(b - a)h^3}{12} \left( 1 - \frac{1}{16 \cos{(kh/4)}} \right) \sin \frac{kh}{2} f^{(4)}(\xi), \qquad a < \xi < b.$$

$$(2.10.2.12)$$

An extension of Filon's method has been made by Flinn, who uses fifth-degree polynomials, found by interpolating to the values of $f(x)$ and of its first derivative at the above points.

**References.** Buyst and Schotsmans [1], Filon [1], Flinn [1], Hamming [1], Kruglikova [1], Teijelo [A1].

**Examples.** In the following examples, $G_{32}$ designates a Gauss 32-point rule; $2n \times L_4$ and $2n \times L_5$ designate, respectively, the result of a 4- and 5-point Lobatto rule inserted into each arch of the sine curve; $F_i$ designates the Filon rule with $h = 2\pi/in$. Thus, in $F_{11}$, $nh = \theta = 2\pi/11 \approx .57$.

It is interesting to note the poor quality of $G_{32}$ as $n$ becomes large. However, for small $n$, a high-order Gauss rule seems to be competitive, as is seen in the following tables.

$$\int_0^{2\pi} x \sin nx \cos x \, dx = \begin{cases} -\dfrac{\pi}{2}, & n = 1, \\[2ex] -\dfrac{2n\pi}{n^2 - 1}, & n \neq 1. \end{cases}$$

| $n$ | Exact | $G_{32}$ | $2n \times L_4$ | $2n \times L_5$ |
|---|---|---|---|---|
| 1 | $-1.5707\,9633$ | $-1.5704\,811$ | $-2.4368\,252$ | |
| 2 | $-4.1887\,902$ | $-4.1842\,807$ | $-4.7246\,829$ | |
| 4 | $-1.6755\,161$ | $-1.6756\,476$ | $-1.8613\,529$ | |
| 10 | $-.6346\,6518$ | $-.6340\,2069$ | $-.7020\,6954$ | $-.5587\,594$ |
| 20 | $-.3149\,4663$ | $-1.2092\,524$ | $-.3481\,8404$ | $-.2778\,962$ |
| 30 | $-.2096\,7247$ | $-1.5822\,272$ | $-.2317\,7723$ | $-.1850\,8448$ |

| | $F_7$ | $F_9$ | $F_{11}$ |
|---|---|---|---|
| 10 | $-.6346\,766$ | $-.6346\,740$ | $-.6346\,739$ |
| 20 | $-.3149\,717$ | $-.3149\,685$ | $-.3149\,549$ |
| 30 | $-.2096\,831$ | $-.2096\,940$ | $-.2096\,922$ |

$$\int_0^{2\pi} x \sin nx \cos 50x \, dx = \frac{2n\pi}{2500 - n^2} \quad (n \neq 50).$$

| $n$ | Exact | $G_{32}$ | $2n \times L$ | $2n \times L_5$ |
|---|---|---|---|---|
| 1 | .0025\,1428 | 2.1561\,858 | .5631\,2612 | |
| 2 | .0050\,3460 | .8756\,9672 | 4.7048\,779 | |
| 4 | .0101\,1785 | $-.0974\,2242$ | .6975\,8325 | |
| 10 | .0261\,7994 | .1058\,5082 | 9.3325\,313 | .3305\,4736 |
| 20 | .0598\,3986 | $-.8128\,6374$ | .1110\,445 | $-.3301\,2624$ |
| 30 | .1178\,0972 | $-.6453\,4403$ | .1639\,1873 | $-.0304\,516$ |

| | $F_7$ | $F_9$ | $F_{11}$ |
|---|---|---|---|
| 10 | .1104\,744 | .2979\,713 | .2905\,720 |
| 20 | .0939\,910 | .0391\,049 | .0534\,536 |
| 30 | .1020\,426 | .1134\,099 | .1159\,873 |

$$\int_0^{2\pi} \frac{x \sin nx}{\sqrt{1 - x^2/4\pi^2}} \, dx = 2\pi^3 J_1(2\pi n) \approx 62.012553 J_1(2\pi n).$$

| $n$ | Exact | $G_{32}$ | $2n \times L_4$ | $2n \times L_5$ |
|---|---|---|---|---|
| 1 | $-13.1702$ | $-13.1715\,25$ | $-13.9910\,48$ | |
| 2 | $-9.5828$ | $-9.5829\,142$ | $-10.2182\,90$ | |
| 4 | $-6.8760$ | $-6.8777\,809$ | $-7.3418\,421$ | |
| 10 | $-4.3874$ | $-4.3941\,584$ | $-4.6871\,704$ | $-4.4389\,57$ |
| 20 | $-3.1068$ | $-1.2103\,556$ | $-3.3245\,016$ | $-3.1460\,04$ |
| 30 | $-2.5431$ | $-7.5194\,213$ | $-2.7171\,478$ | $-2.5706\,44$ |

|    | $F_7$ | $F_9$ | $F_{11}$ |
|----|-------|-------|----------|
| 10 | $-4.0380\,496$ | $-4.1804\,932$ | $-4.2486\,224$ |
| 20 | $-2.8740\,128$ | $-2.9753\,827$ | $-3.0161\,137$ |
| 30 | $-2.3445\,709$ | $-2.4349\,045$ | $-2.4735\,530$ |

$$\int_0^{2\pi} \log x \sin nx \, dx = -\frac{1}{n} [\gamma + \log 2n\pi - \text{Ci}(2n\pi)], \qquad \gamma \approx .5772\,1566\,5,$$

$$\text{Ci} = \text{cosine integral}.$$

| $n$ | Exact | $G_{32}$ | $2n \times L_4$ | $2n \times L_5$ |
|-----|-------|----------|-----------------|-----------------|
| 1  | $-2.4376$ | $-2.4377\,894$ | $-2.4379\,902$ |            |
| 2  | $-1.5572$ | $-1.5569\,920$ | $-1.5879\,795$ |            |
| 4  | $-.9507$  | $-.9506\,9323$ | $-.9830\,4071$ |            |
| 10 | $-.4718$  | $-.4721\,4693$ | $-.4940\,6296$ | $-.4410\,448$ |
| 20 | $-.2705$  | $.1237\,0883$  | $-.2852\,8092$ | $-.2511\,1912$ |
| 30 | $-.1939$  | $-1.1143\,265$ | $-.2051\,162$  | $-.1793\,4632$ |

|    | $F_7$ | $F_9$ | $F_{11}$ |
|----|-------|-------|----------|
| 10 | $-.4569\,386$ | $-.4645\,544$ | $-.4676\,223$ |
| 20 | $-.2622\,322$ | $-.2665\,889$ | $-.2683\,037$ |
| 30 | $-.1879\,863$ | $-.1911\,092$ | $-.1923\,261$ |

## 2.10.3   Application of Speedup Methods

It is also possible to break up an oscillatory integral into a series of integrands of alternating sign and to apply a transformation designed to "speed up" the convergence of such a series.

The following formula, which is a variation of the much employed Euler transformation,† was developed by Longman.

Let

$$S = v_0 - v_1 + v_2 - \cdots + (-1)^n v_n. \tag{2.10.3.1}$$

Write

$$S(x) = v_0 - v_1 x + v_2 x^2 - \cdots + (-1)^n v_n x^n. \tag{2.10.3.2}$$

† For the Euler transformation, see Section 3.8.

Then

$$(1 + x)S(x) = v_0 - (v_1 - v_0)x + (v_2 - v_1)x^2 - \cdots + (-1)^n(v_n - v_{n-1})x^n$$
$$+ (-1)^n v_n x^{n+1}$$

$$= v_0 - (\Delta v_0)x + (\Delta v_1)x^2 - \cdots + (-1)^n(\Delta v_{n-1})x^n$$
$$+ (-1)^n v_n x^{n+1}. \tag{2.10.3.3}$$

Here we use the notation

$$\Delta v_k = v_{k+1} - v_k, \tag{2.10.3.4}$$
$$\Delta^{r+1} v_k = \Delta^r v_{k+1} - \Delta^r v_k.$$

From (2.10.3.3) we obtain

$$S(x) = \frac{v_0 + (-1)^n v_n x^{n+1}}{1 + x}$$
$$- y[\Delta v_0 - (\Delta v_1)x + (\Delta v_2)x^2 - \cdots + (-1)^{n-1}(\Delta v_{n-1})x^{n-1}], \tag{2.10.3.5}$$

where

$$y = \frac{x}{1 + x}. \tag{2.10.3.6}$$

Applying this transformation again to the bracketed series in (2.10.3.5), we obtain

$$S(x) = \frac{v_0 + (-1)^n v_n x^{n+1}}{1 + x} - \frac{\Delta v_0 + (-1)^{n-1}(\Delta v_{n-1})x^n}{1 + x} y$$
$$+ y^2[\Delta^2 v_0 - (\Delta^2 v_1)x + (\Delta^2 v_2)x^2 - \cdots + (-1)^{n-2}(\Delta^2 v_{n-2})x^{n-2}]. \tag{2.10.3.7}$$

If $p \leqslant n$, then $p$ applications yield

$$S(x) =$$
$$\frac{v_0 - y\Delta v_0 + y^2\Delta^2 v_0 - \cdots + (-1)^{p-1}y^{p-1}\Delta^{p-1}v_0}{1 + x}$$
$$+ \frac{(-1)^n[v_n x^{n+1} + (\Delta v_{n-1})x^n y + (\Delta^2 v_{n-2})x^{n-1}y^2 + \cdots + (\Delta^{p-1}v_{n-p+1})x^{n-p+2}y^{p-1}]}{1 + x}$$
$$+ (-1)^p y^p[\Delta^p v_0 - (\Delta^p v_1)x + (\Delta^p v_2)x^2 - \cdots + (-1)^{n-p}(\Delta^p v_{n-p})x^{n-p}]. \tag{2.10.3.8}$$

Set $x = 1$, and we obtain the formal identity

$$S = \tfrac{1}{2}v_0 - \tfrac{1}{4}\Delta v_0 + \tfrac{1}{8}\Delta^2 v_0 - \cdots + (-1)^{p-1}2^{-p}\Delta^{p-1}v_0$$
$$+ (-1)^n[\tfrac{1}{2}v_n + \tfrac{1}{4}\Delta v_{n-1} + \tfrac{1}{8}\Delta^2 v_{n-2} + \cdots + 2^{-p}\Delta^{p-1}v_{n-p+1}]$$
$$+ 2^{-p}(-1)^p[\Delta^p v_0 - \Delta^p v_1 + \Delta^p v_2 - \cdots + (-1)^{n-p}\Delta^p v_{n-p}], \, p \leqslant n. \tag{2.10.3.9}$$

Assuming now that $n$ and $p$ are large and that the high-order differences are small, we neglect the last bracket and obtain

$$S \approx \tfrac{1}{2}v_0 - \tfrac{1}{4}\Delta v_0 + \tfrac{1}{8}\Delta^2 v_0 - \cdots$$

$$+ (-1)^n[\tfrac{1}{2}v_n + \tfrac{1}{4}\Delta v_{n-1} + \tfrac{1}{8}\Delta^2 v_{n-2} + \cdots]. \qquad (2.10.3.10)$$

**Example** (Longman). Determine $I = \int_0^{100\pi} (100^2\pi^2 - x^2)^{1/2} \sin x \, dx$. Write

$$I = \sum_{r=0}^{99} (-1)^r \int_0^{\pi} [100^2\pi^2 - (r\pi + x)^2]^{1/2} \sin x \, dx$$

$$= \sum_{r=0}^{99} (-1)^r v_r,$$

where $v_r$ are the integrals in the above sum. For values of $r$ near 0 and near 99, the quantities $v_r$ were computed by use of a 16-point Gauss rule.

| $r$ | $v_r$ | $r$ | $v_r$ |
|---|---|---|---|
| 1 | 628.30915 | 89 | 280.25486 |
| 2 | 628.24630 | 90 | 267.27464 |
| 3 | 628.12061 | 91 | 253.47487 |
| 4 | 627.93204 | 92 | 238.71325 |
| 5 | 627.68049 | 93 | 222.79836 |
| 6 | 627.36594 | 94 | 205.46181 |
| $\vdots$ | $\vdots$ | 95 | 186.30583 |
| 85 | 325.85292 | 96 | 164.30583 |
| 86 | 315.26077 | 97 | 139.47917 |
| 87 | 304.17027 | 98 | 108.12528 |
| 88 | 292.52472 | 99 | 60.96022 |

Since $v_r$ changes rapidly near $r = 99$, it is more expeditious to write

$$I = \sum_{r=0}^{85} (-1)^r v_r + \sum_{r=86}^{99} (-1)^r v_r$$

and to apply the summation formula (2.10.3.10) only to the first sum above. This yields (we omit the computation of the differences)

$$I = 298.43558.$$

The exact value is $I = 50\pi^2 H_1(100\pi) = 298.435716$, where $H_1$ is the Struve function, so that disagreement occurs only in the last two places of the approximation.

**References.** Longman [4], NBS Handbook [1, p. 496], Rosser [1], Shanks [1].

### 2.10.4   Special Methods

The schemes just presented should not camouflage the fact that difficult integrals requiring special study and treatment may occur from time to time. For example, the integral

$$C(x, y, \beta) = \frac{1}{2\beta} \int_{-\beta}^{\beta} \cos (x \cos \theta - y \sin \theta) \cos \theta \, d\theta,$$

where $x$ and $y$ are large, is in this category and has been analyzed by Hartree.

**Reference.**   Hartree [1].

### 2.11   Contour Integrals

By a contour integral, we mean an integral of the form $\int_C f(x, y) \, dx$, $\int_C f(x, y) \, dy$, or $\int_C f(x, y) \, ds$, extended over a contour $C$ in the $xy$-plane. If the contour $C$ can be conveniently parameterized as

$$C: \begin{cases} x = x(t), \\ y = y(t), \end{cases} \quad t_0 \leqslant t \leqslant t_1, \tag{2.11.1}$$

these integrals can be transformed to ordinary integrals of a single variable

$$\int_{t_0}^{t_1} f\big(x(t), y(t)\big) \frac{dx}{dt} \, dt, \qquad \int_{t_0}^{t_1} f\big(x(t), y(t)\big) \frac{dy}{dt} \, dt,$$

$$\int_{t_0}^{t_1} f\big(x(t), y(t)\big) \frac{ds}{dt} \, dt, \tag{2.11.2}$$

and can then be treated by the rules discussed.

An interesting special case occurs when $C$ is a closed contour. It may be possible to write a parametric representation in terms of a central angle $\theta$. The integrand is then a periodic function of $\theta$ and, if it is sufficiently smooth, can be very accurately integrated by use of a mean value as developed in Section 2.9. Thus, if $\mathscr{E}$ designates the ellipse

$$\begin{aligned} x &= a \cos \theta, \\ y &= b \sin \theta, \end{aligned} \quad 0 \leqslant \theta \leqslant 2\pi,$$

then

$$\int_{\mathscr{E}} f(x, y) \, ds = \int_0^{2\pi} f(a \cos \theta, b \sin \theta) \sqrt{a^2 \sin^2 \theta + b^2 \cos^2 \theta} \, d\theta$$

$$\approx \frac{2\pi}{N} \sum_{k=0}^{N-1} f\left(a \cos \frac{2\pi k}{N}, b \sin \frac{2\pi k}{N}\right) \sqrt{a^2 \sin^2 \frac{2\pi k}{N} + b^2 \cos^2 \frac{2\pi k}{N}}. \tag{2.11.3}$$

**Example.**  Compute the length of the perimeters of ellipses of various eccentricities, using 60 points.

| $a$ | $b$ | Approximate value of $\frac{1}{4}$ perimeter | Exact value |
|-----|-----|----------------------------------------------|-------------|
| 1.0 | .80 | 1.4180 830 | 1.4180 834 |
| 1.0 | .40 | 1.1506 554 | 1.1506 556 |
| 1.0 | .20 | 1.0505 019 | 1.0505 022 |
| 1.0 | .10 | 1.0159 888 | 1.0159 935 |

### 2.11.1  Contour Integrals in the Complex Plane

Suppose that $z = x + iy$ and $f(z)$ is a function of a complex variable. Write $f(z) = R(x, y) + iI(x, y)$. Then

$$\int_C f(z)\, dz = \int_C (R + iI)(dx + i\, dy)$$

$$= \int_C (R\, dx - I\, dy) + i \int_C (I\, dx + R\, dy). \quad (2.11.1.1)$$

In this way, a complex contour integral may be expressed as the sum of real contour integrals and can be treated as before.

If $f(z)$ is a *regular analytic* function in a simply connected region $B$ that contains an open contour $C$ in its interior, then, by Cauchy's Theorem in the theory of analytic functions, the contour $C$ may be replaced by any other contour that lies in $B$ and starts and ends at the same points as $C$. In particular, under proper conditions of regularity, $C$ may be replaced by the straight line joining its end points, or by two straight lines—one parallel to the $x$-axis and one to the $y$-axis.

If $f(z)$ is analytic, it is also possible to give rules of approximate integration which involve values of the function that are off the contour $C$. The following formula of interpolatory type has been derived by Birkhoff and Young:

$$\int_{z_0 - h}^{z_0 + h} f(z)\, dz = \frac{h}{15} \left[ 24f(z_0) + 4[f(z_0 + h) + f(z_0 - h)] \right.$$

$$\left. - [f(z_0 + ih) + f(z_0 - ih)] + R. \quad (2.11.1.2) \right.$$

The remainder $R$ satisfies

$$|R| \leqslant \tfrac{1}{1890} |h|^7 \max_{z \in S} |f^{(6)}(z)|, \quad (2.11.1.3)$$

where $S$ denotes the square whose vertices are $z_0 + i^k h$ ($k = 0, 1, 2, 3$; $i = \sqrt{-1}$).

**References.**  Birkhoff and Young [1], D. Young [1].

## 2.12   Improper Integrals

Improper integrals occur with great frequency in computational work and must be handled by special devices.

Let us assume that the integral to be evaluated is in the form $\int_0^1 f(x)\, dx$, where $f(x)$ is continuous in $0 < x \leqslant 1$ but not in $0 \leqslant x \leqslant 1$. For example, $(x)$ may be unbounded in the vicinity of $x = 0$.

### 2.12.1   Proceeding to the Limit

The basic definition

$$\int_0^1 f(x)\, dx = \lim_{r \to 0^+} \int_r^1 f(x)\, dx \qquad (2.12.1.1)$$

suggests a primitive mode of procedure. Let $1 > r_1 > r_2 > \cdots$ be a sequence of points that converge to 0, for example $r_n = 2^{-n}$. Write

$$\int_0^1 f(x)\, dx = \int_{r_1}^1 f(x)\, dx + \int_{r_2}^{r_1} f(x)\, dx + \int_{r_3}^{r_2} f(x)\, dx + \cdots. \qquad (2.12.1.2)$$

Each of the integrals on the right-hand side is proper, and the evaluations are terminated when $\left| \int_{r_n}^{r_{n+1}} f(x)\, dx \right| \leqslant \varepsilon$. This is only a practical criterion and is not correct theoretically.

**Example**

$$I = \int_0^1 \frac{dx}{x^{1/2} + x^{1/3}}, \qquad I_n = \int_{r_n}^1 \frac{dx}{x^{1/2} + x^{1/3}}, \qquad r_n = 2^{-n}.$$

| $n$ | $I_n$ | Number of functional evaluations |
|---|---|---|
| 1 | .2849 2598 | 9 |
| 2 | .4744 8022 | 18 |
| 4 | .6832 3927 | 44 |
| 8 | .8128 0497 | 80 |
| 16 | .8402 9678 | 176 |
| 32 | .8411 1612 | 344 |
| 40 | .8411 1663 | 432 |
| Exact value | .8411 1692 | |

Each integral $\int_{r_{n-1}}^{r_n}$ was computed (presumably correct to five figures) by an adaptive modification of the Romberg integration scheme available on the Brown University computer. (See Section 6.3.)

### 2.12.2    Truncation of the Interval

In some instances it might be possible to obtain an estimate of $\int_0^r f(x)\,dx$ without much difficulty. If $\left|\int_0^r f(x)\,dx\right| \leqslant \varepsilon$, then we can simply evaluate the proper integral $\int_r^1 f(x)\,dx$.

**Example.**   Estimate

$$\int_0^r \frac{g(x)}{x^{1/2} + x^{1/3}}\,dx,$$

where $g(x)$ is in $C[0, 1]$ and satisfies $|g(x)| \leqslant 1$. Since $x^{1/2} \leqslant x^{1/3}$ in $[0, 1]$, we have

$$\left|\frac{g(x)}{x^{1/2} + x^{1/3}}\right| \leqslant \frac{1}{2x^{1/2}}.$$

Hence

$$\left|\int_0^r \frac{g(x)}{x^{1/2} + x^{1/3}}\,dx\right| \leqslant \frac{1}{2}\int_0^r \frac{dx}{x^{1/2}} = r^{1/2}.$$

This suggests that we take $r \leqslant 10^{-6}$ for an accuracy of $10^{-3}$.

### 2.12.3    Change of Variable

A change of variable which will eliminate the singularity can sometimes be found. For example, if $f(x) \in C[0, 1]$, the change of variable $t^n = x$ transforms the integral

$$\int_0^1 x^{-1/n} f(x)\,dx, \qquad n \geqslant 2,$$

into $n\int_0^1 f(t^n)t^{n-2}\,dt$, which is a proper integral.

If the improper integral $\int_0^1 f(x)\log x\,dx, f(x) \in C[0, 1], f(0) \neq 0$ is treated by the obvious substitution $t = -\log x$, we obtain $-\int_0^\infty te^{-t}f(e^{-t})\,dt$, an integral with an infinite range of integration. This sort of transformation may result only in exchanging one kind of difficulty for another.

### 2.12.4    Elimination of the Singularity

It may be possible to "subtract out" the singularity. For example, evaluate

$$\int_0^1 \frac{\cos x}{\sqrt{x}}\,dx.$$

Write

$$\int_0^1 \frac{\cos x}{\sqrt{x}}\, dx = \int_0^1 \frac{dx}{\sqrt{x}} + \int_0^1 \frac{\cos x - 1}{\sqrt{x}}\, dx = 2 + \int_0^1 \frac{\cos x - 1}{\sqrt{x}}\, dx.$$

Now, since $\cos x - 1 \approx x^2/2$ near $x = 0$, this last integrand is now in $C[0,1]$. For accurate numerical work it would be better to subtract off more and write

$$\int_0^1 \frac{\cos x}{\sqrt{x}}\, dx = \int_0^1 \frac{1 - \frac{1}{2}x^2}{\sqrt{x}}\, dx + \int_0^1 \frac{\cos x - 1 + \frac{1}{2}x^2}{\sqrt{x}}\, dx.$$

With this simple integrand, the whole expansion of $\cos x$ can, of course, be used.

The method of eliminating the singularity may be particularly valuable in the case of an indefinite integral. Let

$$I(x) = \int_0^x \frac{e^{-t}\, dt}{1 - t}. \tag{2.12.4.1}$$

In the neighborhood of $t = 1$, the integrand behaves like $e^{-1}/(1 - t)$. Hence we write

$$I(x) = e^{-1} \int_0^x \frac{dt}{1 - t} + \int_0^x \left( \frac{e^{-t} - e^{-1}}{1 - t} \right) dt$$

$$= -e^{-1} \log (1 - x) + \int_0^x \left( \frac{e^{-t} - e^{-1}}{1 - t} \right) dt. \tag{2.12.4.2}$$

The second integrand is now in $C[0, 1]$.

The general method is to subtract from the singular integrand $f(x)$ a function $g(x)$ whose integral is known in closed form and is such that $f(x) - g(x)$ is no longer singular. The function $g(x)$ must therefore mimic the behavior of $f(x)$ closely at its singular point.

Integration by parts may be used from time to time. For example, integrating by parts, we have

$$\int_0^1 \frac{\cos x}{\sqrt{x}}\, dx = 2\sqrt{x} \cos x \Big|_0^1 - 2 \int_0^1 \sqrt{x} \sin x\, dx.$$

The burden is now on the integrand $\sqrt{x} \sin x$, which is no longer unbounded (but has an unbounded derivative).

**References.** Abramowitz [1], Fröberg [1, pp. 172–175], Mineur [1, Chap. 13].

### 2.12.5 Integration Formulas of Interpolatory Type

Let $w(x)$ be a fixed function with a singularity in the neighborhood of $x = 0$, but such that $\int_0^1 w(x)x^k \, dx$ exists for $k = 0, 1, \ldots, n$. For a given sequence of abscissas $0 < x_0 < x_1 < \cdots < x_n \leqslant 1$, we can determine weights $w_i$ such that

$$\int_0^1 w(x)f(x) \, dx = \sum_{i=0}^{n} w_i f(x_i) \tag{2.12.5.1}$$

whenever $f(x) \in \mathscr{P}_n$. This leads to the approximate integration formula

$$\int_0^1 w(x)f(x) \, dx \approx \sum_{i=0}^{n} w_i f(x_i). \tag{2.12.5.2}$$

For example, let $w(x) = x^{-1/2}$, $x_0 = \frac{1}{3}$, $x_1 = \frac{2}{3}$, $x_2 = 1$. Then the $w_i$ are determined by the linear system

$$w_1 + w_2 + w_3 = \int_0^1 x^{-1/2} \, dx = 2,$$

$$\frac{w_1}{3} + \frac{2w_2}{3} + w_3 = \int_0^1 x^{-1/2}x \, dx = \frac{2}{3}, \tag{2.12.5.3}$$

$$\frac{w_1}{9} + \frac{4w_2}{9} + w_3 = \int_0^1 x^{-1/2}x^2 \, dx = \frac{2}{5}.$$

This leads to the rule

$$\int_0^1 x^{-1/2} f(x) \, dx \approx \tfrac{14}{5}f(\tfrac{1}{3}) - \tfrac{8}{5}f(\tfrac{2}{3}) + \tfrac{4}{5}f(1). \tag{2.12.5.4}$$

It may be more convenient to use it in the form

$$\int_0^r x^{-1/2}f(x) \, dx \approx r^{1/2}\left(\frac{14}{5}f\left(\frac{r}{3}\right) - \frac{8}{5}f\left(\frac{2}{3}r\right) + \frac{4}{5}f(r)\right). \tag{2.12.5.5}$$

As a second example, we quote the formula of A. Young,

$$\int_{-1}^1 \frac{f(x)}{\sqrt{1-x^2}} \, dx \approx \frac{\pi}{6}\left[f(-1) + 2f\left(-\frac{1}{2}\right) + 2f\left(\frac{1}{2}\right) + f(1)\right]. \tag{2.12.5.6}$$

**References.** Abramowitz [1], Kaplan [1], Luke [1], [3], A. Young [1].

### 2.12.6 Formulas of Gauss Type

Singularities may also be accommodated by means of Gauss-type formulas. The integral is written in the form

$$I = \int_a^b w(x)f(x) \, dx, \tag{2.12.6.1}$$

where $w(x)$ is a fixed nonnegative weight function. The moments $\int_a^b w(x)x^n\, dx$ are assumed to exist for $n = 0, 1, 2, \ldots$, but $w(x)$ may have one or more singularities in the interval $[a, b]$.

The most thoroughly investigated case is that of the Jacobi weight

$$w(x) = (1 - x)^\alpha (1 + x)^\beta, \qquad \alpha > -1, \qquad \beta > -1. \quad (2.12.6.2)$$

If either $\alpha < 0$ or $\beta < 0$, we have an unbounded singularity. The Gauss–Jacobi formulas were discussed in Section 2.7. Some special cases should be noted.

$$\int_0^1 \sqrt{1 - x}\, f(x)\, dx = \sum_{k=1}^n w_k f(x_k)$$
$$+ \frac{2^{4n+3}[(2n + 1)!]^4}{(2n)!(4n + 3)[(4n + 2)!]^2} f^{(2n)}(\xi), \qquad 0 < \xi < 1. \quad (2.12.6.3)$$

In this formula, $x_k = 1 - \xi_k^2$, where $\xi_k$ is the $k$th positive zero of the Legendre polynomial $P_{2n+1}(x)$, and $w_k = 2\xi_k^2 w_k^{(2n+1)}$, where $w_k^{(2n+1)}$ is the weight corresponding to $\xi_k$ in the rule $G_{2n+1}$.

$$\int_0^1 \frac{f(x)}{\sqrt{1 - x}} dx = \sum_{k=1}^n w_k f(x_k) + \frac{2^{4n+1}}{4n + 1} \frac{[(2n)!]^3}{[(4n)!]^2} f^{(2n)}(\xi), \qquad 0 < \xi < 1. \quad (2.12.6.4)$$

Here $x_k = 1 - \xi_k^2$, where $\xi_k$ is the $k$th positive zero of $P_{2n}(x)$, and $w_k = 2 w_k^{(2n)}$ where $w_k^{(2n)}$ is the weight corresponding to $\xi_k$ in the rule $G_{2n}$.

$$\int_{-1}^1 \frac{f(x)}{\sqrt{1 - x^2}} dx = \frac{\pi}{n} \sum_{k=1}^n f(x_k) + \frac{\pi}{(2n)!\,2^{2n-1}} f^{(2n)}(\xi), \qquad -1 < \xi < 1; \quad (2.12.6.5)$$

$$x_k = \cos \frac{(2k - 1)}{2n} \pi.$$

$$\int_{-1}^1 \sqrt{1 - x^2}\, f(x)\, dx = \sum_{k=1}^n w_k f(x_k) + \frac{\pi}{(2n)!\,2^{2n+1}} f^{(2n)}(\xi), \qquad -1 < \xi < 1; \quad (2.12.6.6)$$

$$x_k = \cos \frac{k + 1}{n + 1} \pi, \qquad w_k = \frac{\pi}{n + 1} \sin^2 \frac{k + 1}{n + 1} \pi.$$

$$\int_0^1 \sqrt{\frac{x}{1 - x}}\, f(x)\, dx = \sum_{k=1}^n w_k f(x_k) + \frac{\pi}{(2n)!\,2^{4n+1}} f^{(2n)}(\xi), \qquad 0 < \xi < 1; \quad (2.12.6.7)$$

$$x_k = \cos^2 \frac{2k - 1}{2n + 1} \frac{\pi}{2}, \qquad w_k = \frac{2\pi}{2n + 1} x_k.$$

Weights and abscissas for Gaussian formulas for the integral $\int_0^1 \log(1/x)f(x)\,dx$ can be found in Anderson. Similar tables for $\int_0^h \log x\,f(x)\,dx$ can be found in Price.

**References.** Anderson [1], Krylov, Lugin, and Ianovitch [1], NBS Handbook [1, p. 920], Price [1], Stroud and Secrest [1].

### 2.12.7 Ignoring the Singularity

It is also possible to ignore the fact that the integrand has a singularity and merely use standard rules for approximate integration. Suppose we would like to compute $\int_0^1 f(x)\,dx$, where $f(x)$ is unbounded in the neighborhood of $x = 0$. We can arbitrarily set $f(0) = 0$ (or any other value) and use a sequence of trapezoidal rules or any sequence of rules. Or we might use a sequence of rules that do not involve the value of $f(x)$ at $x = 0$.

**Example**

$$\int_0^1 \frac{dx}{\sqrt{x}} = 2.0$$

| | | | |
|---|---|---|---|
| $32 \times S$ | 1.8427 | $G_2$ | 1.65068 |
| $64 \times S$ | 1.8887 | $G_3$ | 1.75086 |
| $128 \times S$ | 1.9213 | $G_4$ | 1.80634 |
| $256 \times S$ | 1.9444 | $G_{10}$ | 1.91706 |
| $512 \times S$ | 1.9606 | $G_{16}$ | 1.94722 |
| $1024 \times S$ | 1.9721 | $G_{32}$ | 1.97321 |
| | $S$ = Simpson | $G$ = Gauss | |

The convergence of $n \times S$ is very slow, and the comparison with $G_n$ is striking.

The method of "ignoring the singularity" *may not work if the integrand is oscillatory.*

**Example**

$$\int_0^1 \frac{1}{x}\sin\frac{1}{x}\,dx = \int_1^\infty \frac{\sin x}{x}\,dx = .624713$$

| | |
|---|---|
| $32 \times S$ | 2.3123 |
| $64 \times S$ | 1.6946 |
| $128 \times S$ | $-.6083$ |
| $256 \times S$ | 1.2181 |
| $512 \times S$ | .7215 |
| $1024 \times S$ | .3178 |

No pattern of convergence is discernible from these computations. However, if the integrand is monotonic in a neighborhood of its singularity, it can be shown that the method is convergent to the proper answer. More precisely, let $R$ designate a fixed $m$-point rule of approximate integration in $[0, 1]$:

$$R(f) = \sum_{k=1}^{m} w_k f(x_k)$$

with

$$0 \leqslant x_1 < x_2 < \cdots < x_m \leqslant 1, \qquad w_k > 0, \qquad \sum_{k=1}^{m} w_k = 1,$$

and let $R_n$ designate the compound rule that arises by applying $R$ to each of the $n$ subintervals $[0, 1/n], [1/n, 2/n], \ldots, [(n-1)/n, 1]$.

THEOREM.   *If $f(x)$ is a monotonic increasing integrable singular function with a singularity at $x = 0$, then*

$$\lim_{n \to \infty} R_n(f) = \int_0^1 f(x)\, dx. \tag{2.12.7.1}$$

On the whole, ignoring the singularity is a tricky business and should be avoided whenever possible.

**Reference.**   Davis and Rabinowitz [7].

### 2.12.8   *Numerical Evaluation of the Cauchy Principal Value*

Suppose that $a < c < b$ and that $f(x)$ is unbounded in the neighborhood of $x = c$. Suppose, however, that the Cauchy principal value of $\int_a^b f(x)\, dx$,

$$\lim_{r \to 0^+} \left[ \int_a^{c-r} f(x)\, dx + \int_{c+r}^b f(x)\, dx \right],$$

exists. The following analytical device is occasionally useful to obtain this value. It is no restriction to take $c = 0$ and to take the integral in the form $\int_{-a}^a f(x)\, dx$. Set

$$g(x) = \tfrac{1}{2}[f(x) - f(-x)], \qquad h(x) = \tfrac{1}{2}[f(x) + f(-x)]. \tag{2.12.8.1}$$

Then

$$f(x) = g(x) + h(x), \tag{2.12.8.2}$$

where $g(x)$ is an odd function,

$$g(x) = -g(-x), \tag{2.12.8.3}$$

and $h(x)$ is an even function,

$$h(x) = h(-x). \tag{2.12.8.4}$$

Hence

$$\int_{-a}^{-r} f(x)\, dx + \int_r^a f(x)\, dx$$

$$= \int_{-a}^{-r} g(x)\, dx + \int_r^a g(x)\, dx + \int_{-a}^{-r} h(x)\, dx + \int_r^a h(x)\, dx = 2\int_r^a h(x)\, dx. \tag{2.12.8.5}$$

Therefore,

$$P\int_{-a}^a f(x)\, dx = 2 \lim_{r \to 0^+} \int_r^a h(x)\, dx = 2\int_0^a h(x)\, dx$$

$$= \int_0^a (f(x) + f(-x))\, dx. \tag{2.12.8.6}$$

It is possible that $h(x)$ has no singularity at $x = 0$. In most cases, however, this device reduces the determination of a Cauchy principal value to that of an ordinary integral with a singularity at $x = 0$.

The same device can be used for Cauchy principal values at $\infty$. We have

$$P\int_{-\infty}^{\infty} f(x)\, dx = 2\int_0^{\infty} h(x)\, dx. \tag{2.12.8.7}$$

**Examples**

(1) $$P\int_{-1}^1 \frac{dx}{x}$$

Here

$$h(x) = \frac{1}{2}\left(\frac{1}{x} - \frac{1}{x}\right) = 0,$$

so that

$$P\int_{-1}^1 \frac{dx}{x} = 0.$$

(2) $$P\int_{-1}^1 \frac{e^x}{x}\, dx$$

Here

$$h(x) = \frac{1}{2}\left(\frac{e^x}{x} + \frac{e^{-x}}{-x}\right) = \frac{1}{x}\sinh x.$$

Hence

$$P \int_{-1}^{1} \frac{e^x}{x} \, dx = 2 \int_{0}^{1} \frac{\sinh x}{x} dx.$$

The function $\sinh x/x$ has no singularity at $x = 0$.

The method of subtracting the singularity may also be used. Suppose we consider an integral of the form

$$I = P \int_{a}^{b} \frac{f(t)}{t - x} \, dt, \qquad a < x < b. \tag{2.12.8.8}$$

The integral

$$\int_{a}^{b} \frac{f(t)}{t - x} \, dt$$

is known as the *Hilbert transform* of $f(t)$. We have

$$I = P \int_{a}^{b} \frac{f(t)}{t - x} \, dt = \int_{a}^{b} \frac{f(t) - f(x)}{t - x} \, dt + f(x) P \int_{a}^{b} \frac{dt}{t - x}$$

$$= \int_{a}^{b} \frac{f(t) - f(x)}{t - x} \, dt + f(x) \log \frac{b - x}{x - a}. \tag{2.12.8.9}$$

If we assume that the function

$$\phi(t, x) = \frac{f(t) - f(x)}{t - x} \tag{2.12.8.10}$$

is of class $C^1$ for fixed $x$ and variable $t$, then $\phi(x, x) = f'(x)$ and the integral $\int_{a}^{b} \phi(t, x) \, dt$ in (2.12.8.9) has no difficulties associated with it.

It may be useful to consider

$$\int_{x-h}^{x+h} \phi(t, x) \, dt = \int_{-h}^{h} \frac{f(t + x) - f(x)}{t} \, dt. \tag{2.12.8.11}$$

If $f(t)$ can be expanded in a Taylor series at $t = x$, then we have

$$\int_{x-h}^{x+h} \phi(t, x) \, dt = \int_{-h}^{h} \left( f'(x) + \frac{t f''(x)}{2!} + \frac{t^2 f'''(x)}{3!} + \cdots \right) dt$$

$$= 2h f'(x) + \frac{h^3}{9} f'''(x) + \cdots. \tag{2.12.8.12}$$

**References.** Bareiss and Neuman [1], Longman [3], Stewart [1].

Interpolatory-type and Gauss-type formulas can be developed for Cauchy principal value integrals. Thus, Price has worked out the following rules. The first rule is a nine-point formula (the coefficient of $f(0)$ is 0), which is exact for $f(t) \in \mathscr{P}_8$.

$$P \int_{-1}^{1} \frac{f(t)\,dt}{t} \approx [Af(1) - f(-1)] + B[f(\tfrac{3}{4}) - f(-\tfrac{3}{4})]$$
$$+ C[f(\tfrac{1}{2}) - f(-\tfrac{1}{2})] + D[f(\tfrac{1}{4}) - f(-\tfrac{1}{4})]. \qquad (2.12.8.13)$$

Here

$$A = \tfrac{2459}{3307} \approx .7435742365,$$
$$B = \tfrac{1856}{3675} \approx .5050340136,$$
$$C = \tfrac{592}{4725} \approx .1252910052, \qquad (2.12.8.14)$$
$$D = \tfrac{9152}{4725} \approx 1.936931217.$$

The second rule is a four-point formula exact for $f(t) \in \mathscr{P}_7$ and, hence, is of Gauss type.

$$P \int_{-1}^{1} \frac{f(t)}{t}\,dt \approx w_1[f(x_1) - f(-x_1)] + w_2[f(x_2) - f(-x_2)]. \qquad (2.12.8.15)$$

Here

$$w_1 = .40394864, \qquad x_1 = .86113631,$$
$$w_2 = 1.91818095, \qquad x_2 = .33998104. \qquad (2.12.8.16)$$

The weight function $1/t$ is not of one sign over $[-1, 1]$, and this is reflected in the fact that the weights in the rule (2.12.8.15) are not of one sign.

**Reference.** Price [1].

A special treatment of the Cauchy principal value integral,

$$T(f) = \frac{1}{2\pi} \int_{-\pi}^{\pi} \cot \frac{1}{2}(\theta - \phi) f(\phi)\,d\phi, \qquad (2.12.8.17)$$

which occurs in aerodynamics can be found in Serbin. A deeper study of the numerical treatment of Hilbert transforms is given in Bareiss and Neuman.

**References.** Bareiss and Neuman [1], Serbin [1].

### 2.13 Indefinite Integration

The problem here is the computation of

$$F(x) = \int_{a}^{x} f(t)\,dt, \qquad a \leqslant x \leqslant b. \qquad (2.13.1)$$

We shall also consider briefly the more complicated indefinite integral in which the integrand also depends on $x$:

$$F(x) = \int_a^x f(x, t)\, dt, \qquad a \leqslant x \leqslant b. \tag{2.13.2}$$

The integral (2.13.1) may be considered from several points of view. These include (1) regarding (2.13.1) as a definite integral over a variable range and (2) regarding $F(x)$ as the solution to the differential equation

$$\frac{dF}{dx} = f(x), \qquad F(a) = 0. \tag{2.13.3}$$

The simple (and often very satisfactory) approach consists in dividing the interval of integration $a \leqslant x \leqslant b$ into a set of subintervals and applying a rule of approximate integration to each subinterval. Simpson's rule is widely used for this purpose despite the fact that it advances the integration two steps at a time. To get started, we may use, for example, the following rule (of "overhanging" type):

$$\int_a^{a+h} f(x)\, dx \approx \frac{h}{12}\, [5f(a) + 8f(a + h) - f(a + 2h)]. \tag{2.13.4}$$

*Indefinite Integration via Differential Equations*

Some of the standard techniques reduce to familiar rules. Consider, for example, the classical Runge–Kutta method for the solution of

$$\frac{dy}{dx} = g(x, y), \qquad y(x_0) = y_0. \tag{2.13.5}$$

The relevant formulas are

$$y_{m+1} = y_m + \frac{h}{6}(k_1 + 2k_2 + 2k_3 + k_4),$$

$$k_1 = g(x_m, y_m),$$

$$k_2 = g\left(x_m + \frac{h}{2}, y_m + \frac{hk_1}{2}\right), \tag{2.13.6}$$

$$k_3 = g\left(x_m + \frac{h}{2}, y_m + \frac{hk_2}{2}\right),$$

$$k_4 = g(x_m + h, y_m + hk_3).$$

Here $y_m$ is the computed value of the solution at $x_m$ and $x_{m+1} - x_m = h$. When $g(x, y) = f(x)$, these formulas reduce to

$$y_{m+1} = y_m + \frac{h}{6}\left[f(x_m) + 4f\left(x_m + \frac{h}{2}\right) + f(x_m + h)\right]. \quad (2.13.7)$$

This is equivalent to

$$\int_{x_m}^{x_{m+1}} f(x)\, dx \approx \frac{h}{6}\left[f(x_m) + 4f\left(x_m + \frac{h}{2}\right) + f(x_m + h)\right], \quad (2.13.8)$$

which is merely Simpson's rule applied to $[x_m, x_{m+1}]$.

Other Runge–Kutta rules may reduce to higher order integration formulas when $g$ is independent of $y$. For example, King has developed Runge–Kutta rules which reduce to 5th-order Radau integration and 6th-order Lobatto integration.

A general *multistep method* for indefinite integration would consist in computing the value of the integral at the next step, $y_{n+1}$, in terms of values of the integral previously computed, $y_n, y_{n-1}, \ldots$, and in terms of the values of the integrand $f(x_{n+1}), f(x_n), f(x_{n-1}), \ldots$. For example, a formula of this type is

$$y_{n+1} = \tfrac{1}{8}[9y_n - y_{n-2} + 3h(f(x_{n+1}) + 2f(x_n) - f(x_{n-1}))] - \tfrac{1}{40}h^4(f^{(5)}(\xi)), \quad (2.13.9)$$

sometimes used. Multistep methods are of interest principally in the solution of differential equations. They lead immediately to questions of numerical stability, and the subject will not be pursued here.

The corrector formula in the predictor–corrector pair

$$P: \quad \bar{y}_{m+1} = y_{m-1} + 2hf(x_m, y_m),$$

$$C: \quad y_{m+1} = y_m + \frac{h}{2}[f(x_m, y_m) + f(x_{m+1}, \bar{y}_{m+1})], \quad (2.13.10)$$

reduces to the trapezoidal rule.

When the indefinite integral is desired, it may be convenient to exhibit the computation as a simple recurrence. For example, the trapezoidal rule may be written in the form

$$y_{n+1} = y_n + \frac{h}{2}[f(x_n) + f(x_{n+1})]. \quad (2.13.11)$$

**Example.**  Compute

$$y(x) = \int_0^x e^t\, dt = e^x - 1 \qquad \text{for} \quad x = 0(.1)1,$$

using the trapezoidal rule.

| $x$ | $y_n$ | Error $= y_n - y$ |
|------|--------|--------|
| .0 | .0000 | .0000 |
| .1 | .1053 | .0001 |
| .2 | .2216 | .0002 |
| .3 | .3501 | .0003 |
| .4 | .4922 | .0004 |
| .5 | .6493 | .0005 |
| .6 | .8228 | .0007 |
| .7 | 1.0146 | .0008 |
| .8 | 1.2266 | .0010 |
| .9 | 1.4608 | .0012 |
| 1.0 | 1.7197 | .0014 |

**References.** Hamming [1, Chap. 13], King [1], Krylov [1, Chaps. 13–16].

## 2.13.1 Application of Approximation Theory; Tschebyscheff Series

Suppose that it is desired to compute

$$F(x) = \int_a^x f(t)\,dt, \qquad a \leqslant x \leqslant b, \quad -\infty < a < b < \infty, \qquad (2.13.1.1)$$

for a given integrand $f(x)$. Suppose, further, that we are in possession of an approximation to $f(x)$:

$$f(x) = \phi_0(x) + \phi_1(x) + \cdots + \phi_n(x) + \varepsilon(x), \qquad a \leqslant x \leqslant b, \qquad (2.13.1.2)$$

where

$$|\varepsilon(x)| \leqslant \varepsilon, \qquad a \leqslant x \leqslant b \qquad (2.13.1.3)$$

and where each of the approximating functions $\phi_i(x)$ has an indefinite integral

$$\psi_i(x) = \int_a^x \phi_i(t)\,dt, \qquad (2.13.1.4)$$

which is simple to handle. Then, integrating (2.13.1.2), we obtain

$$F(x) = \int_a^x f(t)\,dt = \psi_0(x) + \psi_1(x) + \cdots + \psi_n(x) + \eta(x), \qquad a \leqslant x \leqslant b, \qquad (2.13.1.5)$$

where

$$|\eta(x)| = \left| \int_a^x \varepsilon(t)\,dt \right| \leqslant (b - a)\varepsilon. \qquad (2.13.1.6)$$

The closed form (2.13.1.5) of the indefinite integral may be very convenient for further manipulation. In principle, we may employ any sort of approximation of form (2.13.1.2), but in practice it turns out to be particularly convenient to use expansions in terms of *Tschebyscheff polynomials*.

We begin with a brief introduction to the Tschebyscheff polynomials. The fundamental interval on which we work will be assumed for convenience as $[-1, 1]$. If this is not the case, a simple linear transformation will make it so. The Tschebyscheff polynomials (of the first kind) are defined by

$$T_n(x) = \cos{(n \arccos x)} = x^n + \binom{n}{2} x^{n-2}(x^2 - 1) + \cdots,$$

$$n = 0, 1, \ldots, \quad -1 \leqslant x \leqslant 1. \tag{2.13.1.7}$$

It is easy to compute the first few Tschebyscheff polynomials explicitly by using (2.13.1.7). We find

$$\begin{aligned}
T_0(x) &= 1, \\
T_1(x) &= x, \\
T_2(x) &= 2x^2 - 1, \\
T_3(x) &= 4x^3 - 3x, \\
T_4(x) &= 8x^4 - 8x^2 + 1, \\
&\vdots
\end{aligned} \tag{2.13.1.8}$$

The Tschebyscheff polynomials satisfy a three-term recurrence relationship:

$$T_{n+1}(x) = 2xT_n(x) - T_{n-1}(x), \quad n = 1, 2, \ldots. \tag{2.13.1.9}$$

*Proof.*

$$\cos{(n + 1)\theta} = \cos{n\theta} \cos{\theta} - \sin{n\theta} \sin{\theta},$$

$$\cos{(n - 1)\theta} = \cos{n\theta} \cos{\theta} + \sin{n\theta} \sin{\theta}.$$

Adding and rearranging, we have

$$\cos{(n + 1)\theta} = 2 \cos{n\theta} \cos{\theta} - \cos{(n - 1)\theta}.$$

Now we set $\cos{\theta} = x$, $\cos{n\theta} = T_n(x)$, and (2.13.1.9) is obtained.

The Tschebyscheff polynomials are easily bounded:

$$|T_n(x)| \leqslant 1, \quad -1 \leqslant x \leqslant 1. \tag{2.13.1.10}$$

This follows from the fact that on $-1 \leqslant x \leqslant 1$, $T_n$ is a cosine.

The indefinite integrals of Tschebyscheff polynomials are themselves linear combinations of Tschebyscheff polynomials:

$$\int_{-1}^{x} T_0(x)\, dx = T_1(x) + 1,$$

$$\int_{-1}^{x} T_1(x)\, dx = \tfrac{1}{4}T_2(x) - \tfrac{1}{4}, \qquad\qquad\qquad (2.13.1.11)$$

$$\int_{-1}^{x} T_n(x)\, dx = \frac{1}{2}\left(\frac{T_{n+1}(x)}{n+1} - \frac{T_{n-1}(x)}{n-1}\right) + (-1)^{n-1}\frac{1}{n^2-1}, \qquad n = 2, 3, \ldots .$$

*Proof.* The cases $n = 0, 1$ can be had by inspection. For $n > 1$, we have

$$\int_{-1}^{x} T_n(x)\, dx = \int_{-1}^{x} \cos(n \arccos x)\, dx = \int_{\cos^{-1}x}^{\pi} \cos n\theta \sin\theta\, d\theta$$

$$= \left[-\frac{\cos(n+1)\theta}{n+1} + \frac{\cos(n-1)\theta}{n-1}\right]_{\cos^{-1}x}^{\pi}$$

$$= \frac{1}{2}\left[\frac{1}{n+1}T_{n+1}(x) - \frac{1}{n-1}T_{n-1}(x)\right]$$

$$+ \frac{1}{2}\left[\frac{(-1)^{n-1}}{n-1} - \frac{(-1)^{n+1}}{n+1}\right].$$

We have used the identity

$$\cos n\theta \sin\theta = \tfrac{1}{2}[\sin(n+1)\theta - \sin(n-1)\theta]$$

in this derivation.

The Tschebyscheff polynomials are orthogonal in two ways:

$$\int_{-1}^{1} \frac{T_m(x)T_n(x)}{\sqrt{1-x^2}}\, dx = \begin{cases} \pi, & m = n = 0, \\ \dfrac{\pi}{2}, & m = n \neq 0, \\ 0, & m \neq n; \end{cases} \qquad (2.13.1.12)$$

$$\sum_{j=0}^{n}{}'' T_r(x_j)T_s(x_j) = \begin{cases} n, & r = s = 0 \quad\text{or}\quad n, \\ \dfrac{n}{2}, & r = s \neq 0 \quad\text{or}\quad n, \\ 0, & r \neq s. \end{cases} \qquad (2.13.1.13)$$

Here $x_j = \cos(\pi j/n)$; $n > 0$; $r, s \leqslant n$. The double prime on the sigma indicates that in forming the sum, the terms with subscripts $j = 0$ and $j = n$ are to be halved. (See, for example, Lanczos [1, pp. vii, xvii].)

It can be shown that under mild conditions on the function $f(x)$, for example if $f(x)$ is of class $C^1$ in $[-1, 1]$, then $f(x)$ may be expanded in a uniformly convergent series of $T$'s:

$$f(x) = \tfrac{1}{2}a_0 + a_1 T_1(x) + a_2 T_2(x) \cdots . \tag{2.13.1.14}$$

The constants $a_r$ are the "Fourier–Tschebyscheff" coefficients of $f(x)$ and are given by the formula

$$a_r = \frac{2}{\pi} \int_{-1}^{1} \frac{f(x)T_r(x)}{\sqrt{1 - x^2}} \, dx = \frac{2}{\pi} \int_0^\pi f(\cos \theta) \cos r\theta \, d\theta. \tag{2.13.1.15}$$

For many functions the sequence $a_0, a_1, \ldots$ decreases to zero rapidly. Furthermore, the partial sum $\tfrac{1}{2}a_0 + a_1 T_1(x) + \cdots + a_N T_N(x)$ is a polynomial of degree $\leqslant N$, which is very close to the best approximation to $f(x)$ by polynomials $p_N(x)$ of this degree, approximation being measured in the sense of $\max_{-1 \leqslant x \leqslant 1} |f(x) - p_N(x)|$. (See, for example, Davis [6, pp. 174–175].) In any case, we have the estimate

$$|f(x) - (\tfrac{1}{2}a_0 + \cdots + a_N T_N(x))|$$

$$= \left| \sum_{j=N+1}^{\infty} a_j T_j(x) \right| \leqslant \sum_{j=N+1}^{\infty} |a_j|, \quad -1 \leqslant x \leqslant 1. \tag{2.13.1.16}$$

For a general sort of function, the coefficients $a_k$ cannot be evaluated in terms of closed expressions, and we must seek an approximation to them. What we shall do essentially is to apply a trapezoidal rule of a certain order $n$ to the second integral in (2.13.1.15).

We define constants $\alpha_0, \alpha_1, \ldots, \alpha_n$ by means of

$$\alpha_r = \frac{2}{n} \sum_{j=0}^{n}{}'' f(x_j)T_r(x_j) = \frac{2}{n} \sum_{j=0}^{n}{}'' f\left(\cos \frac{\pi j}{n}\right) \cos \frac{\pi r j}{n}. \tag{2.13.1.17}$$

To see how $\alpha_r$ differs from $a_r$, we have, from (2.13.1.17),

$$\alpha_r = \frac{2}{n} \sum_{s=0}^{\infty}{}' a_s \sum_{j=0}^{n}{}'' T_s(x_j) \, T_r(x_j)$$

$$= a_r + a_{2n-r} + a_{2n+r} + a_{4n-r} + \cdots . \tag{2.13.1.18}$$

The single prime over the sigma means that the term with subscript $s = 0$ is halved. Thus, if $n$ is sufficiently large and if the coefficients $a_0, a_1, \ldots$ decrease rapidly, we have very closely

$$f(x) \approx \frac{a_0}{2} + a_1 T_1(x) + \cdots + a_n T_n(x) \tag{2.13.1.19}$$

with

$$a_r = \frac{2}{n} \sum_{j=0}^{n}{}'' f\left(\cos \frac{\pi j}{n}\right) \cos \frac{\pi r j}{n}. \tag{2.13.1.20}$$

The coefficients $a_r$ are available computationally through (2.13.1.20).

If we integrate the uniformly convergent series (2.13.1.14) term by term, we obtain

$$\int f(x)\, dx = \frac{a_0}{2} T_1(x) + \frac{a_1}{4} T_2(x)$$

$$+ \sum_{r=2} \frac{a_r}{2}\left(\frac{T_{r+1}(x)}{r+1} - \frac{T_{r-1}(x)}{r-1}\right) + \text{constant}$$

$$= \sum_{r=0}{}' A_r T_r(x), \tag{2.13.1.21}$$

where

$$A_r = \frac{a_{r-1} - a_{r+1}}{2r}, \qquad r > 0. \tag{2.13.1.22}$$

The constant $A_0$ should be selected so that the indefinite integral is zero at the lower limit of integration. (See also Section 6.4.)

**References.** Clenshaw [1], Clenshaw and Curtis [1], Davis [6, pp. 60–64, Chap. 10], Lanczos [1].

### 2.13.2 *Indefinite Integration and Approximation*

Indefinite integrals or integrals with a parameter may be used to obtain approximations to functions.

**Example**

$$\arctan x = \int_0^x \frac{dt}{1 + t^2}.$$

Change the interval of integration to $[-1, 1]$ and obtain

$$\arctan x = 2x \int_{-1}^{1} \frac{du}{4 + x^2(u + 1)^2}.$$

Now use a 5-point Gauss rule on this definite integral:

$$\arctan x \approx 2x \left[\frac{w_1}{4 + (1 + x_1)^2 x^2} + \frac{w_2}{4 + (1 + x_2)^2 x^2} + \frac{2 - 2w_1 - 2w_2}{4 + x^2}\right.$$

$$\left. + \frac{w_2}{4 + (1 - x_2)^2 x^2} + \frac{w_1}{4 + (1 - x_1)^2 x^2}\right], \tag{2.13.2.1}$$

where

$$x_1 = .9061\ 7985, \qquad w_1 = .2369\ 2689,$$
$$x_2 = .5384\ 6931, \qquad w_2 = .4786\ 2867.$$

This yields an approximation to arctan $x$, which is accurate to at least seven figures over $0 \leqslant x \leqslant 1$.

### 2.13.3  Indefinite Integration of Nonequally Spaced Data

We may use the trapezoidal rule or, if something "better" is desired, the rule based on overlapping parabolas explained in Section 2.3. For repeated integrals of a function defined on nonequally spaced abscissas, see Thacher.

**Reference.**  Thacher [5].

### 2.13.4  Computation of Integrals of the Form $\int_a^x f(x, t)\, dt$

In general, the integral must be treated as a sequence of definite integrals for $x_0, x_1, \ldots$ . Some computational economies can be obtained when $f(x, t)$ is of a certain form. For example, suppose we have to compute the *convolution integral* $\int_0^x K(x - t) f(t)\, dt$, over the range $0 \leqslant x \leqslant 1$. We make a table of $f(t)$ over the range $0 \leqslant t \leqslant 1$ and of $K(x)$ over the range $0 \leqslant x \leqslant 1$. Referring to the values in this table, we avoid duplication of computing functional values. When convolution integrals are carried out on desk computers, work is facilitated by use of the "moving-strip" technique, wherein the tables are prepared on two strips of paper and placed one on top of the other. The strips are then shifted with each step in $x$.

# CHAPTER 3

# APPROXIMATE INTEGRATION OVER INFINITE INTERVALS

### 3.1  Change of Variable

The substitution $x = e^{-y}$ changes the interval $0 \leqslant y \leqslant \infty$ into the interval $0 \leqslant x \leqslant 1$. Hence, we have the formula

$$\int_0^\infty f(y)\, dy = \int_0^1 \frac{f(-\log x)}{x}\, dx = \int_0^1 \frac{g(x)}{x}\, dx. \qquad (3.1.1)$$

This reduces an integral over an infinite range to one over a finite range. If $g(x)/x$ is bounded in the neighborhood of $x = 0$, then the second integral will be proper. If not, the integral will be improper and we have only exchanged one sort of difficulty for another. An alternative form of this transformation is

$$\int_0^\infty e^{-x} f(x)\, dx = \int_0^1 f\left(\log \frac{1}{x}\right) dx. \qquad (3.1.2)$$

Additional transformations that are useful include

$$\int_a^b f(x)\, dx = (b - a) \int_0^\infty f\left(\frac{a + bt}{1 + t}\right) \frac{dt}{(1 + t)^2}, \qquad (3.1.3)$$

$$\int_0^{\pi/2} f(x)\, dx = \int_0^\infty f(x) \frac{\sin x}{x}\, dx, \qquad (3.1.4)$$

provided that

$$f(x + \pi) = f(x) \quad \text{and} \quad f(x) = f(-x),$$

89

and

$$\int_0^{\pi/2} f(x) \cos x \, dx = \int_0^{\infty} f(x) \frac{\sin x}{x} \, dx, \qquad (3.1.5)$$

provided that

$$f(x + \pi) = -f(x) \qquad \text{and} \qquad f(x) = f(-x).$$

## 3.2  Proceeding to the Limit

The basic definition

$$\int_0^{\infty} f(x) \, dx = \lim_{r \to \infty} \int_0^r f(x) \, dx \qquad (3.2.1)$$

suggests a primitive mode of procedure. Let $0 < r_1 < r_2 < \cdots$ be a sequence of numbers that converge to $\infty$. Write

$$\int_0^{\infty} f(x) \, dx = \int_0^{r_1} f(x) \, dx + \int_{r_1}^{r_2} f(x) \, dx + \cdots. \qquad (3.2.2)$$

Each of the integrals on the right-hand side is proper, and the evaluations are terminated when $\left| \int_{r_n}^{r_{n+1}} f(x) \, dx \right| \leqslant \varepsilon$. This is only a practical termination criterion and is not correct theoretically. For example, when the divergent integral $\int_1^{\infty} dx/x$ is evaluated by such a procedure, a finite answer will be printed out. The interval is frequently doubled at each step; that is, $r_n = 2^n$. The idea behind this selection is that if an arithmetic sequence is used ($r_n = cn$) the contribution of each additional step may be too insignificant to be worth a special computation. Furthermore, it may be less than $\varepsilon$, thus stopping the process.

### Example

$$I_n = \int_0^{r_n} \frac{e^{-x}}{1 + x^4}, \qquad r_n = 2^n.$$

| $n$ | $I_n$ | Number of functional evaluations |
|---|---|---|
| 0 | .5720 2582 | 35 |
| 1 | .6274 5952 | 52 |
| 2 | .6304 3990 | 100 |
| 3 | .6304 7761 | 178 |
| 4 | .6304 7766 | 322 |

### 3.3  Truncation of the Infinite Interval

We may also reduce the infinite interval to a finite interval by ignoring the "tail" of the integrand. Rigorous application of this method requires that the analyst be able to estimate this tail by some simple analytical device.

**Example.** Determine numerically $\int_0^\infty e^{-x^2}\,dx$. We estimate $\int_k^\infty e^{-x^2}\,dx$. For $x \geqslant k$, we have $x^2 \geqslant kx$. Hence

$$\int_k^\infty e^{-x^2}\,dx \leqslant \int_k^\infty e^{-kx}\,dx = \frac{e^{-k^2}}{k}.$$

For $k = 4$, we have $e^{-k^2}/k \approx 10^{-8}$. For a seven-figure computation, it suffices therefore to evaluate $\int_0^4 e^{-x^2}\,dx$ by some standard method.

**Example.** Determine numerically

$$\int_0^\infty \frac{\sin x}{1 + x^2}\,dx.$$

We have

$$\left| \int_{2k\pi}^\infty \frac{\sin x}{1 + x^2}\,dx \right| = |r_1 + r_2 + \cdots|, \qquad \text{where } r_j = \int_{(2k+j-1)\pi}^{(2k+j)\pi} \frac{\sin x}{1 + x^2}\,dx.$$

Since $r_{2n} < 0$, $r_{2n+1} > 0$, and $|r_1| > |r_2| > \cdots$, we have

$$|r_1 + r_2 + \cdots| < r_1 = \int_{2k\pi}^{(2k+1)\pi} \frac{\sin x\,dx}{1 + x^2} < \int_{2k\pi}^{(2k+1)\pi} \frac{dx}{x^2} < \frac{1}{4\pi k^2}.$$

For a truncation error of $10^{-4}$, this analysis suggests that $k \approx 28$.

### 3.4  Primitive Rules for the Infinite Interval

The simple Riemann sum takes on the form

$$h[f(h) + f(2h) + \cdots] = h \sum_{k=1}^\infty f(kh) \tag{3.4.1}$$

in the case of a singly infinite integral.

**Theorem.** *Let $f(x)$ be monotonic for $x \geqslant 0$ and suppose that $\int_0^\infty f(x)\,dx$ exists. Then*

$$\lim_{h \to 0} h \sum_{k=1}^\infty f(kh) = \int_0^\infty f(x)\,dx. \tag{3.4.2}$$

*Proof.* Since $\int_0^\infty f(x)\,dx$ exists, and $f(x)$ is monotonic, it follows that $\lim_{x \to \infty} f(x) = 0$. Furthermore, $f(x)$ must have the same sign throughout

$x \geqslant 0$. Without loss of generality, we can assume $f(x)$ to be positive and decreasing. Since $f(x)$ is decreasing,

$$0 \leqslant \int_{h}^{(n+1)h} f(x)\,dx \leqslant h[f(h) + f(2h) + \cdots + f(nh)] \leqslant \int_{0}^{nh} f(x)\,dx. \qquad (3.4.3)$$

Allow $n \to \infty$, and we have

$$\int_{h}^{\infty} f(x)\,dx \leqslant h \sum_{k=1}^{\infty} f(kh) \leqslant \int_{0}^{\infty} f(x)\,dx. \qquad (3.4.4)$$

Allowing $h \to 0$, we obtain (3.4.2).

COROLLARY. *The theorem holds if $f(x)$ is ultimately monotonic, that is, if there is an $x_0 \geqslant 0$ such that $f(x)$ is monotonic for $x \geqslant x_0$.*

From the inequality (3.4.4) we obtain the error estimate

$$0 \leqslant \int_{0}^{\infty} f(x)\,dx - h \sum_{k=1}^{\infty} f(kh) \leqslant \int_{0}^{h} f(x)\,dx \leqslant hf(0). \qquad (3.4.5)$$

This is an indication of very slow convergence in general.

Under certain circumstances, the trapezoidal rule can give very good approximations to infinite integrals. For the development of this result, we make use of the Euler–Maclaurin formula.

THEOREM. *Let $a$ and $k$ be fixed and let $f(x) \in C^{2k+1}[a, b]$ for all $b \geqslant a$. Suppose, further, that $\int_{a}^{\infty} f(x)\,dx$ exists, that*

$$M = \int_{a}^{\infty} |f^{(2k+1)}(x)|\,dx < \infty,$$

*and that*

$$f'(a) = f'''(a) = \cdots = f^{(2k-1)}(a) = 0,$$

$$f'(\infty) = f'''(\infty) = \cdots = f^{(2k-1)}(\infty) = 0. \qquad (3.4.6)$$

*Then, for fixed $h > 0$,*

$$\left| \int_{a}^{\infty} f(x)\,dx - h\left[ \frac{1}{2}f(a) + f(a+h) + f(a+2h) + \cdots \right] \right| \leqslant \frac{h^{2k+1} M \zeta(2k+1)}{2^{2k}\pi^{2k+1}}. \qquad (3.4.7)$$

*Here $\zeta(k) = \sum_{j=1}^{\infty} j^{-k}$ is the Riemann zeta function.*

*Proof.* From (2.9.15) we have

$$\left| h\left[ \frac{1}{2} f(a) + f(a + h) + \cdots + f(a + (n - 1)h) \right.\right.$$

$$\left. + \frac{1}{2} f(a + nh) \right] - \int_a^{a + nh} f(x)\,dx \bigg| \leq \left| \frac{B_2}{2!} h^2 [f'(a + nh) - f'(a)] \right|$$

$$+ \cdots + \left| \frac{B_{2k}}{(2k)!} h^{2k} [f^{(2k-1)}(a + nh) - f^{(2k-1)}(a)] \right|$$

$$+ h^{2k+1} \int_a^{a+nh} \left| P_{2k+1}\left( \frac{x - a}{h} \right) \right| |f^{(2k+1)}(x)|\,dx.$$

Now allow $n \to \infty$, and use conditions (3.4.6), the definition of $M$, and the inequality (2.9.17) for the periodic function $P_{2k+1}(x)$.

This theorem tells us that if the integrand and all of its odd-order derivatives up to order $2k - 1$ vanish at both ends of an infinite interval, then, as $h \to 0$, the trapezoidal rule will converge to the proper answer with the rapidity of $h^{2k+1}$. If all odd-order derivatives vanish, then the rapidity exceeds $h^{2k+1}$ for *all k*.

A similar theorem can be formulated for integrals of the type $\int_{-\infty}^{\infty} f(x)\,dx$. The Poisson formula related to (3.4.7) is

$$\int_0^\infty f(x)\,dx = h\left\{ \frac{1}{2} f(0) + \sum_{k=1}^\infty f(kh) \right\} - 2 \sum_{k=1}^\infty g\left( \frac{2k\pi}{h} \right), \qquad (3.4.8)$$

where

$$g(x) = \int_0^\infty f(t) \cos xt\,dt. \qquad (3.4.9)$$

**Example** (Hartree)

$$I = \int_0^\infty e^{-x^2}\,dx = \tfrac{1}{2}\sqrt{\pi}.$$

| $h$ | Trapezoidal rule |
|---|---|
| 1.1 | .88674 |
| 1.0 | .88632 0 |
| .9 | .88623 598 |
| .8 | .88622 72808 |
| .7 | .88622 69285 |
| .6 | .88622 69254 8 |
| .5 | .88622 69254 5 |
| Exact value | .88622 69254 5 |

**Example** (Milne)

$$I = \int_{-\infty}^{\infty} \operatorname{sech}^2 x \, dx = 2.0.$$

| $h$ | Trapezoidal rule |
|---|---|
| 1.0 | 2.00408 43212 |
| .8 | 2.00043 29224 |
| .6 | 2.00000 94492 |
| .4 | 2.00000 00036 |
| .2 | 2.00000 00000 |
| Exact value | 2.00000 00000 |

**References.** Hartree [2, p. 116], Goodwin [1], Milne [2].

## 3.5  Formulas of Interpolatory Type

Formulas of the interpolatory type may be developed for infinite intervals as well as for finite intervals. One example will suffice to show how this can be done. Suppose it is desired to obtain a formula for $\int_0^\infty e^{-x} f(x) \, dx$ in terms of the values $f(0), f(h), \ldots, f(nh)$. Write the formal *Newton Series*

$$f(x) \sim \sum_{k=0}^{\infty} \frac{\Delta^k f(0)}{k! h^k} (x)(x - h) \cdots \Big( x - (k - 1)h \Big). \tag{3.5.1}$$

Finite segments of this series interpolate to $f(x)$ at $x = 0, h, \ldots, nh$. Then, formally at least,

$$\int_0^\infty e^{-x} f(x) \, dx \sim \int_0^\infty e^{-x} \sum_{k=0}^{\infty} \frac{\Delta^k f(0)}{k! h^k} x(x - h) \cdots (x - (k - 1)h) \, dx$$

$$\sim \sum_{k=0}^{\infty} \frac{\Delta^k f(0)}{k! h^k} \int_0^\infty e^{-x} x(x - h) \cdots (x - (k - 1)h) \, dx$$

$$= \sum_{k=0}^{\infty} \frac{\Delta^k f(0) m_k}{k! h^k}, \tag{3.5.2}$$

where

$$m_k = \int_0^\infty x(x - h) \cdots (x - (k - 1)h) e^{-x} \, dx$$

$$= h^{k+1} \int_0^\infty t(t - 1) \cdots (t - (k - 1)) e^{-ht} \, dt. \tag{3.5.3}$$

The constants $m_k$ are now precomputed (recurrence is convenient), and we have the approximate integration formula

$$\int_0^\infty e^{-x} f(x)\, dx \approx \sum_{k=0}^n \frac{\Delta^k f(0) m_k}{k!\, h^k}. \tag{3.5.4}$$

It is clear that similar formulas can be developed with other interpolation formulas of the difference calculus such as Stirling's formula, and for weights other than $e^{-x}$. If an unequal spacing of abscissas is desired, Lagrange interpolation would be indicated.

**Example.**  Compute numerically

$$\int_0^\infty \frac{e^{-x}}{2x + 100}\, dx,$$

using $h = \frac{1}{2}$.

| $n$ | |
|-----|----------|
| 0 | .0100 0000 |
| 1 | .0098 0198 |
| 2 | .0098 0780 |
| 3 | .0098 0757 |
| Exact | .0098 0757 |

In view of the fact that a Newton series converges only for a very restricted class of functions $f(x)$, we cannot expect that, as $n \to \infty$, the above integration rule will converge to the proper value with any frequency.

**References.**  Burgoyne [1], Davis [6, pp. 51–52].

### 3.6  *Gaussian Formulas for the Infinite Interval*

The ultimate in the interpolatory formula is, of course, the formula of Gauss type

$$\int_0^\infty w(x) f(x)\, dx \approx \sum_{k=1}^n w_k f(x_k) \tag{3.6.1}$$

or

$$\int_{-\infty}^\infty w(x) f(x)\, dx \approx \sum_{k=1}^n w_k f(x_k), \tag{3.6.2}$$

where the $x_k$ and the $w_k$ have been determined so that the formula is exact for functions $f(x)$ of class $\mathscr{P}_{2n-1}$. The general theory of the Gauss formula has already been discussed in Section 2.7. A set of tables can be developed for any weight function with $\int w(x)\, dx < \infty$, but the most widely employed Gauss-type formulas are the Laguerre formulas and the Hermite formulas.

*Laguerre Formula*

$$\int_0^\infty e^{-x} f(x)\, dx = \sum_{k=1}^n w_k f(x_k) + \frac{(n!)^2}{(2n)!} f^{(2n)}(\xi), \qquad 0 < \xi < \infty. \quad (3.6.3)$$

Here the abscissas $x_k$ are the zeros of the Laguerre polynomials $L_n(x)$ $[L_n(x) = (-1)^n x^n + \cdots]$ and

$$w_k = \frac{(n!)^2 x_k}{[L_{n+1}(x_k)]^2}. \qquad (3.6.4)$$

*Generalized Laguerre Formula*

A more general weight function is $w(x) = x^\alpha e^{-x}$, $\alpha > -1$. We have

$$\int_0^\infty x^\alpha e^{-x} f(x)\, dx = \sum_{k=1}^n w_k f(x_k) + \frac{n!\,\Gamma(n + \alpha + 1)}{(2n)!} f^{(2n)}(\xi), \qquad 0 < \xi < \infty. \quad (3.6.5)$$

The abscissas $x_k$ are the zeros of the generalized or associated Laguerre polynomial $L_n^{(\alpha)}(x)$ and

$$w_k = \frac{n!\,\Gamma(n + \alpha + 1) x_k}{[L_{n+1}^{(\alpha)}(x_k)]^2}. \qquad (3.6.6)$$

*Hermite Formula*

$$\int_{-\infty}^\infty e^{-x^2} f(x)\, dx$$

$$= \sum_{k=1}^n w_k f(x_k) + \frac{n!\sqrt{\pi}}{2^n (2n)!} f^{(2n)}(\xi), \qquad -\infty < \xi < \infty. \quad (3.6.7)$$

The abscissas $x_k$ are the zeros of the Hermite polynomial $H_n(x)$, where

$$H_n(x) = 2^n x^n + \cdots$$

and

$$w_k = \frac{2^{n+1} n!\,\sqrt{\pi}}{[H_{n+1}(x_k)]^2}. \qquad (3.6.8)$$

Information on Gaussian formulas for $\int_{-\infty}^\infty (1 + x^2)^{-k-1} f(x)\, dx$ can be found in Harper and in Haber.

For convergent integrals of the form $\int_0^\infty f(x)\,dx$ and $\int_{-\infty}^\infty f(x)\,dx$, we may also use the Laguerre and Hermite integration formulas, for example in the Laguerre case, by writing

$$\int_0^\infty f(x)\,dx = \int_0^\infty e^{-x}e^x f(x)\,dx \approx \sum_{k=1}^n w_k e^{x_k} f(x_k)$$

$$= \sum_{k=1}^n V_k f(x_k), \qquad \text{where} \quad V_k = w_k e^{x_k}. \qquad (3.6.9)$$

In many tabulations of zeros and weights for Laguerre and Hermite integration, $V_k$ is tabulated along with $x_k$ and $w_k$.

**References.** Aizenshtat, Krylov, and Metleskii [1], Concus, Cassatt, Jaehnig, and Melby [1], Haber [1], Harper [1], NBS Handbook of Mathematical Tables [1, Chap. 25], Rabinowitz and Weiss [1], Shao, Chen, and Frank [1], [2], Stroud and Secrest [1], [2].

### 3.7 Convergence of Formulas of Gauss type for Singly and Doubly Infinite Intervals

Consider the family of Laguerre formulas

$$L_n(f) = \sum_{k=1}^n w_{nk} f(x_{nk}) \approx \int_0^\infty e^{-x} x^\alpha f(x)\,dx, \qquad \alpha > -1, \qquad (3.7.1)$$

which are exact for $f(x) \in \mathscr{P}_{2n-1}$.

THEOREM. *If for all sufficiently large values of x the function $f(x)$ satisfies the inequality*

$$|f(x)| \leqslant \frac{e^x}{x^{\alpha+1+\rho}}, \qquad \text{for some } \rho > 0, \qquad (3.7.2)$$

*then*

$$\lim_{n\to\infty} L_n(f) = \int_0^\infty e^{-x} x^\alpha f(x)\,dx. \qquad (3.7.3)$$

A similar convergence theorem holds for the Hermite formulas

$$H_n(f) = \sum_{k=1}^n w_{nk} f(x_{nk}) \approx \int_{-\infty}^\infty e^{-x^2} f(x)\,dx. \qquad (3.7.4)$$

THEOREM. *If for all sufficiently large values of $|x|$, $f(x)$ satisfies the inequality*

$$|f(x)| \leqslant \frac{e^{x^2}}{|x|^{1+\rho}}, \qquad \text{for some } \rho > 0, \qquad (3.7.5)$$

*then*

$$\lim_{n \to \infty} H_n(f) = \int_{-\infty}^{\infty} e^{-x^2} f(x) \, dx. \tag{3.7.6}$$

The proofs of these theorems, together with some generalizations, can be found in the work of Uspensky.

**Reference.**  Uspensky [1].

**Examples**

1
$$e^{-2} \int_{2}^{\infty} \frac{dx}{x(\log x)^2}$$

2
$$e^{-2} \int_{2}^{\infty} \frac{dx}{x(\log x)^{3/2}}$$

3
$$e^{-2} \int_{2}^{\infty} \frac{dx}{x^{1.01}}$$

4
$$e^{-2} \int_{2}^{\infty} \left(\frac{\sin x}{x}\right) dx \qquad \text{(Sine integral)}$$

5
$$e^{-2} \int_{2}^{\infty} \cos\left(\frac{\pi}{2} x^2\right) dx \qquad \text{(Fresnel integral)}$$

6
$$e^{-2} \int_{2}^{\infty} e^{-x^2} dx \qquad \text{(Complementary error function)}$$

7
$$e^{-2} \int_{2}^{\infty} \frac{\sin (x - 1) \, dx}{\sqrt{x(x - 2)}} \qquad \text{(Bessel function)}$$

8
$$e^{-2} \int_{2}^{\infty} \frac{x \, dx}{(e^x - 1)} \qquad \text{(Debye function)}$$

| Integral | $L_4$ | $L_8$ | $L_{16}$ |
|---|---|---|---|
| 1 | .1451 0750 | .1554 3187 | .1662 3627 |
| 2 | .1610 1337 | .1783 2886 | .1914 2399 |
| 3 | .2701 1936 | .3587 1939 | .4499 6932 |
| 4 | − .0587 1937 6 | − .0407 9735 8 | − .0392 5869 6 |
| 5 | − 1.3992 326 | − 2.0529 382 | − .0678 5954 5 |
| 6 | .0005 1218 446 | .0005 6386 851 | .0005 6100 775 |
| 7 | .0367 1888 3 | .0395 0364 6 | .0970 8306 4 |
| 8 | .0583 3517 7 | .0583 3484 7 | .0583 3484 1 |

| Integral | $L_{32}$ | Exact |
|----------|----------|-------|
| 1 | .1670 8562 | .1952 4753 |
| 2 | .2016 3572 | .3251 0855 |
| 3 | .5414 5344 | 13.628 |
| 4 | $-.0002\ 3993\ 672$ | $-.0046\ 984$ |
| 5 | 1.1197 176 | .0015 8973 |
| 6 | .0005 6103 72 | .0005 6103 71 |
| 7 | .1007 0835 | .1626 6891 |
| 8 |  | .0583 349 |

$L_4$ = Laguerre 4-point rule; $L_8$, 8-point; etc.

The only integrands on this list that are covered by the convergence theorem are 3, 6, and 8. The last two indeed exhibit strong convergence toward the proper answer. Integrand 3 is something of a numerical joke inasmuch as it is scarcely distinguishable from the divergent integrand $x^{-1}$. The values for 1 and 2 are increasing monotonically and might conceivably be convergent, though slowly, to the correct value. The values for 4 and 5 are very bad.

## 3.8   Oscillatory Integrands

In computing the value of an integral whose integrand oscillates over $[0, \infty]$, it may be useful to compute the positive and negative contributions individually and to sum the resulting infinite series. This series, however, may be slowly convergent.

Numerous devices that can transform a slowly convergent series into one more rapidly convergent are available. We make a slight digression here to describe *Euler's transformation*, which is the one most commonly employed.

The formal transformation is most expeditiously derived by means of the calculus of finite differences. Let $\Delta u_0 = u_1 - u_0, \Delta^2 u_0 = \Delta(\Delta u_0) = \Delta(u_1 - u_0) = u_2 - 2u_1 + u_0$, and so on. Let $Eu_0 = u_1, E^2 u_0 = u_2$, and so on. We have $E = \Delta + I$, where $I$ is the identity operator. Then, with these operators, we may write formally

$$u_0 - u_1 + u_2 - \cdots = u_0 - E_1 u_0 + E^2 u_0 - E^3 u_0 + \cdots$$

$$= (I - E + E^2 - \cdots)u_0 = (I + E)^{-1}u_0$$

$$= (2I + E - I)^{-1}u_0 = (2I + \Delta)^{-1}u_0$$

$$= \tfrac{1}{2}(I + \tfrac{1}{2}\Delta)^{-1}u_0$$

$$= \tfrac{1}{2}u_0 - \tfrac{1}{4}\Delta u_0 + \tfrac{1}{8}\Delta^2 u_0 - \tfrac{1}{16}\Delta^3 u_0 + \cdots. \tag{3.8.1}$$

Euler's transformation is

$$u_0 - u_1 + u_2 - \cdots = \tfrac{1}{2}u_0 - \tfrac{1}{4}\Delta u_0 + \tfrac{1}{8}\Delta^2 u_0 - \cdots. \qquad (3.8.2)$$

It can be proved that if the left-hand series is convergent, the right-hand series is also convergent and to the same value. In numerous cases of practical interest (but not always), the right-hand series will converge more rapidly than the left-hand series.

**Example.** The slowly convergent series

$$S = \frac{1}{\log 2} - \frac{1}{\log 3} + \frac{1}{\log 4} - \cdots$$

may be speeded up by the use of Euler's transformation. Writing

$$S = \left(\frac{1}{\log 2} - \frac{1}{\log 3}\right) + \frac{1}{\log 4} - \cdots,$$

we apply the transformation to the infinite series

$$S' = \frac{1}{\log 4} - \frac{1}{\log 5} + \cdots.$$

We have $u_0 = .721350$, $\Delta u_0 = -.100016$, $\Delta^2 u_0 = .036792$, $\Delta^3 u_0 = -.01778$, $\Delta^4 u_0 = .00299$. Therefore

$$S' = \tfrac{1}{2}(.721350) + \tfrac{1}{4}(.100016) + \tfrac{1}{8}(.036792) + \tfrac{1}{16}(.01788) + \tfrac{1}{32}(.00299) + \cdots$$
$$= .3915.$$

Hence, $S = .9239$.

In the next example, the Euler's transformation is applied to an integral with an oscillatory integrand.

**Example** (Longman)

$$I = \int_0^\infty J_0(2x)\frac{f(x)}{g(x)}\,dx,$$

where

$$f(x) = x(x^2+\tfrac{1}{3})^{1/2}[2x^2\exp\{-\tfrac{1}{5}(x^2+1)^{1/2}\} - (2x^2+1)\exp\{-\tfrac{1}{5}(x^2+\tfrac{1}{3})^{1/2}\}],$$
$$g(x) = (2x^2+1)^2 - 4x^2(x^2+\tfrac{1}{3})^{1/2}(x^2+1)^{1/2}.$$

The zeros $x_1, x_2, \ldots$ of the Bessel function $J_0(2x)$ are readily available. See, for example, NBS Handbook [1, p. 409].

Set

$$x_0 = 0 \quad \text{and} \quad u_i = (-1)^{i+1}\int_{x_i}^{x_{i+1}}.$$

Performing approximate integration between zeros, we find $u_0 = .145234$, $u_1 = .206401$, $u_2 = .150723$, $u_3 = .108661$, $u_4 = .079288$, $u_5 = .058351$, $u_6 = .043165$, $u_7 = .032028$. In order to deal with small differences, we begin the Euler transformation with the third term. Therefore

$$\int_0^\infty \approx -.145234 + .206401 - [\tfrac{1}{2}(.150723) + \tfrac{1}{4}(.042062)$$

$$+ \tfrac{1}{8}(.012689) + \tfrac{1}{16}(.004253) + \tfrac{1}{32}(.001568) + \tfrac{1}{64}(.000585)]$$

$$= -.02662.$$

**References.** Hurwitz and Zweifel [1], Hurwitz, Pfeiffer, and Zweifel [1], Knopp [1, pp. 244–246], Longman [1], [2], Lubkin [1], Shanks [1].

# CHAPTER 4

# ERROR ANALYSIS

## 4.1  Types of Error

In the preceding chapters, we have dealt with errors from time to time, treating them informally. In the present chapter we deal with them on a more systematic basis.

In approximate integration, we replace the value of an integral $\int_a^b f(x)\,dx$ by a finite sum $\sum_{i=1}^n w_i f(x_i)$, and in so doing we incur two sorts of error. In the first place, there is the *truncation error*, E, that arises from the fact that the sum is only approximately equal to the integral:

$$\int_a^b f(x)\,dx = \sum_{i=1}^n w_i f(x_i) + E. \tag{4.1.1}$$

In the second place, there is the *roundoff error*, R, which arises from the fact that we have computed $\sum_{i=1}^n w_i f(x_i)$ only approximately, due to the limitation of accuracy of the computer. We have produced and accepted a value $\Sigma^*$ such that

$$\Sigma^* = \sum_{i=1}^n w_i f(x_i) + R. \tag{4.1.2}$$

The estimate of total error is therefore

$$\left| \int_a^b f(x)\,dx - \Sigma^* \right| \leqslant |E| + |R|. \tag{4.1.3}$$

In the analysis of the present chapter, we assume that $f$ is a function defined mathematically (that is, $f$ does not consist of experimental data) and that we are able to compute $f$ to within the accuracy of the computer word length. We do not present error analyses based either on statistical assumptions of roundoff or on the assumption that the function $f$ is extracted from an ensemble of functions with certain statistical properties.

In practice, roundoff error is usually negligible; but it should be pointed out that with the high speeds of present computers, there is a temptation to use large values of $n$ in the sum (4.1.1) and this may take the roundoff error out of the negligible category. For this reason, the principal concern of this chapter is with the truncation error. It is precisely in the area of truncation-error analysis that some of the most brilliant contributions to the theory of approximate integration lie.

In laboratory practice exact error analysis is usually omitted. There are many reasons for this: (1) it is difficult or impossible to carry out, (2) many of the mathematical theorems are irrelevant to machine computation, (3) the estimates are too pessimistic, (4) it is replaced by an automatic or approximate sort of analysis. Error analysis is the tithe that intelligence demands of action, but it is rarely paid.

## 4.2  Roundoff Error for a Fixed Integration Rule

In this section, we shall analyze the effect of roundoff in the computation of the rule

$$\int_a^b f(x) \, dx \approx \sum_{k=1}^{n} w_k f(x_k). \tag{4.2.1}$$

We are particularly interested in what happens when $n$ becomes large. The analysis below follows, in large measure, the analysis given by Wilkinson of a general roundoff error.

We assume that the right-hand sum in (4.2.1) is computed on a computer that works with $t$ binary (or decimal) digits and that the computation is carried out in *floating-point* arithmetic. We assume, further, that our computer has a single precision accumulator. If $fl(x_1 + x_2)$ designates the result of adding $x_2$ to $x_1$ in the floating-point mode, then it can be shown that

$$fl(x_1 + x_2) = x_1(1 + \varepsilon') + x_2(1 + \varepsilon''), \tag{4.2.2}$$

where

$$|\varepsilon'|, |\varepsilon''| \leqslant (\tfrac{3}{2})2^{-t} \tag{4.2.3a}$$

if one uses a binary machine, or

$$|\varepsilon'|, |\varepsilon''| \leqslant (5.5)10^{-t} \tag{4.2.3b}$$

if one uses a decimal machine.

If $fl\,(x_1 x_2)$ correspondingly is the result of multiplying $x_2$ by $x_1$ in floating, then it can be shown that

$$fl(x_1 x_2) = x_1 x_2 (1 + \varepsilon'''), \tag{4.2.4}$$

where

$$|\varepsilon'''| \leqslant 2^{-t} \tag{4.2.5a}$$

for a binary machine, or

$$|\varepsilon'''| \leqslant \tfrac{1}{2}(10^{1-t}) \tag{4.2.5b}$$

for a decimal machine.

With these basic inequalities at hand, we are in a position to analyze the error made in computing a sum of products (i.e., an inner product) such as that which appears in (4.2.1).

We let

$$s_n = fl(a_1 b_1 + a_2 b_2 + \cdots + a_n b_n). \tag{4.2.6}$$

By this is meant that we compute the products $a_i b_i$ in floating and then add them in floating in the order indicated. The computation (4.2.6) is really an abbreviation for the following computation indicated recursively:

$$\begin{aligned}
s_1 &= t_1 = fl(a_1 b_1), \\
t_r &= fl(a_r b_r), \\
s_r &= fl(s_{r-1} + t_r), \qquad r > 1.
\end{aligned} \tag{4.2.7}$$

Using (4.2.4) and (4.2.2), we obtain

$$\begin{aligned}
t_r &= a_r b_r (1 + \xi_r), \\
s_r &= s_{r-1}(1 + \eta_r') + t_r(1 + \eta_r''),
\end{aligned} \tag{4.2.8}$$

where the quantities $\xi_r$, $\eta_r'$, and $\eta_r''$ satisfy

$$|\eta_r'|, |\eta_r''| \leqslant \Omega_1, \qquad |\xi_r| \leqslant \Omega_2, \tag{4.2.9}$$

with

$$\Omega_1 = (\tfrac{3}{2})2^{-t}, \qquad \Omega_2 = 2^{-t}$$

for a binary machine†, or

$$\Omega_1 = (5.5)10^{-t}, \qquad \Omega_2 = \tfrac{1}{2}(10)^{1-t}$$

for a decimal machine.

† On some binary computers, one must take $\Omega_1 = 2^{2-t}$, $\Omega_2 = 2^{1-t}$.

By recurrence we find

$$s_n = a_1 b_1 (1 + \varepsilon_1) + a_2 b_2 (1 + \varepsilon_2) + \cdots + a_n b_n (1 + \varepsilon_n), \quad (4.2.10)$$

where

$$(1 + \varepsilon_1) = (1 + \xi_1)(1 + \eta_2') \cdots (1 + \eta_n'),$$

$$(1 + \varepsilon_r) = (1 + \xi_r)(1 + \eta_r'')(1 + \eta_{r+1}') \cdots (1 + \eta_n'), \quad r = 2, \ldots, n - 1,$$

$$(1 + \varepsilon_n) = (1 + \xi_n)(1 + \eta_n''). \quad (4.2.11)$$

Using (4.2.9) and (4.2.11), we have

$$(1 - \Omega_2)(1 - \Omega_1)^{n-1} \leqslant 1 + \varepsilon_1 \leqslant (1 + \Omega_2)(1 + \Omega_1)^{n-1},$$
$$(4.2.12)$$

$$(1 - \Omega_2)(1 - \Omega_1)^{n-r+1} \leqslant 1 + \varepsilon_r \leqslant (1 + \Omega_2)(1 + \Omega_1)^{n-r+1},$$
$$r = 2, 3, \ldots, n.$$

This implies the uniform estimate for $r = 1, 2, \ldots, n$:

$$(1 - \Omega_2)(1 - \Omega_1)^{n-r+1} \leqslant 1 + \varepsilon_r \leqslant (1 + \Omega_2)(1 + \Omega_1)^{n-r+1}. \quad (4.2.13)$$

Now

$$\begin{aligned}
(1 + \Omega)^k &= 1 + k\Omega + \frac{k(k-1)}{2!}\Omega^2 + \cdots \\
&= 1 + k\Omega\left(1 + \frac{k-1}{2!}\Omega + \frac{(k-1)(k-2)}{3!}\Omega^2 + \cdots\right) \\
&\leqslant 1 + k\Omega\left(1 + \frac{k}{2!}\Omega + \frac{k^2}{3!}\Omega^2 + \cdots\right) \\
&= 1 + k\Omega\left(\frac{e^{k\Omega} - 1}{k\Omega}\right). \quad (4.2.14)
\end{aligned}$$

Similarly

$$(1 - \Omega)^k \geqslant 1 - k\Omega\left(\frac{e^{k\Omega} - 1}{k\Omega}\right). \quad (4.2.15)$$

If we assume that

$$n\Omega_1 \leqslant \tfrac{1}{10} \quad (4.2.16)$$

(which will certainly be the case with the $n$'s occurring in approximate integration), then since $(e^{.1} - 1)/.1 \leqslant 1.06$, we have, from (4.2.13), (4.2.14), (4.2.15),

$$(1 - \Omega_2)[1 - (n - r + 1)\Omega_1(1.06)] \leqslant 1 + \varepsilon_r$$
$$\leqslant (1 + \Omega_2)[1 + (n - r + 1)\Omega_1(1.06)].$$
$$(4.2.17)$$

Hence

$$|\varepsilon_r| \leqslant \Omega_2 + (n - r + 1)\Omega_1(1 + \Omega_2)(1.06), \qquad r = 1, 2, \ldots, n. \qquad (4.2.18)$$

Now, from (4.2.6) and (4.2.10), we have

$$\sum_{i=1}^{n} a_i b_i - f\ell \left( \sum_{i=1}^{n} a_i b_i \right) = \sum_{i=1}^{n} a_i b_i \varepsilon_i. \qquad (4.2.19)$$

This identity will be applied to $\sum_{i=1}^{n} w_i f(x_i)$. We designate by $\bar{f}_i$ the result of computing $f(x_i)$ in the floating mode. We shall assume that

$$\bar{f}_i = f(x_i)(1 + \theta_i), \qquad i = 1, 2, \ldots, n, \qquad (4.2.20)$$

where

$$|\theta_i| \leqslant \theta, \qquad i = 1, 2, \ldots, n, \qquad (4.2.21)$$

and $\theta$ is a small quantity of the order of magnitude of $\Omega_1$. (This assumption may not be fulfilled in practice. In the first place, there may be roundoff error in the computation of the abscissas and, as we run through the abscissas, the error may propagate, affecting the computation of $f(x)$ adversely. In the second place, $f$ itself may be given by a complicated formula and substantial roundoff error may result. In computing higher dimensional integrals these errors are compounded even more. A larger number of points are used and care must be taken in interpreting the results.) We have

$$R = \sum_{i=1}^{n} w_i f(x_i) - f\ell \left( \sum_{i=1}^{n} w_i \bar{f}_i \right). \qquad (4.2.22)$$

By (4.2.19), we obtain

$$R = \sum_{i=1}^{n} w_i f(x_i) - \sum_{i=1}^{n} w_i \bar{f}_i + \sum_{i=1}^{n} w_i \bar{f}_i \varepsilon_i. \qquad (4.2.23)$$

Therefore, by (4.2.20) and (4.2.21), it follows that

$$|R| \leqslant \theta \sum_{i=1}^{n} |w_i| \, |f(x_i)| + (1 + \theta) \sum_{i=1}^{n} |w_i| \, |f(x_i)| \, |\varepsilon_i|. \qquad (4.2.24)$$

If we set

$$M = \max_{a \leqslant x \leqslant b} |f(x)|, \qquad (4.2.25)$$

then (4.2.24) reduces to

$$|R| \leqslant \theta M \sum_{i=1}^{n} |w_i| + (1 + \theta)M \sum_{i=1}^{n} |w_i| \, |\varepsilon_i|, \qquad (4.2.26)$$

and, from (4.2.18),

$$|R| \leqslant \theta M \sum_{i=1}^{n} |w_i| + (1 + \theta)M\Omega_2 \sum_{i=1}^{n} |w_i|$$

$$+ (1.06)(1 + \theta)M\Omega_1(1 + \Omega_2) \sum_{i=1}^{n} |w_i|(n - i + 1). \qquad (4.2.27)$$

This is as far as we can carry the analysis without further assumptions as to the nature of the rule (4.2.1). At this point we therefore assume that

$$w_i \geqslant 0, \qquad \sum_{i=1}^{n} w_i = b - a, \qquad \text{and} \qquad w_i \leqslant \frac{A}{n}, \qquad i = 1, 2, \ldots, n,$$

$$(4.2.28)$$

where $A$ is a constant independent of $n$. These assumptions are fulfilled for the trapezoidal, Simpson's, and all compound rules formed from simple rules with positive coefficients. We have from (4.2.27) our final estimate:

$$|R| \leqslant \theta(b - a)M + (1 + \theta)M\Omega_2(b - a)$$

$$+ 1.06(1 + \theta)M\Omega_1(1 + \Omega_2)A \frac{(n + 1)}{2}. \qquad (4.2.29)$$

The conclusion to be reached from this analysis is that roundoff error in approximate integration can be expected to grow, at worst, as the first power of $n$. In ordinary circumstances, $n \approx 10^1$ to $10^2$, so that no great damage is done. Some machines have the facility of accumulating inner products in double precision. In such a case, the roundoff will be even less. On the other hand, if vast numbers of abscissas are used (as sometimes occurs in multi-dimensional integrals), some thought must be given to the roundoff error.

The appearance of $|w_i|$ and $\sum_{i=1}^{n} |w_i|$ in formula (4.2.27) shows that rules with both plus and minus weights are less favorable in regard to roundoff. The quantity $\sum_{i=1}^{n} |w_i|$ in such instances may even be unbounded as $n \to \infty$. The error estimate just carried out is conservative in that it assumes the worst possible build-up of error. A statistical approach might yield an estimate $\sim \sqrt{n}$.

The total error committed in the approximation (4.2.1) consists of the roundoff error plus the truncation error. For the usual rules employed, the truncation error is $\sim n^{-1}$ or better. As $n$ increases, roundoff goes up and truncation goes down, the most favorable selection of $n$ being at some intermediate value.

**References.** Henrici [2, pp. 41–58], McCracken and Dorn [1, pp. 166–171], Wilkinson [1, pp. 7–19].

**Example.**  Integrate $\int_0^1 \sin \pi x \, dx$, using the trapezoidal rule (see Section 2.1).

| Number of intervals | Total error |
|:---:|:---:|
| 2 | .1366 1977 |
| 4 | .0330 6640 |
| 8 | .0082 0237 |
| 16 | .0020 4671 |
| 32 | .0005 1149 |
| 64 | .0001 2801 |
| 128 | .0000 3223 |
| 256 | .0000 0833 |
| 512 | .0000 0333 |
| 1024 | .0000 0187 |
| 2048 | .0000 0195 |
| 4096 | .0000 0934 |
| 8192 | .0000 1950 |

In this example, $a = 0$, $b = 1$, $A = 1$, $\theta = \Omega_1 = 5.5 \times 10^{-8}$, $\Omega_2 = \frac{1}{2}(10^{-7})$, $M = 1$. Hence an upper band for $|R|$ is approximately $[.53(n + 1) + 2]5.5 \times 10^{-8}$. The truncation error $E$ is bounded by $|E| \leqslant \pi^2/12n^2$. For $n = 8192$, $|E| \approx 1.2 \times 10^{-8}$, so that the observed error at this stage is largely roundoff. The predicted roundoff error bound at $n = 8192$ is $|R| \leqslant .00024$, and this overestimates the observed error of $.00002$ by an order of magnitude. Note that the total error bound is of the form $c_1 + c_2 n + c_3 n^{-2}$ and that the predicted behavior of steady improvement followed by deterioration due to roundoff is borne out.

### 4.3  Truncation Error Through Peano's Theorem

In discussing the truncation error of approximate integration, it is frequently useful to regard the error

$$E = E(f) = \int_a^b f(x) \, dx - \sum_{i=1}^n w_i f(x_i) \qquad (4.3.1)$$

as a *linear functional* defined over a certain class of functions. Linear functionals $E$ have the property that

$$E(cf(x)) = cE(f(x)) \qquad (4.3.2)$$

for any constant $c$, and

$$E(f(x) + g(x)) = E(f(x)) + E(g(x)). \qquad (4.3.3)$$

In the theorem that follows, we consider integrands of class $C^{n+1}[a, b]$ and linear functionals of the following structure:

$$E(f) = \int_a^b [a_0(x)f(x) + a_1(x)f'(x) + \cdots + a_n(x)f^{(n)}(x)] \, dx$$

$$- \sum_{i=1}^{j_0} b_{i0}f(x_{i0}) - \sum_{i=1}^{j_1} b_{i1}f'(x_{i1}) - \cdots - \sum_{i=1}^{j_n} b_{in}f^{(n)}(x_{in}). \quad (4.3.4)$$

Here it is assumed that the functions $a_i(x)$ are piecewise continuous over $[a, b]$ and that the points $x_{ij}$ lie in $[a, b]$.

PEANO'S THEOREM. *Let* $E(p(x)) = 0$ *whenever* $p(x) \in \mathscr{P}_n$. *Then, for all* $f(x) \in C^{n+1}[a, b]$,

$$E(f) = \int_a^b f^{(n+1)}(t)K(t) \, dt, \quad (4.3.5)$$

*where*

$$K(t) = \frac{1}{n!} E_x[(x - t)_+^n] \quad (4.3.6)$$

*and*

$$(x - t)_+^n = \begin{cases} (x - t)^n, & x \geq t, \\ 0, & x < t. \end{cases} \quad (4.3.7)$$

The notation $E_x$ means the linear functional $E$ is applied to the $x$-variable in $(x - t)_+^n$. The function $K(t)$ is called the *Peano kernel* for the linear functional $E$.

*Proof.* By Taylor's theorem with exact remainder,

$$f(x) = f(a) + f'(a)(x - a) + \cdots + \frac{f^{(n)}(a)(x - a)^n}{n!}$$

$$+ \frac{1}{n!} \int_a^x f^{(n+1)}(t)(x - t)^n \, dt. \quad (4.3.8)$$

The integral remainder may be written as

$$\frac{1}{n!} \int_a^b f^{(n+1)}(t)(x - t)_+^n \, dt.$$

We apply $E$ to both sides of equation (4.3.8) and use the fact that $E$ vanishes on polynomials of class $\mathscr{P}_n$:

$$E(f(x)) = \frac{1}{n!} E_x \int_a^b f^{(n+1)}(t)(x - t)_+^n \, dt. \quad (4.3.9)$$

Now the type of functional we are working with allows the interchange of $E$ and the integral; hence,

$$E(f) = \frac{1}{n!} \int_a^b f^{(n+1)}(t) E_x(x - t)_+^n \, dt. \tag{4.3.10}$$

COROLLARY

$$|E(f)| \leqslant (b - a) \max_{a \leqslant x \leqslant b} |f^{(n+1)}(x)| \int_a^b |K(x)| \, dx. \tag{4.3.11}$$

If the Peano kernel does not change its sign over the interval $[a, b]$, then $E$ may be expressed essentially as $f^{(n+1)}$ evaluated at an intermediate point.

COROLLARY.  *If, in addition, $K(t)$ does not change its sign on $[a, b]$, then*

$$E(f) = \frac{f^{(n+1)}(\xi)}{(n+1)!} E(x^{n+1}), \qquad a < \xi < b. \tag{4.3.12}$$

*Proof.* Under the additional hypotheses we may use the mean-value theorem for integrals and obtain

$$E(f) = f^{(n+1)}(\xi) \int_a^b K(t) \, dt. \tag{4.3.13}$$

Now we insert $f(x) = x^{n+1}$ in (4.3.13) and obtain

$$E(x^{n+1}) = (n + 1)! \int_a^b K(t) \, dt. \tag{4.3.14}$$

This yields (4.3.12).

**Example.**  If we set

$$E(f) = \int_a^b f(x) \, dx - \frac{b-a}{2} [f(a) + f(b)],$$

then $E(f)$ is the truncation error in the trapezoidal rule. We may select $n = 1$ in Peano's theorem and obtain

$$K(t) = \int_a^b (x - t)_+ \, dx - \frac{b-a}{2} [(a - t)_+ + (b - t)_+]$$

$$= \int_t^b (x - t) \, dx - \frac{b-a}{2} (b - t) = \tfrac{1}{2}(a - t)(b - t). \tag{4.3.15}$$

Therefore

$$\int_a^b f(x) \, dx - \frac{b-a}{2} [f(a) + f(b)] = -\frac{1}{2} \int_a^b f''(t)(a - t)(b - t) \, dt. \tag{4.3.16}$$

The kernel $K(t)$ is nonpositive throughout $[a, b]$; hence we may apply the second corollary. Now

$$E(x^2) = \int_a^b x^2 \, dx - \frac{b-a}{2}(a^2 + b^2) = -\frac{1}{6}(b-a)^3; \qquad (4.3.17)$$

thus

$$\int_a^b f(x) \, dx = \frac{b-a}{2}[f(a) + f(b)] - \frac{1}{12}(b-a)^3 f''(\xi), \qquad a < \xi < b. \quad (4.3.18)$$

**Example.**  Let

$$E(f) = \int_{-1}^1 f(x) \, dx - \tfrac{1}{3}f(-1) - \tfrac{4}{3}f(0) - \tfrac{1}{3}f(1).$$

Now $E(p(x)) = 0$ if $p(x) \in \mathscr{P}_3$. Hence, we may take $n = 3$ in Peano's theorem. We find that $K(t) = \tfrac{1}{6}E_x[(x - t)_+^3]$. When this expression is computed out, we find that

$$K(t) = \begin{cases} -\tfrac{1}{72}(1 - t)^3(3t + 1), & 0 \leqslant t \leqslant 1, \\ K(-t), & -1 \leqslant t \leqslant 0. \end{cases} \qquad (4.3.19)$$

Now $K(t) \leqslant 0$ in $[-1, 1]$ so that the second corollary is applicable. Since $E(x^4) = -\tfrac{4}{15}$, this leads to the error in Simpson's rule:

$$\int_{-1}^1 f(x) \, dx = \frac{1}{3}f(-1) + \frac{4}{3}f(0) + \frac{1}{3}f(1) - \frac{f^{(4)}(\xi)}{90}, \qquad -1 < \xi < 1.$$
$$(4.3.20)$$

For an arbitrary rule of approximate integration

$$\int_a^b f(x) \, dx \approx \sum_{k=1}^n w_k f(x_k),$$

there is no reason for the Peano kernel to have one sign. However, for integration rules of Newton–Cotes type, it can be shown that the kernel does have one sign. (See Steffensen.)

COROLLARY.  *If a rule R has a Peano kernel that does not change sign and if R is compounded, then the compound rule has a kernel that does not change sign.*

*Proof.*  For simplicity, we work with two intervals $[a, a + h]$, and $[a + h, a + 2h]$. We have

$$\int_a^{a+h} f(x) \, dx = \sum w_k f(x_k) + \int_a^{a+h} f^{(n+1)}(t)K(t) \, dt,$$

$$\int_{a+h}^{a+2h} f(x) \, dx = \sum w_v f(x_k') + \int_{a+h}^{a+2h} f^{(n+1)}(t)K(t - h) \, dt,$$

where $x_k' = x_k + h$.

Hence

$$\int_a^{a+2h} f(x)\, dx = \sum w_k f(x_k) + \sum w_k f(x_k') + \int_a^{a+2h} f^{(n+1)}(t) K_1(t)\, dt,$$

where

$$K_1(t) = \begin{cases} K(t), & a \leqslant t \leqslant a + h, \\ K(t - h), & a + h \leqslant t \leqslant a + 2h. \end{cases}$$

The kernel $K_1(t)$ clearly does not change its sign on $[a, a + 2h]$. Application of the previous two corollaries leads to error terms for compound rules.

A function such as $(x - t)_+^n$, which is a piecewise polynomial and which has continuous derivatives up to a certain order, is known as a *spline function*. The kernel $K(t)$ is a spline function. The theory of spline functions has many intimate connections with approximate integration, which unfortunately we shall not be able to pursue here.

For the development of Peano's theorem in several dimensions, the reader is referred to the work of Sard.

**References.** Davis [6, pp. 69–75], Krylov [1, pp. 82–92], Milne [1], Sard [2. Chap. 4], Schoenberg [1], Steffensen [1, pp. 154–165].

### 4.4 Special Devices

Peano's theorem is of great generality, but the price one pays for this is that the kernel $K(t) = E_x[(x - t)_+^n]$ may be difficult to convert to a neat, easily handled form. Other devices are available. We shall exhibit the method used to obtain the error in the Gaussian integration formula.

Let $w(x) \geqslant 0$ be a weight function defined on $[a, b]$, let $p_n(x)$ be the corresponding orthogonal polynomials, and let

$$p_n^*(x) = k_n x^n + \cdots, \qquad k_n > 0,$$

be the orthonormal polynomials. The numbers $x_k$ and $w_k$ are the abscissas and weights of the Gauss rule of order $n$, related to $p_n(x)$ as explained in Section 2.7.

THEOREM. *If $f(x) \in C^{2n}[a, b]$, then*

$$E_{G_n}(f) = \int_a^b w(x) f(x)\, dx - \sum_{k=1}^n w_k f(x_k) = \frac{f^{(2n)}(\eta)}{(2n)! k_n^2}, \qquad a < \eta < b. \tag{4.4.1}$$

*Proof.* Let $h_{2n-1}(x)$ be that unique polynomial of class $\mathscr{P}_{2n-1}$ for which $h_{2n-1}(x_k) = f(x_k)$, $h_{2n-1}'(x_k) = f'(x_k)$, $k = 1, 2, \ldots, n$. Then, according to the remainder theorem for polynomial interpolation (see, for example, Davis), we have

$$f(x) = h_{2n-1}(x) + \frac{f^{(2n)}(\xi(x))}{(2n)!} (x - x_1)^2(x - x_2)^2 \cdots (x - x_n)^2 \qquad (4.4.2)$$

for $a \leqslant x \leqslant b$ and $a < \xi(x) < b$. The function

$$\frac{(2n)!(f(x) - h_{2n-1}(x))}{(x - x_1)^2 \cdots (x - x_n)^2} = f^{(2n)}(\xi(x))$$

is continuous in $a \leqslant x \leqslant b$. Now, multiply (4.4.2) by $w(x)$:

$$w(x)f(x) = w(x)h_{2n-1}(x) + \frac{f^{(2n)}(\xi(x))}{(2n)!} w(x) \frac{p_n^*(x)^2}{k_n^2}. \qquad (4.4.3)$$

Integrate (4.4.3) and employ the general mean-value theorem for integrals:

$$\int_a^b w(x)f(x)\, dx = \int_a^b w(x)h_{2n-1}(x)\, dx + \frac{1}{(2n)!k_n^2} \int_a^b f^{(2n)}(\xi(x))w(x)[p_n^*(x)]^2\, dx$$

$$= \int_a^b w(x)h_{2n-1}(x)\, dx + \frac{f^{(2n)}(\eta)}{(2n)!k_n^2} \int_a^b w(x)[p_n^*(x)]^2\, dx. \qquad (4.4.4)$$

Now, since $G_n$ integrates members of $\mathscr{P}_{2n-1}$ exactly, then

$$\int_a^b w(x)h_{2n-1}(x)\, dx = \sum_{k=1}^n w_k h_{2n-1}(x_k) = \sum_{k=1}^n w_k f(x_k).$$

Since $p_n^*$ is orthonormal, then $\int_a^b w(x)[p_n^*(x)]^2\, dx = 1$. These equalities reduce (4.4.4) to (4.4.1).

Explicit forms of the Gauss remainder have already been given in Sections 2.7 and 3.6 for the most commonly employed cases.

**Reference.**  Davis [6, p. 67].

### 4.5  *Error Estimates Through Differences*

Error expressions of the usual sort involve high-order derivatives, $f^{(M)}(\xi)$, of the integrand. In the case of Simpson's rule, $E = cf^{(4)}(\xi)$. In the case of a Gauss 96-point rule (which has actually been used in machine calculation), we should have to compute $f^{(192)}(\xi)$. If the integrand is sufficiently elementary, it may be possible to obtain the appropriate derivative $f^{(M)}(x)$ and from it to estimate $\max_{a \leqslant x \leqslant b} |f^{(M)}(x)|$. For example, we can obtain the $n$th derivative of certain types of rational functions quite easily through interpolation formulas. Let $z_0, z_1, \ldots, z_p$ be $p + 1$ distinct numbers. Set

$$w(z) = (z - z_0)(z - z_1) \cdots (z - z_p). \qquad (4.5.1)$$

Then, for a given $f(z)$, the polynomial

$$p(f; z) = \sum_{i=0}^{p} f(z_i) \frac{w(z)}{(z - z_i)w'(z_i)} \tag{4.5.2}$$

interpolates to $f$ at $z_0, \ldots, z_p$. [See (1.11.6–1.11.13).] If $f(z)$ is itself a polynomial of degree $\leqslant p$, then $f(z)$ and $p(f; z)$ would coincide at the $p + 1$ points $z_0, \ldots, z_p$ and hence must be identical. Therefore

$$f(z) = \sum_{i=0}^{p} f(z_i) \frac{w(z)}{(z - z_i)w'(z_i)} \tag{4.5.3}$$

and

$$\frac{f(z)}{w(z)} = \sum_{i=0}^{p} \frac{f(z_i)}{w'(z_i)} \frac{1}{(z - z_i)}. \tag{4.5.4}$$

Thus, finally,

$$\frac{d^n}{dz^n}\left(\frac{f(z)}{w(z)}\right) = (-1)^n n! \sum_{i=0}^{p} \frac{f(z_i)}{w'(z_i)} \frac{1}{(z - z_i)^{n+1}}. \tag{4.5.5}$$

**Example.**   Estimate

$$\max_{0 \leqslant x \leqslant 1}\left|\frac{d^n}{dx^n}\left(\frac{1}{1 + x^4}\right)\right|.$$

Here

$$f(z) \equiv 1, \qquad w(z) = z^4 + 1 = (z - z_0)(z - z_1)(z - z_2)(z - z_3),$$

where $z_0 = e^{\pi i/4}$, $z_1 = e^{3\pi i/4}$, $z_2 = e^{5\pi i/4}$, $z_3 = e^{7\pi i/4}$, $w'(z) = 4z^3$. Hence

$$\frac{d^n}{dz^n}\left(\frac{1}{1 + z^4}\right)$$
$$= \frac{(-1)^n n!}{4}\left[\frac{1}{z_1(z - z_0)^{n+1}} + \frac{1}{z_0(z - z_1)^{n+1}} + \frac{1}{z_3(z - z_2)^{n+1}} + \frac{1}{z_2(z - z_3)^{n+1}}\right].$$

Since the minimum distance from $z_0$ or $z_3$ to $[0, 1]$ is $\frac{1}{2}\sqrt{2}$, and the minimum distance from $z_1$ or $z_2$ to $[0, 1]$ is 1, we have

$$\max_{0 \leqslant x \leqslant 1}\left|\frac{d^n}{dx^n}\left(\frac{1}{1 + x^4}\right)\right| \leqslant \frac{n!}{4}\left[(\sqrt{2})^{n+1} + (1)^{n+1} + (1)^{n+1} + (\sqrt{2})^{n+1}\right]$$

$$= \frac{n!}{2}\left[2^{(1/2)(n+1)} + 1\right].$$

For some additional algebraic devices that are useful in computing formal high-order derivatives, the reader is referred to Steffensen. Also, computer programs have been written for the formal calculation of higher derivatives. But even with simple integrands, high-order derivatives can lead to expressions of enormous complexity. We are, of course, interested in ways of avoiding this formidable computation.

**Reference.** Steffensen [1, pp. 231–241].

An $n$th derivative may be approximated by an $n$th difference. Let $a \leqslant x_0 < x_1 < x_2 < \cdots < x_n \leqslant b$ be $n + 1$ equally spaced points of distance $h$ apart. If $f(x) \in C^n[a, b]$, then

$$\Delta^n f(x_0) = h^n f^{(n)}(\xi), \qquad x_0 < \xi < x_n. \tag{4.5.6}$$

Thus, $f^{(n)}(x)$ may be approximated by $(1/h^n)\Delta^n f(x_0)$. *Markoff's formulas*, which are Newton forward-difference formulas differentiated, provide complete expansions of derivatives in terms of differences. The first few expansions are

$$hf'(x_0) = \Delta_0 - \tfrac{1}{2}\Delta_0^2 + \tfrac{1}{3}\Delta_0^3 - \tfrac{1}{4}\Delta_0^4 + \cdots,$$
$$h^2 f''(x_0) = \Delta_0^2 - \Delta_0^3 + \tfrac{11}{12}\Delta_0^4 - \cdots,$$
$$h^3 f'''(x_0) = \Delta_0^3 - \tfrac{3}{2}\Delta_0^4 + \tfrac{7}{4}\Delta_0^5 - \cdots,$$
$$h^4 f^{(4)}(x_0) = \Delta_0^4 - 2\Delta_0^5 + \tfrac{17}{6}\Delta_0^6 - \tfrac{7}{2}\Delta_0^7 + \cdots,$$
$$\vdots$$

**Example.** $\int_{1.5}^{1.6} \Gamma(x)\, dx$ has been evaluated by use of a 3-point Simpson rule. Estimate the error $E$. It involves the fourth derivative of the gamma function $\Gamma(x)$. The following tabulation of values is from the NBS Handbook of Mathematical Tables [1].

| $x$ | $\Gamma(x)$ | $\Delta$ | $\Delta^2$ | $\Delta^3$ | $\Delta^4$ |
|------|-----------|----------|-----------|-----------|-----------|
| 1.50 | .8862 269 | | | | |
| 1.52 | .8870 388 | .0008 119 | | | |
| 1.54 | .8881 777 | .0011 389 | .0003 270 | | |
| 1.56 | .8896 392 | .0014 615 | .0003 226 | − .0000 044 | |
| 1.58 | .8914 196 | .0017 804 | .0003 189 | − .0000 037 | − .0000 007 |
| 1.60 | .8935 154 | .0020 958 | .0003 154 | − .0000 035 | − .0000 002 |

We have $|\Delta^{(4)}\Gamma| \approx 7.0 \times 10^{-7}$, so that $|\Gamma^{(4)}| \approx (7.0 \times 10^{-7})/(.02)^4 \approx 5.0$. Hence

$$|E| \approx \frac{(b-a)^5}{2880}\, \Gamma^{(4)} \approx \frac{5(10^{-1})^5}{2880} \approx 2 \times 10^{-8}.$$

## 4.6   Error Estimates Through the Theory of Analytic Functions

If the integrand is an *analytic* function, then the high derivatives relevant to error estimation may be bounded by use of Cauchy's theorem. This theorem is as follows.

Let $B$ be a simply connected region in the complex $z(= x + iy)$-plane. Suppose that $f(z)$ is analytic in $B$. Let $z_0$ lie in $B$. Suppose that $C$ is a simple contour which lies in $B$ and goes around $z_0$ in the positive sense; then

$$f^{(n)}(z_0) = \frac{n!}{2\pi i} \int_C \frac{f(z)}{(z - z_0)^{n+1}} \, dz. \tag{4.6.1}$$

Suppose next that the real-line segment $a \leqslant x \leqslant b$ is contained in $B$. Select a $C$ that lies in $B$ and that contains this segment in its interior. Introduce this notation: $L(C) = $ length of $C$, $M_C = \max_{z \in C} |f(z)|$, $\delta = $ minimum distance from points of $C$ to points of the segment $a \leqslant x \leqslant b$. We now have

$$|f^{(n)}(x)| \leqslant \frac{n!}{2\pi} \int_C \frac{|f(z)| \, |dz|}{|z - x|^{n+1}} \leqslant \frac{n! L(C) M_C}{2\pi \delta^{n+1}}. \tag{4.6.2}$$

Therefore

$$\max_{a \leqslant x \leqslant b} |f^{(n)}(x)| \leqslant \frac{n! L(C) M_C}{2\pi \delta^{n+1}}, \tag{4.6.3}$$

and the right-hand number provides an estimate of $f^{(n)}(x)$ in terms of the maximum modulus of $f$ along $C$. Note that the terms $L(C)$ and $M_C$, as well as $\delta$, depend on $C$. As $C$ becomes larger, $L(C)$, $M_C$, and $\delta$ all increase in value, and the minimum (or nearly minimum) value of the estimate can be found if we vary $C$.

**Example.** Estimate $\max_{-1 \leqslant x \leqslant 1} |f^{(10)}(x)|$, where $f(x) = \exp [e^x]$. Take $C$ as the circle $|z| = R$, $R > 1$. Now

$$|f(z)| = | \exp [e^z]| = | \exp [e^x \cos y + i e^x \sin y]| = | \exp [e^x \cos y]| \leqslant \exp [e^R].$$

Hence, since $\delta = R - 1$,

$$\max_{-1 \leqslant x \leqslant 1} |f^{(10)}(x)| \leqslant \frac{(10)! \, 2\pi R \exp [e^R]}{2\pi (R - 1)^{11}}.$$

This inequality is valid for all $R > 1$. A coarse calculation shows that $R \exp [e^R] \times (R - 1)^{-11}$ has a minimum of about $2.46 \times 10^3$ at $R = 2.2$. Hence,

$$\max_{-1 \leqslant x \leqslant 1} |f^{(10)}(x)| \leqslant (10)! \times 2.46 \times 10^3.$$

It is also possible to obtain derivative-free error estimates without first going through the real variable work that leads to expressions of the type $f^{(n)}(\xi)$.

If $f(z)$ is a regular analytic function in a simply connected region $B$, then we can write

$$f(z) = \frac{1}{2\pi i} \int_C \frac{f(t)}{t - z} \, dt, \tag{4.6.4}$$

where $C$ is a simple contour lying in $B$ and containing $z$ in its interior. Suppose that $E$ is a linear functional. Then

$$E(f(z)) = \frac{1}{2\pi i} E \int_C \frac{f(t)}{t - z} \, dt. \tag{4.6.5}$$

Under certain mild restrictions as to the nature of $E$, it will be possible to interchange the operator $E$ with $\int_C$ and obtain

$$E(f(z)) = \frac{1}{2\pi i} \int_C E_z\left(\frac{1}{t - z}\right) f(t) \, dt. \tag{4.6.6}$$

Thus

$$E(f(z)) = \frac{1}{2\pi i} \int_C k(t) f(t) \, dt, \tag{4.6.7}$$

where

$$k(t) = E_z\left(\frac{1}{t - z}\right). \tag{4.6.8}$$

Formula (4.6.7) can be regarded as the complex variable analog of Peano's formula. We have

$$|E(f(z))| \leqslant \frac{1}{2\pi} \int_C |k(t)| \, |f(t)| \, |dt|, \tag{4.6.9}$$

so that an error estimate may be found in terms of the size of $|f(t)|$ on the contour $C$. The problem now is how to obtain good estimates for

$$|k(t)| = \left| E_z\left(\frac{1}{t - z}\right) \right|.$$

For approximate integration of interpolatory type, interpolatory formulas in the complex plane may be used to good effect. Let $z_0, z_1, \ldots, z_n$ be $n + 1$ distinct points lying in the complex plane. Suppose that $f(z)$ is a regular analytic function in a simply connected region $B$ that contains these points in its interior. Let

$$w(z) = (z - z_0)(z - z_1) \cdots (z - z_n). \tag{4.6.10}$$

Then

$$p_n(z) = \sum_{k=0}^{n} f(z_k) \frac{w(z)}{(z - z_k) w'(z_k)} \tag{4.6.11}$$

is the polynomial of class $\mathscr{P}_n$, which interpolates to $f(z)$ at $z_k$:

$$p_n(z_k) = f(z_k), \qquad k = 0, 1, \ldots, n. \tag{4.6.12}$$

According to a theorem of Hermite (see, for example, Davis [6, p. 68]) the error in polynomial interpolation can be expressed as a contour integral:

$$f(z) = p_n(z) + \frac{1}{2\pi i} \int_C \frac{w(z)f(t)}{w(t)(t-z)} \, dt, \qquad (4.6.13)$$

where $C$ is a simple contour contained in $B$ and containing the points $z_0, \ldots, z_n$ in its interior. If now the points $z = a$ and $z = b$ also lie inside $C$, then, integrating (4.6.13), we obtain

$$\int_a^b f(z) \, dz = \sum_{k=0}^n f(z_k) \int_a^b \frac{w(z)}{(z-z_k)w'(z_k)} \, dz + \int_a^b dz \frac{1}{2\pi i} \int_C \frac{w(z)f(t)}{w(t)(t-z)} \, dt. \qquad (4.6.14)$$

Hence, interchanging the order of integration, we have

$$\int_a^b f(z) \, dz = \sum_{k=0}^n a_k f(z_k) + \frac{1}{2\pi i} \int_C \frac{f(t)}{w(t)} u(t) \, dt, \qquad (4.6.15)$$

where $a_0, \ldots, a_n$ are the weights for interpolatory integration at $z_0, \ldots, z_n$ and $u(t)$ designates the function

$$u(t) = \int_a^b \frac{w(z) \, dz}{t-z}. \qquad (4.6.16)$$

If we now write

$$E(f) = \int_a^b f(z) \, dz - \sum_{k=0}^n a_k f(z_k) = \frac{1}{2\pi i} \int_C \frac{f(t)u(t)}{w(t)} \, dt, \qquad (4.6.17)$$

we can obtain an upper bound for $E$ that does not involve derivatives:

$$E(f) = \frac{1}{2\pi i} \int_C \frac{f(t)}{w(t)} \left( \int_a^b \frac{w(z) \, dz}{t-z} \right) dt. \qquad (4.6.18)$$

Hence

$$|E(f)| \leq \frac{1}{2\pi} \int_C \frac{|f(t)|}{|t-z_0| \, |t-z_1| \cdots |t-z_n|}$$
$$\times \left( \int_a^b \frac{|z-z_0| \, |z-z_1| \cdots |z-z_n|}{|t-z|} \, |dz| \right) |dt|. \qquad (4.6.19)$$

The following notations will be used: length of $C$, $L(C)$; minimum distance from $[a, b]$ to $C$, $\delta_C$; maximum distance from $z_0, z_1, \ldots, z_n$ to $[a, b]$, $D$; minimum distance from $z_0, z_1, \ldots, z_n$ to $C$, $d$. Then, from (4.6.19), we have

$$|E(f)| \leq \frac{L(C)}{2\pi} \max_{t \in C} |f(t)| \frac{1}{d^{n+1}} \frac{(b-a)D^{n+1}}{\delta_C} = \text{const} \max_{t \in C} |f(t)|, \qquad (4.6.20)$$

where

$$\text{const} = \frac{L(C)(b - a)}{2\pi\delta_C} \left(\frac{D}{d}\right)^{n+1}. \tag{4.6.21}$$

These identities have been applied by McNamee to Gaussian integration. Let $z_0, z_1, \ldots, z_{n-1}$ be the $n$ abscissas of the $G_n$ rule. Then

$$w(z) = (z - z_0)\cdots(z - z_{n-1}) = c_n P_n(z), \tag{4.6.22}$$

where $P_n(z)$ is the Legendre Polynomial of order $n$ and $c_n$ is a normalizing constant. Then the remainder is given by

$$\int_{-1}^{1} f(x)\, dx - G_n(f) = \frac{1}{2\pi i} \int_C \frac{f(t)}{P_n(t)} \left(\int_{-1}^{1} \frac{P_n(z)}{t - z} dz\right) dt. \tag{4.6.23}$$

The functions

$$Q_n(t) = \frac{1}{2} \int_{-1}^{1} \frac{P_n(z)}{t - z}\, dz \tag{4.6.24}$$

are commonly called the *Legendre functions of the second kind*. They are regular, single-valued functions in the whole plane with the segment $[-1 \leqslant t \leqslant 1]$ deleted. Therefore

$$\int_{-1}^{1} f(x)\, dx - G_n(f) = \frac{i}{\pi i} \int_C \frac{f(t) Q_n(t)}{P_n(t)}\, dt. \tag{4.6.25}$$

An upper bound for the integral on the right can now be obtained in terms of $\max_{t \in C} |f(t)|$, as was worked out before. An alternative method is to use an asymptotic expression for $Q_n(t)/P_n(t)$ and to employ a very large contour $C$. It is known that, as $t \to \infty$,

$$\frac{Q_n(t)}{P_n(t)} = c_n t^{-2n-1} \left[1 + \frac{2n^3 + 3n^2 - n - 1}{(2n + 3)(2n - 1)t^2} + \cdots\right], \tag{4.6.26}$$

where

$$c_n = \frac{2^{2n}(n!)^4}{(2n)!(2n + 1)!}. \tag{4.6.27}$$

**Example** (McNamee). Take $f(t) = e^t t^3$ and select $n = 5$. On the circle $|t| = R$, the modulus of the integrand in (4.6.25) is dominated by

$$c_5 \exp\left[-[7 \log R - R]\right].$$

We therefore choose $R = 7$. This leads to

$$\left|\int_{-1}^{1} e^t t^3\, dt - G_5(e^t t^3)\right| \leqslant 4 \times 10^{-6}.$$

Exact error: $1.0 \times 10^{-7}$.

**Reference.**   McNamee [1].

### 4.7   Error Estimates Through Functional Analysis

In this approach to error analysis, one works with a normed linear space of functions and estimates the norm of the truncation error operator, which has been considered as a linear functional defined over the space of functions. We cannot go into the deeper aspects of the method but will content ourselves with a simple example.

Let $f(z)$ be a regular analytic function in $|z| < 1$ and suppose that $f(z)$ is also continuous on $|z| = 1$. Let $-1 < a < b < 1$ and set

$$E(f) = \int_a^b f(x)\, dx - \sum_{k=1}^n w_k f(x_k). \tag{4.7.1}$$

For simplicity, assume that $-1 \leqslant x_i \leqslant 1$. By Cauchy's theorem, we have

$$f(z) = \frac{1}{2\pi i} \int_C \frac{f(t)}{t - z}\, dt = \frac{1}{2\pi} \int_C \frac{f(t)}{1 - z\bar{t}}\, ds. \tag{4.7.2}$$

In this last integral, $\bar{t}$ is the complex conjugate of $t$ and $ds$ is the element of length along the unit circle $C$. Applying $E$ to both sides of (4.7.2) and interchanging $E$ and $\int$, we obtain

$$E(f) = \frac{1}{2\pi} \int_C E\left(\frac{1}{1 - z\bar{t}}\right) f(t)\, ds. \tag{4.7.3}$$

From the Schwarz inequality, we have

$$|E(f)|^2 \leqslant \frac{1}{4\pi^2} \int_C \left| E\left(\frac{1}{1 - z\bar{t}}\right) \right|^2 ds \int_C |f(t)|^2\, ds. \tag{4.7.4}$$

Now

$$\frac{1}{1 - z\bar{t}} = \sum_{n=0}^\infty z^n \bar{t}^n, \quad \text{so that} \quad E\left(\frac{1}{1 - z\bar{t}}\right) = \sum_{n=0}^\infty E(z^n)\bar{t}^n.$$

Hence

$$\int_C \left| E\left(\frac{1}{1 - z\bar{t}}\right) \right|^2 ds = \int_C E\left(\frac{1}{1 - z\bar{t}}\right) \overline{E\left(\frac{1}{1 - z\bar{t}}\right)}\, ds$$

$$= \int_C \sum_{n=0}^\infty E(z^n)\bar{t}^n \sum_{m=0}^\infty \overline{E(z^m)} t^m\, ds.$$

In view of the fact that $\int_C \bar{t}^n t^m\, ds = 0$ if $m \neq n$ and $2\pi$ if $m = n$, we conclude that

$$\frac{1}{4\pi^2} \int_C \left| E\left(\frac{1}{1 - z\bar{t}}\right) \right|^2 ds = \frac{1}{2\pi} \sum_{n=0}^\infty |E(z^n)|^2. \tag{4.7.5}$$

If the rule of approximation is exact for polynomials of class $\mathscr{P}_N$, then this sum simplifies to

$$\frac{1}{2\pi} \sum_{N+1=n}^{\infty} |E(z^n)|^2.$$

The error estimate (4.7.4) may be written as

$$|E(f)| \leqslant \sigma \|f\|, \tag{4.7.6}$$

where

$$\sigma^2 = \frac{1}{2\pi} \sum_{n=0}^{\infty} |E(z^n)|^2 \tag{4.7.7}$$

and

$$\|f\|^2 = \int_C |f(z)|^2 \, ds. \tag{4.7.8}$$

The quantity $\|f\|$ is called the *norm of $f$*, and $\sigma$ is the *norm of $E$*. This estimate is *derivative-free* insofar as it requires only a knowledge of the values of $f(z)$ along $|z| = 1$. The norm $\|f\|$ may be estimated from

$$\|f\|^2 = \int_C |f(z)|^2 \, ds \leqslant 2\pi \max_{|z|=1} |f(z)|, \tag{4.7.9}$$

so that (4.7.6) leads to

$$|E(f)| \leqslant \sqrt{2\pi} \, \sigma \max_{|z|=1} |f(z)|. \tag{4.7.10}$$

The constant $\sigma$ is independent of $f$ and depends merely on the rule of approximate integration. It may be computed directly from (4.7.7) by machine or it may be handled analytically.

On the basis of a number of summation identities, Hämmerlin has computed the following values for $\sigma$.

| Interval | Rule | Error norm |
|---|---|---|
| $(-\frac{1}{2}, \frac{1}{2})$ | $h^{-1} \times T$ | $\sqrt{2\pi} \, \sigma < .189h^2$ |
| $(-\frac{1}{2}, \frac{1}{2})$ | $h^{-1} \times S$ | $\sqrt{2\pi} \, \sigma < .253h^4$ |
| $(-\frac{1}{2}, \frac{1}{2})$ | $h^{-1} \times N$ | $\sqrt{2\pi} \, \sigma < .569h^4$ |

*Note*: $T$ = trapezoidal rule, $S$ = Simpson's rule, $N$ = Simpson's $\frac{3}{8}$ rule.

**References.**   Chai and Wertz [1], Davis [1], [5], Davis and Rabinowitz [1], Hämmerlin [2], [3], Lo, Lee, and Sun [1], Stroud and Secrest [2].

The basic normed linear space relevant to the above work is the Hilbert space of analytic functions in $|z| < 1$, for which $\int_C |f(z)|^2 \, ds < \infty$. Numerous other spaces of functions, both real and complex, have been considered. In the real cases, they do not lead to derivative-free error estimates.

For a given normed linear space of functions, we may obtain error estimates in the form

$$|E(f)| \leqslant \sigma \, \|f\|. \tag{4.7.11}$$

As noted before, the constant $\sigma$ depends merely on the rule of approximate integration and not on the particular function to be integrated. For fixed $n$, we may therefore inquire as to the rule

$$\sum_{k=1}^{n} w_k f(x_k) \approx \int f(x) \, dx,$$

which minimizes $\sigma$. Such a rule is called an *optimum rule of integration* with respect to the space of functions chosen. Many optimum rules have been determined and, although they are of great interest from the theoretical point of view, their utility in practice has not, at the time of writing, been established.

**References.** Davis [1], Ghizetti [1], Golomb and Weinberger [1], Meyers and Sard [1], Nikolsky [1], Sard [1], Valentin [1], Wilf [1].

### 4.8 Errors for Integrands with Low Continuity

The errors incurred in approximate integration formulas are conventionally expressed in terms of the higher derivatives of the integrand and are valid only if the integrand is sufficiently smooth. What is the error when a high-order rule is applied to a function with low-order continuity? One way of obtaining an estimate of error in such an instance is through the use of approximation theory.

THEOREM. *Let $f(x) \in C[a, b]$, and suppose that there exists a polynomial of degree $\leqslant n$, $p_n(x)$, such that*

$$|f(x) - p_n(x)| \leqslant \varepsilon, \qquad a \leqslant x \leqslant b. \tag{4.8.1}$$

*Let*

$$R(f) = \sum_{k=1}^{n+1} w_k f(x_k) \approx \int_a^b f(x) \, dx, \qquad a \leqslant x_k \leqslant b$$

*be a rule of approximate integration which is exact for polynomials of class $\mathscr{P}_n$. Then if*

$$E(f) = \int_a^b f(x) \, dx - \sum_{k=1}^{n+1} w_k f(x_k), \tag{4.8.2}$$

*we have*

$$|E(f)| \leqslant \left[ (b - a) + \sum_{k=1}^{n+1} |w_k| \right] \varepsilon. \qquad (4.8.3)$$

*Proof*

$$E(f) = \int_a^b f(x)\, dx - R(f) = \int_a^b (f(x) - p_n(x))\, dx + \int_a^b p_n(x)\, dx - R(f)$$

$$= \int_a^b (f(x) - p_n(x))\, dx + R(p_n - f)$$

*inasmuch as* $\int_a^b p_n(x)\, dx = R(p_n)$. *Hence*

$$|E(f)| \leqslant \int_a^b |f(x) - p_n(x)|\, dx + \sum_{k=1}^{n+1} |w_k|\, |p_n(x) - f(x)|$$

$$\leqslant (b - a)\varepsilon + \varepsilon \sum_{k=1}^{n+1} |w_k|.$$

COROLLARY.  *If* $w_k > 0$, *then*

$$|E(f)| \leqslant 2(b - a)\varepsilon. \qquad (4.8.4)$$

*Proof.*  In this case, we have

$$\sum_{k=1}^{n+1} |w_k| = \sum_{k=1}^{n+1} w_k = \int_a^b dx = b - a.$$

This estimate of error can now be coupled with an estimate of how close a given continuous function may be approximated by a polynomial. The following theorems due to Jackson are relevant.

THEOREM.  *Let* $f(x)$ *be of class* $C[a, b]$ *and have* $\omega(\delta)$ *as its modulus of continuity there. Then for each* $n = 1, 2, 3, \ldots$ *there exists a polynomial of degree* $\leqslant n, p_n(x)$, *such that*

$$|f(x) - p_n(x)| \leqslant 6\omega\left(\frac{b - a}{2n}\right), \qquad a \leqslant x \leqslant b. \qquad (4.8.5)$$

*If* $f(x)$ *is of class* $C[a, b]$ *and has a bounded derivative there,*

$$|f'(x)| \leqslant M, \qquad a \leqslant x \leqslant b, \qquad (4.8.6)$$

*then for each* $n = 1, 2, \ldots$ *there exists a polynomial* $p_n(x)$ *of degree* $\leqslant n$ *such that*

$$|f(x) - p_n(x)| \leqslant \frac{3(b - a)M}{n}, \qquad a \leqslant x \leqslant b. \qquad (4.8.7)$$

*Let $f(x) \in C^p[a, b]$ $(p > 1)$ and have a bounded $(p + 1)$th derivative there:*

$$|f^{(p+1)}(x)| \leqslant M_{p+1}, \qquad a \leqslant x \leqslant b. \tag{4.8.8}$$

*Then for each $n = 1, 2, \ldots$ there exists a polynomial $p_n(x)$ of degree $\leqslant n$ such that*

$$|f(x) - p_n(x)| \leqslant \frac{6^{p+1}p^p}{p!n^{p+1}}(p + 1)(b - a)^{p+1}M_{p+1}. \tag{4.8.9}$$

**Example.** The function $f(x) = x^{3/2}$ is in $C^1[0, 1]$ and satisfies $|f'(x)| \leqslant \frac{3}{2}$ there. It is not in class $C^2[0, 1]$. Hence, by (4.8.7), there exists a $p_n(x) \in \mathscr{P}_n$ such that

$$|f(x) - p_n(x)| \leqslant 3 \cdot 1 \cdot \tfrac{3}{2} \cdot n^{-1} = 9/2n = \varepsilon.$$

The $n$-point Gauss rule is exact for polynomials of degree $\leqslant 2n - 1$. Hence, by (4.8.4), we have

$$|E_{G_n}(f)| \leqslant \frac{2 \cdot 9}{2(2n - 1)} = \frac{9}{2n - 1}.$$

The table in Section 2.7 displays an error much smaller than this bound.

**References.** Korovkin [1, pp. 86–88], Natanson [1, p. 129].

CHAPTER 5

# APPROXIMATE INTEGRATION IN
# TWO OR MORE DIMENSIONS

## 5.1 Introduction

The object of our investigation can be described in the following general way. Let $B$ designate a fixed closed region in $d$-dimensional Euclidean space and let $dV$ designate the $d$-dimensional volume element. Find fixed points $P_1, P_2, \ldots, P_n$ (preferably in $B$) and fixed weights $w_1, w_2, \ldots, w_n$ such that

$$\int_B f(P) \, dV \approx \sum_{k=1}^{n} w_k f(P_k) \qquad (5.1.1)$$

is a useful approximation to the integral on the left for a reasonably large class of functions of $d$ variables defined on $B$. There is also the possibility of using information about the derivatives of $f$ to form the approximation, but this modification will not be considered.

In passing from one dimension to several dimensions, the diversity of integrals and the difficulty in handling them is greatly increased. In the first place, in one dimension we can restrict our attention to three different types of regions of integration: the finite interval, the singly infinite interval, and the doubly infinite interval, whereas in several dimensions, there are potentially an infinite number of different types of regions to contend with. In the second place, the behavior of functions of several variables can be considerably more complicated than that of functions of one variable (for example, we may have singular behavior on a manifold) and our experience and intuition with them is much more limited. Then again, as the dimension becomes higher, more and more points are necessary for successful approximation, and even with current computing speeds the number of functional

125

evaluations may be an important consideration. The necessity for economiza-
tion has, in fact, led to approximate integration by Monte Carlo methods.

In principle, as in the case of one dimension, we should like to discuss
integration over a variety of regions, sequences of rules and their convergence,
error estimates, "automatic" integration, how to handle singularities, how to
handle highly oscillatory integrands, etc. But these matters are only moder-
ately developed or are currently under development, so that our treatment
of this subject will be somewhat superficial.

### 5.2 Some Elementary Multiple Integrals over Standard Regions

In this chapter, the letter $d$ designates the number of dimensions of the
space. The standard bounded regions are the $d$-dimensional cube, the $d$-
dimensional solid sphere (or ball), and the $d$-dimensional simplex (the generalization of the triangle and the tetrahedron). Since the cube is readily handled,
we omit special formulas referring to it.

1. Let $S_d$ denote the simplex

$$x_1 \geqslant 0, x_2 \geqslant 0, \ldots, x_d \geqslant 0 \qquad (x_1 + x_2 + \cdots + x_d \leqslant 1).$$

Then

$$\int_{S_d} x_1^{p_1-1} x_2^{p_2-1} \cdots x_d^{p_d-1} \, dV = \frac{\Gamma(p_1)\Gamma(p_2) \cdots \Gamma(p_d)}{\Gamma(p_1 + p_2 + \cdots + p_d + 1)}. \qquad (5.2.1)$$

The notation $\Gamma(x)$ designates the gamma function. In particular, the volume
$V$ of $S_d$ is given by

$$V = \int_{S_d} dV = \frac{1}{d!}. \qquad (5.2.2)$$

2. Let $\theta_d$ denote the portion of the ball $x_1^2 + x_2^2 + \cdots + x_d^2 \leqslant 1$ with
positive coordinates: $x_1 \geqslant 0, x_2 \geqslant 0, \ldots, x_d \geqslant 0$. Then

$$\int_{\theta_d} x_1^{p_1-1} x_2^{p_2-1} \cdots x_d^{p_d-1} \, dV = \frac{1}{2^d} \frac{\Gamma(p_1/2)\Gamma(p_2/2) \cdots \Gamma(p_d/2)}{\Gamma(\frac{1}{2}(p_1 + p_2 + \cdots + p_d) + 1)}. \qquad (5.2.3)$$

In particular, the volume $V$ of the ball $B_d : x_1^2 + x_2^2 + \cdots + x_d^2 \leqslant 1$ is

$$V = 2^d \int_{\theta_d} dV = \frac{\pi^{d/2}}{\Gamma(d/2 + 1)}. \qquad (5.2.4)$$

3. Let $Q(x_1, x_2, \ldots, x_d)$ be a positive definite symmetric quadratic form.
Then

$$V = \int \cdots \int_{Q < c^2} dx_1 \, dx_2 \cdots dx_d = \frac{\pi^{d/2} c^d}{\Gamma(d/2 + 1) \sqrt{\det Q}}, \qquad (5.2.5)$$

$$\int_{-\infty}^{\infty} \cdots \int_{-\infty}^{\infty} e^{-Q/2} \, dx_1 \cdots dx_d = \frac{(2\pi)^{d/2}}{\sqrt{\det Q}}. \qquad (5.2.6)$$

4. Let $\alpha_1, \alpha_2, \ldots, \alpha_d$ be nonnegative even integers. Then

$$\int_{-\infty}^{\infty} \cdots \int_{-\infty}^{\infty} \exp\left[-x_1^2 - \cdots - x_d^2\right] x_1^{\alpha_1} \cdots x_d^{\alpha_d} \, dx_1 \cdots dx_d$$
$$= \Gamma\left(\frac{\alpha_1 + 1}{2}\right) \Gamma\left(\frac{\alpha_2 + 1}{2}\right) \cdots \Gamma\left(\frac{\alpha_d + 1}{2}\right). \quad (5.2.7)$$

$$\int_{-\infty}^{\infty} \cdots \int_{-\infty}^{\infty} \exp\left[-\sqrt{x_1^2 + \cdots + x_d^2}\right] x_1^{\alpha_1} \cdots x_d^{\alpha_d} \, dx_1 \cdots dx_d$$
$$= 2(\alpha_1 + \cdots + \alpha_d + d - 1)! \, \frac{\Gamma\left(\dfrac{\alpha_1 + 1}{2}\right) \cdots \Gamma\left(\dfrac{\alpha_d + 1}{2}\right)}{\Gamma\left(\dfrac{\alpha_1 + \cdots + \alpha_d + d}{2}\right)}. \quad (5.2.8)$$

**Reference.** Gradstein and Ryshik [1].

## 5.3 *Change of Order of Integration*

Higher dimensional integrals can exhibit a variety of peculiarities. The reader is no doubt familiar with integrals that cannot be evaluated in elementary terms in their original form but can be so evaluated if the order of integration is changed. For example: $\int_0^1 dx \int_x^1 e^{y^2} \, dy$ leads to a nonelementary indefinite integral; but in the reverse order

$$\int_0^1 dx \int_x^1 e^{y^2} \, dy = \int_0^1 e^{y^2} \, dy \int_0^y dx = \tfrac{1}{2}(e - 1).$$

There is a numerical phenomenon that is reminiscent of this. If a multiple integral is expressed as an iterated integral, the order in which it is so expressed may affect the numerical accuracy of the result.

**Example**

$$I = \int_0^1 dy \int_0^{\sqrt{1-y}} dx = \int_0^1 dx \int_0^{1-x^2} dy = \tfrac{2}{3}.$$

If the first iterated integral is computed numerically by use of ordinary rules, for example, Simpson's Rule, it is found that, due to the square-root singularity, the answer is rather less accurate than that obtained from the second iterated integral.

**Reference.** Price [2].

## 5.4 *Change of Variables*

If a given region $B$ can be transformed into a *standard* region $B'$ for which a rule of approximate integration is available, then this rule may be transformed to provide a rule for $B$. We shall show how this works in the case of two dimensions. The device is perfectly general.

Let $B$ be a region in the $xy$-plane and $B'$ (which will be our standard region) be in the $uv$-plane. Let the regions $B$ and $B'$ be related to each other by means of the transformation

$$x = \phi(u, v),$$
$$y = \psi(u, v). \tag{5.4.1}$$

It will be assumed that $\phi$ and $\psi$ have continuous partial derivatives and that the Jacobian

$$J(u, v) = \begin{vmatrix} \dfrac{\partial \phi}{\partial u} & \dfrac{\partial \phi}{\partial v} \\ \dfrac{\partial \psi}{\partial u} & \dfrac{\partial \psi}{\partial v} \end{vmatrix} \tag{5.4.2}$$

does not vanish in $B'$. Suppose, further, that

$$\iint_{B'} h(u, v) \, du \, dv \approx \sum_{k=1}^{n} w_k h(u_k, v_k), \quad (u_k, v_k) \in B' \tag{5.4.3}$$

is a rule of approximate integration over $B'$. Now we have

$$\iint_B f(x, y) \, dx \, dy = \iint_{B'} f(\phi(u, v), \psi(u, v)) \, |J(u, v)| \, du \, dv$$

$$\approx \sum_{k=1}^{n} w_k f(\phi(u_k, v_k), \psi(u_k, v_k)) \, |J(u_k, v_k)|$$

$$= \sum_{k=1}^{n} W_k f(x_k, y_k), \tag{5.4.4}$$

where

$$x_k = \phi(u_k, v_k), \qquad y_k = \psi(u_k, v_k), \qquad \text{and} \quad W_k = w_k \, |J(u_k, v_k)|. \tag{5.4.5}$$

Thus

$$\iint_B f(x, y) \, dx \, dy \approx \sum_{k=1}^{n} W_k f(x_k, y_k), \tag{5.4.6}$$

with abscissas and weights as above, constitutes a rule of approximate integration for $B$.

An important special case occurs when $B$ and $B'$ are related by a non-singular affine transformation:

$$x = au + bv + c,$$
$$y = du + ev + f. \tag{5.4.7}$$

In this case, the Jacobian is constant:

$$|J| = \left| \det \begin{pmatrix} a & b \\ d & e \end{pmatrix} \right| = |ae - bd| \neq 0. \tag{5.4.8}$$

Integration rules over parallelograms, ellipses, etc., and their higher dimensional analogs are therefore easy to develop.

## 5.5   Decomposition into Elementary Regions

Let $B$ designate a bounded region with volume $V$. Suppose that the whole space is divided up by a cubical grid whose side is $h$. Designate by $N$ the number of cubes contained entirely in $B$. Then $N$ (which is the measure of difficulty of obtaining $V$ by the primitive process of counting) satisfies

$$V \sim Nh^d. \tag{5.5.1}$$

The error $E$ made in counting only those cubes that lie in $B$ equals approximately the volume of those cubes which pass through the boundary of $B$; hence

$$E \sim hS, \tag{5.5.2}$$

where $S$ designates the surface measure of the boundary of $B$. Now we have

$$S \sim V^{(d-1)/d}. \tag{5.5.3}$$

Combining these approximations, we obtain

$$\frac{E}{V} \sim \frac{1}{N^{1/d}}. \tag{5.5.4}$$

This is known as the *dimensional effect* and is a very pessimistic (particularly for high $d$) upper bound of the number of functional evaluations necessary to achieve a given accuracy.

The dimensional effect is exhibited in error estimates for multidimensional Riemann sums. Suppose that the function $f = f(x_1, x_2, \ldots, x_d)$ is of bounded variation over the hypercube $0 \leqslant x_i \leqslant 1$ ($i = 1, 2, \ldots, d$). Designate the total variation of $f$ by $V(f)$. Let $n$ be an integer $\geqslant 1$ and set $N = n^d$.

THEOREM.   *Under the above conditions we have*

$$\left| \int_0^1 \cdots \int_0^1 f \, dx_1 \, dx_2 \cdots dx_d - \frac{1}{N} \sum_{k_1, k_2, \ldots, k_d = 0}^{n-1} f\left(\frac{k_1}{n}, \frac{k_2}{n}, \ldots, \frac{k_d}{n}\right) \right| \leqslant \frac{dV(f)}{N^{1/d}}. \tag{5.5.5}$$

**References.**   Hlawka [1], Tocher [1].

## 5.6   Cartesian Products and Product Rules

Let $B$ be a region in $r$-dimensional Euclidean space with points $(x_1, x_2, \ldots, x_r)$, and let $G$ be a region in $s$-dimensional Euclidean space with points $(y_1, y_2, \ldots, y_s)$. The symbol $B \times G$ designates the *Cartesian product of B and G*, and by this we mean the region in the Euclidean space of $r + s$ dimensions with points $(x_1, \ldots, x_r, y_1, \ldots, y_s)$ that satisfy $(x_1, \ldots, x_r) \in B$, $(y_1, \ldots, y_s) \in G$.

**Examples.** $B: 0 \leqslant x \leqslant 1$, $G: 0 \leqslant y \leqslant 1$; then $B \times G$ is the unit square, $0 \leqslant x, y \leqslant 1$. If $B$ is the disc $x^2 + y^2 \leqslant 1$ and $G$ is the segment $0 \leqslant z \leqslant 1$, then $B \times G$ is the right cylinder of height 1 whose base is $B$.

It is convenient to use vector notation and write $\mathbf{x} = (x_1, \ldots, x_r)$ and $\mathbf{y} = (y_1, \ldots, y_s)$. Suppose now that $R$ is an $m$-point rule of integration over $B$,

$$R(f) = \sum_{k=1}^{m} w_k f(\mathbf{x}_k) \approx \int_B f(\mathbf{x})\, dV, \qquad \mathbf{x}_k \in B, \qquad (5.6.1)$$

and $S$ is an $n$-point rule of integration over $G$,

$$S(f) = \sum_{k=1}^{n} v_k f(\mathbf{y}_k) \approx \int_G f(\mathbf{y})\, dV, \qquad \mathbf{y}_k \in G. \qquad (5.6.2)$$

Then by the *product rule of R and S* we mean the $mn$-point rule applicable to $B \times G$ and defined by

$$R \times S(f) = \sum_{j,k=1}^{m,n} w_j v_k f(\mathbf{x}_j, \mathbf{y}_k) \approx \int_{B \times G} f(\mathbf{x}, \mathbf{y})\, dV. \qquad (5.6.3)$$

An obvious extension of the notion of the product of two rules can be made so as to define the product of three or more rules, and similar definitions can be made for weighted integrals. The following theorem holds for errors.

THEOREM.   *If $R$ integrates $f(\mathbf{x})$ exactly over $B$, if $S$ integrates $g(\mathbf{y})$ exactly over $G$, and if $h(\mathbf{x}, \mathbf{y}) = f(\mathbf{x})g(\mathbf{y})$, then $R \times S$ will integrate $h(\mathbf{x}, \mathbf{y})$ exactly over $B \times G$.*

*Proof*

$$\int_{B \times G} h(\mathbf{x}, \mathbf{y})\, dV = \int_{B \times G} f(\mathbf{x})g(\mathbf{y})\, dV = \int_B f(\mathbf{x})\, dV_B \int_G g(\mathbf{y})\, dV_G$$

$$= \sum_{j=1}^{m} w_j f(\mathbf{x}_j) \sum_{k=1}^{n} v_k g(\mathbf{y}_k) = \sum_{j,k=1}^{m,n} w_j v_k f(\mathbf{x}_j)g(\mathbf{y}_k)$$

$$= R \times S(h).$$

**Examples.**   Let $R$ designate the rectangle $a \leqslant x \leqslant b$, $c \leqslant y \leqslant d$. Set $m = \frac{1}{2}(a + b)$, $n = \frac{1}{2}(c + d)$, $b - a = h$, $d - c = k$. The evaluation of $\iint_R f(x, y)\, dx\, dy$ by the product of two Simpson's rules yields

$$\iint_R f(x, y)\, dx\, dy \approx \frac{hk}{36}\, [f(a, c) + f(a, d) + f(b, c) + f(b, d) +$$
$$+ 4(f(a, n) + f(m, c) + f(b, n) + f(m, d)) + 16 f(m, n)].$$
$$(5.6.4)$$

This 9-point rule will integrate exactly all linear combinations of the 16 monomials $x^i y^j$ ($0 \leqslant i, j \leqslant 3$). The appropriate weights for the product of two compound Simpson's rules can be found by the multiplication table following.

|     | 1 | 4 | 2 | 4 | 2 | 4 | $\cdots$ | 2 | 4 | 1 |
|-----|---|---|---|---|---|---|----------|---|---|---|
| 1   | 1 | 4 | 2 | 4 | 2 | 4 | $\cdots$ | 2 | 4 | 1 |
| 4   | 4 | 16 | 8 | 16 | 8 | 16 | $\cdots$ | 8 | 16 | 4 |
| 2   | 2 | 8 | 4 | 8 | 4 | 8 | $\cdots$ | 4 | 8 | 2 |
| 4   | 4 | 16 | 8 | 16 | 8 | 16 | $\cdots$ | 8 | 16 | 4 |
| 2   |   |   |   |   |   |   |          |   |   |   |
| 4   | . |   |   |   |   |   |          |   |   | . |
| $\vdots$ | . |   |   |   |   |   |          |   |   | . |
| 2   |   |   |   |   |   |   |          |   |   |   |
| 4   | 4 | 16 | 8 | 16 | 8 | 16 | $\cdots$ | 8 | 16 | 4 |
| 1   | 1 | 4 | 2 | 4 | 2 | 4 | $\cdots$ | 2 | 4 | 1 |

As a second example of a product rule, consider the integral $I = \int_C f(x, y)\, dx\, dy$, where $C$ is the unit circle $x^2 + y^2 \leqslant 1$. Expressing this integral in polar coordinates, we have

$$I = \int_0^{2\pi} d\theta \int_0^1 f r\, dr. \qquad (5.6.5)$$

In the $r$ variable, we will integrate approximately, using a Gaussian rule of order $n$ corresponding to the weight function $w(r) = r$ with abscissas $r_1, r_2, \ldots, r_n$ and weights $w_1, w_2, \ldots, w_n$. In the $\theta$ variable (since $f$ is periodic in $\theta$) we use a rectangular (trapezoidal) rule with abscissas $\theta_k = (2\pi k / N)$, $k = 0, 1, \ldots, N - 1$, and weights all $1/N$. This yields

$$I \approx \frac{1}{N} \sum_{k=0}^{N-1} \sum_{i=1}^{n} w_i f\left(r_i \cos \frac{2\pi k}{N}, r_i \sin \frac{2\pi k}{N}\right). \qquad (5.6.6)$$

**References.**   Fishman [1], Peirce [1].

**Example.**    Let $G_5$ be the Gaussian 5-point rule over $[0, 1]$. Then $G_5 \times G_5 \times G_5 \times G_5(= (G_5)^4)$ is a product rule of 625 points applicable to the unit 4-dimensional cube. It integrates exactly the $10^4$ monomials of the form $x_1^{m_1} x_2^{m_2} x_3^{m_3} x_4^{m_4}$ with $0 \leqslant m_1, m_2, m_3, m_4 \leqslant 9$. The following numerical example is from Thacher.

$$I(k) = \int_0^1 \int_0^1 \int_0^1 \int_0^1 (k \cos w - 7kw \sin w - 6kw^2 \cos w + kw^2 \sin w) \, dx_1 \, dx_2 \, dx_3 \, dx_4,$$

$$w = kx_1 x_2 x_3 x_4.$$

| $k$ | .1 | .25 | 1.0 | $\pi/2$ | $3\pi/2$ |
|---|---|---|---|---|---|
| Exact value | .0998 334 | .2474 04 | .8414 71 | 1.0000 0 | $-1.0000$ 0 |
| Error in $(G_5)^4$ | .0000 0018 | .0000 005 | .0000 011 | .0000 010 | .0000 282 |

As $k$ becomes larger, the integrand becomes less polynomial-like in its behavior and the error begins to increase.

**Reference.**    Thacher [3].

**Example**

$$I(b) = \frac{1}{\pi^3} \int_0^\pi \int_0^\pi \int_0^\pi \frac{dx \, dy \, dz}{3b - \cos x - \cos y - \cos z}.$$

| $b^{-1}$ | Rule | Approximate value | Exact value |
|---|---|---|---|
| .7 | A | .25767 | .25794 |
| .7 | B | .25792 | .25794 |
| .8 | A | .30786 | .30781 |
| .8 | B | .30780 | .30781 |
| .9 | A | .37231 | .36993 |
| .9 | B | .36990 | .36993 |
| 1.0 | A | .49849 | .50546 |
| 1.0 | B | .50305 | .50546 |

Rule A is $(G_3)^3$, a 27-point rule. Rule B is $(3 \times G_3)^3$, a 729-point rule. Note that the integrand is singular for $b^{-1} = 1.0$.

**References.**    Ryshik and Gradstein [1, p. 217], Tikson [1].

**Example**

$$\int_0^1 \int_0^1 \frac{dx \, dy}{1 - xy} = \frac{\pi^2}{6}.$$

| Rule | Approximate value |
|:---:|:---:|
| $R_1$ | 1.58123 |
| $R_2$ | 1.61213 |
| $R_3$ | 1.62283 |
| $R_4$ | 1.62827 |
| $R_5$ | 1.63156 |
| $R_6$ | 1.63376 |
| Exact value | 1.644934 |

The rule $R_k = (k \times G_3)^2$ and therefore has $9k^2$ points. Note the singularity of the integrand at $x = y = 1$ and also the difficulty of treating the integral as an iterated simple integral. However, the integrand is positive and monotonic in each variable, and the process of ignoring the singularity is working out.

The number of point $N$ in a product rule exhibits a dimensional effect. That is to say, if $R$ is a $p$-point rule on $[0, 1]$, then the corresponding product rule $R^d$ over the $d$-dimensional cube, has $p^d$ points. For a modest value of $p$, say 5, and for a multiple integral of dimension 18, this would amount to $5^{18} \approx 10^{13}$ functional evaluations. Even with present speeds of computors, this amount of computation would be quite out of the question. On the other hand, for multiple integrals of dimension at most 4 or 5, we could take $R$ up to 10 points and compute a product rule of $10^4$ or $10^5$ points without excessive expenditure of time. The method adopted for approximate multiple integration will therefore depend strongly on the dimension number as well as on the complexity of the integrand.

**References.**   Hammer [2], Hammer and Wymore [1].

### 5.6.1   Generalized Product Rules

If the region $B$ is sufficiently simple, the multiple integral $I = \iint \cdots \int_B f\, dx_1$ $dx_2 \cdots dx_d$ may be expressed as an iterated integral of the form

$$I = \int_{L_0}^{U_0} dx_1 \int_{L_1(x_1)}^{U_1(x_1)} dx_2 \cdots \int_{L_{d-1}(x_1,x_2,\ldots,x_{d-1})}^{U_{d-1}(x_1,x_2,\ldots,x_{d-1})} f(x_1, x_2, \cdots, x_d)\, dx_d,$$

$$(5.6.1.1)$$

or as a sum of such integrals. The notion of a product rule may be extended to integrals of this form. For simplicity, we work in two variables, $x, y$, and write

$$I = \int_a^b dx \int_{\psi(x)}^{\phi(x)} f(x, y)\, dy = \int_a^b g(x)\, dx, \qquad (5.6.1.2)$$

where

$$g(x) = \int_{\psi(x)}^{\phi(x)} f(x, y) \, dy. \tag{5.6.1.3}$$

We use an $N$-point rule $R_1$,

$$\int_a^b g(x) \, dx \approx \sum_{k=1}^N w_k g(x_k), \tag{5.6.1.4}$$

to integrate in the $x$-variable. Thus

$$I \approx \sum_{k=1}^N w_k \int_{\psi(x_k)}^{\phi(x_k)} f(x_k, y) \, dy. \tag{5.6.1.5}$$

For each of the $N$ integrals, we use an $M$-point rule $R_2$ for its evaluation:

$$\int_{\psi(x_k)}^{\phi(x_k)} f(x_k, y) \, dy \approx \sum_{j=1}^M v_{jk} f(x_k, y_{jk}). \tag{5.6.1.6}$$

The double subscripts on the right reflect the fact that the abscissas and weights of $R_2$ must be adjusted for each value of $k$ to the interval $\psi(x_k) \leqslant x \leqslant \phi(x_k)$. Thus

$$I \approx \sum_{k=1}^N w_k \sum_{j=1}^M v_{jk} f(x_k, y_{jk}) \tag{5.6.1.7}$$

is an $MN$-point rule for $I$.

**Example**    (Thacher)

$$I = 8 \int_0^1 \int_0^{\sqrt{1-x^2}} \int_0^{\sqrt{1-x^2-y^2}} \frac{dz \, dy \, dx}{x^2 + y^2 + (z - k)^2} = \pi\left(2 + \left(\frac{1}{k} - k\right) \log\left|\frac{1 + k}{1 - k}\right|\right).$$

An $s \times G_p$ ($G$ = Gauss) rule was employed in each variable, and the following values were obtained.

| $k$ | $\frac{1}{2}$ | | 2 | |
|---|---|---|---|---|
| Exact | 11.46027 | | 1.106097 | |
| $s$ | 1 | 2 | 1 | 2 |
| $p = 2$ | 5.45446 | 11.83865 | 1.036877 | 1.118431 |
| $p = 3$ | 9.36167 | 12.40898 | 1.134355 | 1.109428 |

**References.**    Freeman [A1], Thacher [2].

## 5.7   Rules Exact for Monomials

In one dimension we have seen that the program of obtaining rules that are exact for monomials $1, x, x^2, \ldots, x^n$ coincides with the program of integrating an interpolation polynomial. This has no exact generalization in more than one dimension for the simple reason that polynomial interpolation is not always possible in two and more dimensions. For example, given $n$ points $P_1, P_2, \ldots, P_n$ in the plane, and given $n$ monomials in two variables $1, x, y, x^2, xy, \ldots$, it is not always possible to find a linear combination of the monomials which takes on prescribed values at the points $P_i$.

If the points $P_i$ constitute a product lattice, then there exists a generalization of Lagrange's formula. We set

$$u(x) = \prod_{i=0}^{m} (x - x_i), \qquad u_i(x) = \frac{u(x)}{x - x_i},$$

$$v(y) = \prod_{j=0}^{n} (y - y_j), \qquad v_j(y) = \frac{v(y)}{y - y_j}. \tag{5.7.1}$$

Then

$$p_{mn}(x, y) = \sum_{i,j=0}^{m,n} f(x_i, y_j) \frac{u_i(x)v_j(y)}{u_i(x_i)v_j(y_j)} \tag{5.7.2}$$

is a polynomial in $x$ and $y$ which takes on the values $f(x_i, y_j)$ at the $(m + 1) \times (n + 1)$ points $(x_i, y_j)$ $(i = 0, 1, \ldots, m; j = 0, 1, \ldots, n)$, which align themselves in a rectangular lattice. This device carries over to higher dimensions. This formula may be integrated formally to produce integration rules of the type

$$\int\int_B f(x, y)\, dx\, dy \approx \sum_{i,j=0}^{m,n} w_{ij} f(x_i, y_j) \tag{5.7.3}$$

with

$$w_{ij} = \int\int_B \frac{u_i(x)v_j(y)}{u_i(x_i)v_j(y_j)}\, dx\, dy. \tag{5.7.4}$$

There is an interpolation formula due to Biermann that makes use of functional values on a triangular lattice of points

$$(x_0, y_0), (x_1, y_0), \qquad \cdots \qquad , (x_m, y_0)$$
$$(x_0, y_1), (x_1, y_1), \ldots, (x_{m-1}, y_1)$$
$$\vdots$$
$$(x_0, y_m)$$

Biermann's interpolation formula can also be integrated.

**References.**    Stancu [1], Steffensen [1, p. 215].

In order to obtain formulas that involve fewer points than required for a product layout, we abandon the interpolatory point of view and ask for points $P_1, P_2, \ldots, P_n$ and corresponding weights $w_1, w_2, \ldots, w_n$ such that

$$\int f \, dV \approx \sum_{k=1}^{n} w_k f(P_k)$$

is exact for some $n$ monomials. The determination of such points and weights leads to systems of simultaneous nonlinear equations.

We shall exhibit some of the special rules that have been obtained. Particular emphasis has been laid on the development of rules that are precise for monomials up to degree $n$, that is, monomials of the form $\prod_{i=1}^{d} x_i^{a_i}$ where $a_i \geqslant 0$ and $a_1 + a_2 + \cdots + a_d \leqslant n$. Such a rule is said to be of *precision* or of *degree* $n$.

### 1. 2d-Point Rule of Precision 3 for a Hypercube

Designate the hypercube $-1 \leqslant x_i \leqslant 1$, $i = 1, 2, \ldots, d$, by $H_d$. Let $dV = dx_1 \, dx_2 \cdots dx_d$. We shall look for an integration formula of the form

$$\int_{H_d} f \, dV \approx w \sum^{2d} f(\pm u, 0, 0, \ldots, 0). \tag{5.7.5}$$

The sum on the right is extended over all $2d$ possibilities of $\pm u$ in each of the $d$ argument positions. That is to say, $f(0, \pm u, 0, \ldots, 0)$, etc.

Inserting $f \equiv 1$ into (5.7.5), we find that the

$$\text{volume of } H_d = 2^d = 2dw, \tag{5.7.6}$$

or

$$w = \frac{2^{d-1}}{d}. \tag{5.7.7}$$

Formula (5.7.5) is automatically fulfilled for $f = x_i$, $i = 1, \ldots, d$ by symmetry,

Inserting $f = x_1^2$ into (5.7.5), we obtain

$$\int_{H_d} x_1^2 \, dV = \int_{-1}^{1} x_1^2 \, dx_1 \int_{-1}^{+1} \cdots \int_{-1}^{+1} dx_2 \, dx_3 \cdots dx_d$$

$$= \tfrac{2}{3} \cdot 2^{d-1} = w(2u^2), \tag{5.7.8}$$

or

$$u = \left( \frac{2^{d-1}}{3w} \right)^{1/2} = \left( \frac{d}{3} \right)^{1/2}.$$

The formula will be exact for $f = x_i x_j$, $i \neq j$, by symmetry, and for $f = x_2^2, x_3^2, \ldots, x_d^2$, on the basis of the previous equation. Furthermore, by symmetry it will be exact for monomials of degree three. Hence, it is a rule of precision 3.

This method will work for any region that is fully symmetric. A region $B$ is called *fully symmetric* if $(x_1, x_2, \ldots, x_d) \in B$ implies that $(\pm x_1, \pm x_2, \ldots, \pm x_d) \in B$ and $(x_{p(1)}, x_{p(2)}, \ldots, x_{p(d)}) \in B$, where $x_{p(1)} x_{p(2)}, \ldots, x_{p(d)}$ is any permutation of $x_1, x_2, \ldots, x_d$.

We may also add a weight function $g(x_1, \ldots, x_d)$ to the integrand providing that it is also *fully symmetric*. By this is meant that $g(x_1, x_2, \ldots, x_d) = g(\pm x_{p(1)}, \pm x_{p(2)}, \ldots, \pm x_{p(d)})$. We may, therefore, obtain rules, for example, for spheres and for the infinite space, with the weight

$$\exp\,[-(x_1^2 + x_2^2 + \cdots + x_d^2)].$$

For $d > 3$, we have $u > 1$, and the evaluation points are exterior to the cube. This is not a desirable feature of an integration formula. However, Stroud gives the following $2d$-point rule of precision 3 with all points inside the hypercube. Let $P_k$ $(k = 1, \ldots, d)$ denote the point $(x_{1k}, x_{2k}, \ldots, x_{dk})$, where

$$x_{2r-1,\,k} = \sqrt{\frac{2}{3}} \cos \frac{(2r-1)k\pi}{d}, \qquad x_{2r,\,k} = \sqrt{\frac{2}{3}} \sin \frac{(2r-1)k\pi}{d},$$

$$r = 1, 2, \ldots, \left[\frac{d}{2}\right],$$

and if $d$ is odd, $x_{dk} = (-1)^k/\sqrt{3}$. Let $P_{k+d} = -P_k$. Then

$$\int_{H_d} f\,dV \approx \frac{2^d}{2d} \sum_{k=1}^{2d} f(P_k) \tag{5.7.9}$$

is an integration rule of precision 3 over the hypercube $H_d$ with all points inside $H_d$ and with equal weights.

Stroud also gives a similar $(d + 1)$-point rule of precision 2. Let $P_k$, $k = 0$, $\ldots, d$, denote the point $(x_{1k}, x_{2k}, \ldots, x_{dk})$, where

$$x_{2r-1,\,k} = \sqrt{\frac{2}{3}} \cos \frac{2rk\pi}{d+1}, \qquad x_{2r,\,k} = \sqrt{\frac{2}{3}} \sin \frac{2rk\pi}{d+1}, \qquad r = 1, 2, \ldots, \left[\frac{d}{2}\right],$$

and if $d$ is odd, $x_{dk} = (-1)^k/\sqrt{3}$. Then

$$\int_{H_d} f\,dV \approx \frac{2^d}{d+1} \sum_{k=0}^{d} f(P_k) \tag{5.7.10}$$

is an integration rule of precision 2 over the hypercube $H_d$ with all points inside $H_d$ and with equal weights.

**Reference.**   Stroud [1].

2. $(2d^2 + 1)$-*Point Rule of Precision 5 for a Hypercube*

We shall look for an integration formula of the form

$$\iint_{H_d} f \, dV \approx w_1 f(0, 0, \ldots, 0) + w_2 \sum^{2d} f(\pm u, 0, \ldots, 0)$$

$$+ w_3 \sum^{2d(d-1)} f(\pm u, \pm u, 0, \ldots, 0). \qquad (5.7.11)$$

The first sum on the right is extended over the $2d$ possibilities of $\pm u$ in $d$ positions and the second sum is extended over the $2(d)(d-1) = 4\binom{d}{2}$ possibilities of $\pm u, \pm u$ in pairs of positions.

As before, if a monomial contains an odd power, it will satisfy (5.7.11) automatically. Inserting, successively, $f = 1, x_1^2, x_1^4, x_1^2 x_2^2$ into (5.7.11), we obtain

$$w_1 + 2dw_2 + 2d(d-1)w_3 = \int_{H_d} dV = I_0,$$

$$2u^2 w_2 + 4(d-1)u^2 w_3 = \int_{H_d} x_1^2 \, dV = I_2,$$

$$2u^4 w_2 + 4(d-1)u^4 w_3 = \int_{H_d} x_1^4 \, dV = I_4, \qquad (5.7.12)$$

$$4u^4 w_3 = \int_{H_d} x_1^2 x_2^2 \, dV = I_{22}.$$

If we divide the third equation by the second, we obtain $u^2$. The values of $w_i$ then follow immediately:

$$w_1 = I_0 - d\left(\frac{I_2}{I_4}\right)^2 \left(I_4 - \frac{d-1}{2} I_{22}\right) = \frac{2^d}{162} (25d^2 - 115d + 162),$$

$$w_2 = \frac{1}{2} \left(\frac{I_2}{I_4}\right)^2 (I_4 - (d-1)I_{22}) = \frac{2^d}{162} (70 - 25d),$$

$$w_3 = \frac{1}{4} I_{22} \left(\frac{I_2}{I_4}\right)^2 = \frac{25}{324} 2^d, \qquad (5.7.13)$$

$$u = \left(\frac{I_4}{I_2}\right)^{1/2} = \left(\frac{3}{5}\right)^{1/2}.$$

If $d \geqslant 3$, the weights will be of mixed sign, a not too desirable situation.

**References.**   Hammer and Stroud [2], Miller [2], Morrison [1], Stenger [1].

**Example.**   $I(b)$ as in Section 5.6.

| $b^{-1}$ | Rule A | Rule B | Exact value |
|---|---|---|---|
| 1.0† | .42573 | .46375 | .50546 |
| 0.9 | .35960 | .36929 | .36993 |
| 0.8 | .30458 | .30772 | .30781 |
| 0.7 | .25676 | .25792 | .25794 |

Rule A: 5th-degree rule = 19 points.
Rule B: $2^3$ × Rule A = 152 points.

**Examples**

$$I_d^4 = \int_{-1}^1 \cdots \int_{-1}^1 \left( \sum_{i=1}^d x_i \right)^4 dx_1 \cdots dx_d = 2^d[\tfrac{1}{3}d^2 - \tfrac{2}{15}d]$$

| $d$ | Exact | $P_2$ | $P_3$ | $P_5$ |
|---|---|---|---|---|
| 8 | .5188 2667 (4) | .5234 (4) | .5006 (4) | .5188 26 (4) |
| 11 | .7959 8933 (5) | .6550 (5) | .7422 (5) | .7959 88 (5) |
| 14 | .1039 8379 (7) | .1708 (7) | .1682 (7) | .1039 83 (7) |
| 17 | .1232 9506 (8) | .1684 (8) | .1773 (8) | .1232 94  (8) |
| 20 | .1370 1393 (9) | .3146 (9) | .3122 (9) | .1370 12 (9) |
| 23 | .1453 4661 (10) | .2866 (10) | .2944 (10) | .1453 44 (10) |

$$I_d^6 = \int_{-1}^1 \cdots \int_{-1}^1 \left( \sum_{i=1}^d x_i \right)^6 dx_1 \cdots dx_d = 2^d d[(d-1)(5d-1)/9 + \tfrac{1}{7}]$$

| $d$ | Exact | $P_2$ | $P_3$ | $P_5$ |
|---|---|---|---|---|
| 8 | .6241 5237 (5) | .4756 (5) | .4490 (5) | .1458 17 (5) |
| 11 | .1354 8982 (7) | .7498 (6) | .9471 (6) | .2279 83 (6) |
| 14 | .2289 3908 (8) | .4686 (8) | .4652 (8) | .3009 40 (7) |
| 17 | .3330 6640 (9) | .5031 (9) | .5474 (9) | .3591 88 (8) |
| 20 | .4386 0434 (10) | .1763 (11) | .1766 (11) | .4009 73 (9) |
| 23 | .5379 2942 (11) | .1683 (12) | .1756 (12) | .4267 76 (10) |

$$I_d^5 = \int_{-1}^1 \cdots \int_{-1}^1 \left( \sum_{i=1}^d x_i \right)^5 dx_1 \cdots dx_d = 0$$

| $d$ | $P_5$ |
|---|---|
| 8 | $-.34\ (-2)$ |
| 11 | $-.70\ (-1)$ |
| 14 | $-.10\ (1)$ |
| 17 | $-.34\ (2)$ |
| 20 | $-.71\ (3)$ |
| 23 | $-.98\ (4)$ |

†Integrand singular.

The rules $P_2, P_3$, and $P_5$ are the 2nd-, 3rd-, and 5th-degree rules of the text; the parentheses, for example, in .5188 (4), means .5188 $\times$ $10^4$.

We have here striking examples of the difficulties in using rules with negative weights. This shows up in applying $P_5$ to $I_d^5$. Furthermore, the results for $I_d^6$, where $P_3$ and even $P_2$ are closer to the exact answer than $P_5$, would seem to indicate that rules which choose their points along distinguished subspaces of low dimension may lead to poor answers.

**References.** There are a large number of rules that are exact for monomials over a variety of regions. Rules can be developed for integrals with continuous weight functions or for weight functions with integrable singularities. Here is a partial list of papers containing such rules: Hammer, Marlowe, and Stroud [1], Hammer and Stroud [1], [2], Hammer and Wymore [1], Hetherington [1], Lauffer [1], Lyness [1], Mustard [1], Mustard, Lyness, and Blatt [1], Peirce [1], [2], Price [2], Radon [1], Stenger [1], Stroud [1], [3], [5], [6], Stroud and Secrest [1], Thacher [1], Tyler [1].

There is also a large foreign literature, particularly in Russian, to which we have not referred. For some of these items, see Stroud [2], [4].

There appears to be no systematic theoretical approach to monomial rules nor any systematic evaluation of their practical effectiveness.

Two properties of approximate integration rules are considered particularly desirable: The abscissas should lie in the region and the weights should be positive. When *ad hoc* methods are applied to develop monomial rules, there is, as we have seen, little control over these conditions, and they may not be fulfilled. Yet it is theoretically possible to find such rules. This is guaranteed by a theorem of Tchakaloff. We formulate it in the case of two dimensions, but it is perfectly general. Note that the number of monomials $x^p y^q$ of total degree $\leqslant n$ is $N = \frac{1}{2}(n + 1)(n + 2)$.

THEOREM. *Let B be a closed, bounded set in the plane with positive area. Then there exist $N = \frac{1}{2}(n + 1)(n + 2)$ points in B, $P_1, \ldots, P_N$, and N positive weights $w_1, \ldots, w_N$ such that*

$$\iint_B f(x, y)\, dx\, dy = \sum_{i=1}^{N} w_i f(P_i) \tag{5.7.14}$$

*whenever f is a polynomial in x, y of degree $\leqslant n$.*

The proof of this theorem is based on an argument in functional analysis, and numerical procedures for obtaining such rules corresponding to an arbitrary $B$ and $N$ are yet to be devised.

**Reference.**    V. Tchakaloff [1].

## 5.8 Compound Rules

Suppose that we are integrating over a hypercube. We may subdivide the hypercube into a sum of smaller hypercubes by means of a rectangular grid. If we apply a fixed rule $R$ to each of the smaller hypercubes, the net rule that emerges from this process will be called a *compound rule*. If we work in $d$ dimensions and divide the side of the cube into $n$ parts, applying $R$ to each of the $n^d$ smaller cubes, the total rule will be designated by $n^d \times R$.

In one dimension, compound rules are frequently used to good advantage. In higher dimensions, difficulties intervene. The number of points in a compound rule acts like the number of points in a product rule. Both exhibit the dimensional effect $n^d$. For high $d$, this strictly limits the number of subdivisions that can be made.

If compound rules are desired, it is in the interest of economy to use a base rule $R$ whose points are so disposed that they will overlap when the $R$'s of contiguous hypercubes are combined.

Let $H_d$ designate the hypercube $-1 \leqslant x_i \leqslant 1$, $i = 1, 2, \ldots, d$. Lyness has proposed the following rule of degree 5, which has evaluation points at the vertices of the hypercube:

$$\int_{H_d} f\, dV = \frac{2^d}{9}\left[(8 - 5d)f(0, 0, \ldots, 0) + 2^{-d}\sum^{2^d} f(\pm 1, \pm 1, \ldots, \pm 1)\right.$$

$$\left. + \frac{5}{2}\sum^{2d} f(\pm \sqrt{\tfrac{2}{5}}, 0, 0, \ldots, 0)\right] \qquad (5.8.1)$$

In the first $\sum$ on the right, we sum over the $2^d$ possibilities of $\pm 1$ in all the argument positions. In the second $\sum$, we sum over the $2d$ possibilities of $\pm \sqrt{\tfrac{2}{5}}$ in each of the argument positions and 0 elsewhere.

Thacher has adapted to higher dimensions a one-dimensional integration rule of Ralston that has weights of opposite signs and equal magnitude at the end points of the interval. When compounded, the internal points cancel out. Thacher's rule is of degree 2.

Programming difficulties come into play here. We can write a program for any particular dimension, but to write a FORTRAN program with the dimension $d$ as a parameter in such a way that we take advantage of the overlapping points, is rather difficult.

There is also the possibility of using compound rules together with a Richardson speed-up method. For example, we may subdivide the side of the hypercube into two and three equal parts and use the results for $h = 1$, $h = \frac{1}{2}$, $h = \frac{1}{3}$, as the basis for an extrapolation to the limit.

**References.**   Lyness [1], Lyness and McHugh [1], Ralston [1], Thacher [3].

## 5.9 Multiple Integration by Sampling

The method of sampling in numerical analysis can be described quite generally as follows. We wish to compute a number $I$ that arises in a mathematical problem. Suppose it turns out that $I$ is also the *expected value* of a certain *stochastic* (that is, chance) *process*. The expected value of the process is estimated by sampling, and the estimate is used as an approximation to $I$.

These generalities are illustrated by the following simple problem. Suppose we would like to compute

$$I = \int_a^b f(x)\, dx. \tag{5.9.1}$$

The mean value of $f(x)$ over the interval $[a, b]$ is $I/(b - a)$. Let $x_1, x_2, \ldots, x_n$ be $n$ points selected at random in $[a, b]$. We then sample the height of $f(x)$ by computing $f(x_1), f(x_2), \ldots, f(x_n)$ and forming the sample average:

$$\hat{f}_n = \frac{1}{n} \sum_{i=1}^{n} f(x_i). \tag{5.9.2}$$

We would expect that $\hat{f}_n \approx I/(b - a)$ and, hence, that

$$\int_a^b f(x)\, dx \approx \frac{b - a}{n} [f(x_1) + \cdots + f(x_n)]. \tag{5.9.3}$$

When random values are used for $x_i$, this method is also known as the *Monte Carlo method*. As we shall see, various modifications must be used in practice.

**Example.**  Compute $I = \int_0^1 x\, dx = \frac{1}{2}$ by simple Monte Carlo. Select $n = 50$ and choose 50 two-decimal numbers at random from a uniform distribution in the interval $[0, 1]$.

| .37 | .68 | .05 | .63 | .77 |
|-----|-----|-----|-----|-----|
| .40 | .57 | .86 | .93 | .41 |
| .16 | .54 | .23 | .74 | .07 |
| .26 | .47 | .38 | .55 | .11 |
| .74 | .97 | .77 | .53 | .80 |
| .09 | .28 | .52 | .90 | .20 |
| .89 | .16 | .68 | .63 | .87 |
| .74 | .56 | .88 | .92 | .42 |
| .81 | .02 | .15 | .64 | .24 |
| .39 | .99 | .53 | .26 | .71 |

(These numbers were obtained from a table of 2500 random 5-digit numbers in NBS Handbook of Mathematical Tables [1, pp. 991–995].)

This selection of numbers yields the estimate

$$\int_0^1 x \, dx \approx .539.$$  (5.9.4)

A more extensive computation with $n = 100$ yields

$$\int_0^1 x \, dx \approx .527.$$  (5.9.5)

What is behind this computation is the *Law of Large Numbers*. Let $x_1$, $x_2, \ldots, x_n, \ldots$ *be random variables selected according to a probability density function* $\mu(x)$,

$$\int_{-\infty}^{\infty} \mu(x) \, dx = 1.$$

Let $I = \int_{-\infty}^{\infty} f(x)\mu(x) \, dx$ exist. Then, given an $\varepsilon > 0$, we have

$$\lim_{n \to \infty} \text{probability} \left( I - \varepsilon \leqslant \frac{1}{n} \sum_{i=1}^{n} f(x_i) \leqslant I + \varepsilon \right) = 1.$$  (5.9.6)

This tells us that the probability that the sample average is close to the mean value $I$ can be made arbitrarily close to I if we take a sufficiently large sample.

In Monte Carlo computations we are not inclined to consider numerous samples of the same size but, rather, a sequence of individual samples. The *Strong Law of Large Numbers* is therefore particularly relevant:

$$\text{Probability} \left( \lim_{n \to \infty} \frac{1}{n} \sum_{i=1}^{n} f(x_i) = I \right) = 1.$$  (5.9.7)

In the numerical example above, we select $f(x) = x$ and

$$\mu(x) = \begin{cases} 1, & 0 \leqslant x \leqslant 1, \\ 0, & \text{otherwise.} \end{cases}$$

The workings of the Monte Carlo method raise two questions: (1) How can we obtain random sequences of numbers? (2) How can we estimate the error incurred in our approximations? It is possible to use sequences of numbers prepared in advance or to connect up the computer to a physical process with a random feature to it. In practice, however, this is not done. The first requires too much storage. The second has the poor feature (at least from the standpoint of numerical analysis) that the numbers cannot be duplicated easily and, hence, a computation cannot be readily checked. What is done in practice is to generate a so-called *pseudorandom sequence* of numbers and to use it instead. A pseudorandom sequence of numbers is a deterministic sequence of numbers defined mathematically and, according to a much quoted definition of D. H. Lehmer, is "a vague notion embodying the idea of a sequence in which each item is unpredictable to the uninitiated, and whose digits pass a certain number of tests traditional with statisticians and depending somewhat on the uses to which the sequence is to be put." We shall return to the question of pseudorandom sequences in a later section.

If we adopt the statistical point of view, estimates of error may be obtained through the use of the *Central Limit Theorem*. As above, let

$$I = \int_{-\infty}^{\infty} f(x)\mu(x)\,dx \qquad (5.9.8)$$

be the *mean* (or expected value) of $f$, and let

$$\sigma^2 = \int_{-\infty}^{\infty} (f(x) - I)^2\mu(x)\,dx = \int_{-\infty}^{\infty} f^2(x)\mu(x)\,dx - I^2 \qquad (5.9.9)$$

designate the *variance* of $f(x)$. Then the Central Limit Theorem tells us that

$$\text{prob}\left(\left|\frac{1}{n}\sum_{i=1}^{n} f(x_i) - I\right| \leqslant \frac{\lambda\sigma}{\sqrt{n}}\right) = \frac{1}{\sqrt{2\pi}}\int_{-\lambda}^{\lambda} e^{-x^2/2}\,dx + O\left(\frac{1}{\sqrt{n}}\right). \qquad (5.9.10)$$

A similar formula holds for multiple integrals.

A table of the probability integral

$$PI = \frac{1}{\sqrt{2\pi}}\int_{-\lambda}^{\lambda} e^{-x^2/2}\,dx$$

yields the following typical values.

| $\lambda$ | $PI$ |
|---|---|
| .6745 | .50 |
| 1.645 | .90 |
| 1.960 | .95 |
| 2.576 | .99 |
| 3.291 | .999 |
| 3.891 | .9999 |

If we designate the error $(1/n)\sum_{i=1}^{n} f(x_i) - I$ by $E$, then, using these numerical values, we may convert (5.9.10) into the following statements.

$$\text{Error } E \text{ at } 50\% \text{ level of probability} \leqq \frac{.6745\sigma}{\sqrt{n}}.$$

$$\text{Error } E \text{ at } 90\% \text{ level of probability} \leqq \frac{1.645\sigma}{\sqrt{n}}. \qquad (5.9.11)$$

$$\text{Error } E \text{ at } 95\% \text{ level of probability} \leqq \frac{1.960\sigma}{\sqrt{n}}.$$

For a fixed level of confidence (that is, for $\lambda = \text{const}$), the error bound $\lambda\sigma/\sqrt{n}$ varies directly as $\sigma$ and inversely as $n^{1/2}$. This is known as the "$n^{-1/2}$

law," and this rapidity of convergence is typical of Monte Carlo work. While this rate of convergence is slow, the advantage of Monte Carlo is that it is independent of the dimension, except that $\sigma$ seems to increase with $d$.

**Example.** Referring to the previous integration, we have

$$I = \int_0^1 x \, dx = \frac{1}{2}, \qquad \sigma^2 = \int_0^1 x^2 \, dx - \frac{1}{4} = \frac{1}{12}.$$

Error at 95% level $\leq 1.96\sigma/\sqrt{n} = 1.96/\sqrt{50} \, 2\sqrt{3} = .08 \, (n = 50)$. Observed error $= .039$.

Error at 95% level $= 1.96/\sqrt{100} \, 2\sqrt{3} = .057 \, (n = 100)$. Observed error $= .027$.

In a "practical" case, we need an estimate of $\sigma$ in order to compute an error estimate. But the standard deviation $\sigma$ will be unknown. We can, of course, use the sample variance

$$V_s = \frac{1}{n} \sum_{i=1}^{n} f^2(x_i) - \left( \frac{1}{n} \sum_{i=1}^{n} f(x_i) \right)^2 \tag{5.9.12}$$

to estimate $\sigma^2$. It is perhaps better to use $[n/(n-1)]V_s$ to estimate the variance. For, suppose we sample from a parent population of $N$ items, taking all the $\binom{N}{n}$ samples of size $n$. If $\overline{V}$ is the mean of all the sample variances, and if $V$ is the variance of the whole population, it can be shown that

$$\overline{V} = \frac{n-1}{n} V \left( 1 + \frac{1}{N-1} \right). \tag{5.9.13}$$

Hence, if $N$ is very large, we have

$$\overline{V} \approx \frac{n-1}{n} V \tag{5.9.14}$$

and, therefore,

$$V \approx \frac{n}{n-1} \overline{V}. \tag{5.9.15}$$

However, in Monte Carlo computations, $n$ is ordinarily so large that $n/(n-1) \approx 1$ and the correction is negligible.

**References.** Fraser [1, pp. 114–123], Kahn [1].

Let us examine the error bound $\lambda\sigma/\sqrt{n}$ more carefully. In order to reduce this error (for a fixed level of confidence) we can do several things; we can increase $n$, the number of functional evaluations, or we can reduce the variance $\sigma$. If we increase $n$ by a factor of 100, we increase the accuracy of the answer by a factor of only 10. Even though this variation is discouraging, with present computer speeds, we may easily do $10^5$ functional evaluations, and the resulting accuracy of 1 part in $10^2$ or $10^3$ may very well meet the requirements.

In some cases we can replace the original problem by a modified problem, which has the effect of reducing $\sigma$ sharply. This is known as a *variance-reducing* scheme and will be discussed subsequently.

There is another device that can be used for increasing accuracy: to abandon the idea of random sequences of points and to employ sequences of points specifically tailored for integration. Such sequences are known as *equidistributed sequences*, and their theory can be discussed outside the framework of statistics. The use of such sequences leads to error estimates that are roughly of the order of $1/n$ and, hence, converge more rapidly.

### 5.9.1   Variance Reduction

We begin with a simple sort of variance reduction. Suppose we are interested in computing $I = \int_0^1 f(x)\, dx$, and suppose we can find a $g(x)$ such that

$$|f(x) - g(x)| \leqslant \varepsilon, \qquad 0 \leqslant x \leqslant 1, \tag{5.9.1.1}$$

and such that

$$\int_0^1 g(x)\, dx = J \tag{5.9.1.2}$$

is a known quantity. Compute

$$I_1 = \int_0^1 (f(x) - g(x))\, dx \tag{5.9.1.3}$$

by Monte Carlo. The variance in this modified problem equals

$$\sigma_1^2 = \int_0^1 (f - g)^2\, dx - \left(\int_0^1 (f - g)\, dx\right)^2 \tag{5.9.1.4}$$

and, hence, $\sigma_1 \leqslant \varepsilon$.

We therefore take

$$\frac{1}{n} \sum_{i=1}^{n} (f(x_i) - g(x_i)) + J \tag{5.9.1.5}$$

as an estimator for $I$.

It should be observed that the variance has been reduced at the cost of doubling the number of functional evaluations. If one and the same problem is done two ways, by having variances $\sigma_1^2$, $\sigma_2^2$ and by taking times proportional to $N_1$, $N_2$, respectively, then the relative effectiveness of the variance reduction is

$$\frac{\lambda \sigma_1}{\sqrt{n}\,\sqrt{N_2/N_1}} \Big/ \frac{\lambda \sigma_2}{\sqrt{n}} = \frac{\sqrt{N_1}\,\sigma_1}{\sqrt{N_2}\,\sigma_2}. \tag{5.9.1.6}$$

**Example.** Let $f(x) = e^x$ and $g(x) = 1 + x$. The variance of $e^x$ is $\frac{1}{2}(e^2 - 1) - (e - 1)^2 = .242$, and the variance of $e^x - 1 - x$ is $\frac{1}{2}(e - 1)(5 - e) - \frac{23}{12} = .044$. If it takes 20% more time to compute $e^x - 1 - x$ as opposed to $e^x$, then the relative effectiveness of the reduction is 2.6 : 1.

A second method of variance reduction is that of *importance sampling*. Write $I = \int_0^1 f(x)\,dx$ as

$$I = \int_0^1 \frac{f(x)}{p(x)} p(x)\,dx, \tag{5.9.1.7}$$

where $p(x) > 0$ and

$$\int_0^1 p(x)\,dx = 1. \tag{5.9.1.8}$$

Now use as an estimator for $I$

$$\hat{f}_n = \frac{1}{n} \sum_{i=1}^n \frac{f(x_i)}{p(x_i)}, \tag{5.9.1.9}$$

where $x_i$ is a random variable that has been extracted from the probability density distribution of $p(x)$ on $0 \leqslant x \leqslant 1$. The relevant variance is now

$$\sigma^2 = \int_0^1 \frac{f^2(x)}{p^2(x)} p(x)\,dx - \left( \int_0^1 \frac{f(x)}{p(x)} p(x)\,dx \right)^2. \tag{5.9.1.10}$$

Now assuming that $f(x) > 0$ (if it is not, we add a constant), we select

$$p(x) \approx \frac{f(x)}{\int_0^1 f(x)\,dx}. \tag{5.9.1.11}$$

Then we have

$$\sigma^2 \approx 0. \tag{5.9.1.12}$$

Ideally, then, we should sample in proportion to the value of the function. This would yield a 0 variance, but we should then need to know the solution to our problem beforehand. At any rate, we know that, by using a $p(x)$ whose integral is known and whose behavior approximates that of $f(x)$, we should expect to reduce the variance. Again, this gain must be measured against the loss of time involved in computing with random variables selected from a nonconstant probability density $p(x)$.

**Example.** $f(x) = e^x$. Take $p(x) = \frac{2}{3}(1 + x)$. The estimator is

$$\hat{f}_n = \frac{3}{2n} \sum_{i=1}^n \frac{e^{x_i}}{1 + x_i},$$

where the $x_i$ have a probability density distribution $\frac{2}{3}(1 + x)$. The relevant variance is

$$\sigma^2 = \frac{3}{2} \int_0^1 \frac{e^{2x}\, dx}{1 + x} - \left( \int_0^1 e^x\, dx \right)^2 = \frac{3}{2} e^{-2}[Ei(4) - Ei(2)] - (e - 1)^2 = .0269,$$

$$Ei(t) = \int_1^t \frac{e^t}{t}\, dt.$$

Other variance reduction methods are *stratified sampling* and the use of *antithetic variates*. Variation reduction techniques appear to be equivalent to the approximation of the integrand by functions that can be handled analytically and, hence, may not be available when the dimension is high and the integrand is intractable.

**References.**   Hammersley and Handscomb [1], Kahn [1].


*5.9.2   Pseudorandom Sequences*

Pseudorandom sequences are most commonly generated by the power-residue method. The integers $x_1, x_2, \ldots$ are defined recursively by means of

$$x_{n+1} = ax_n \,(\mathrm{mod}\ m), \qquad x_0 = \text{a starting value.} \qquad (5.9.2.1)$$

Here $a$ and $m$ are certain integers and this notation means that $x_{n+1}$ is the remainder when $ax_n$ is divided by $m$. Since division by $m$ can produce at most $m$ different remainders, it is clear that the sequence $x_0, x_1, \ldots$ will be a periodic sequence whose period cannot exceed $m$. Therefore, what is wanted is a selection of $a$ and $m$ which will produce a period that is large relative to the number of random numbers required in a computation. To go into the number theory of (5.9.2.1) would take us away from our main interests, and we shall merely describe a procedure for a binary computer.

The computer is assumed to have a word size of $b$ bits. Arithmetic is carried out with the binary point to the extreme right. For the number $a$, choose an integer of the form $8t \pm 3$ and close to $2^{b/2}$. Choose $m = 2^b$. For $x_0$, choose any odd integer. The multiplication $ax_0$ now produces a product of $2b$ bits. The $b$ high-order bits are discarded and the $b$ low-order bits are the residue $x_1$. The process is now iterated. To obtain numbers in the unit interval, the binary point is considered to be at the far left. The period of the sequence $x_0, x_1, \ldots$ is $2^{b-2}$, so that with a 35-bit machine the sequence has a period of $2^{33} \approx 8.5 \times 10^9$.

In order for a sequence to qualify for the title "pseudorandom," its beginning portions must pass a number of statistical tests. These tests include, for example, tests for uniform distribution, for independence of successive numbers, for autocorrelation between $x_n$ and $x_{n+p}$, for runs up and down, "poker" tests on combinations of digits, etc. The power-residue method has passed these tests for numerous selections of $a$ and $m$, and it is assumed that this is the case for the reader's specific pseudorandom number generator.

**References.** Hull and Dobell [1], IBM Reference Manual [1], Taussky and Todd [1].

**Example.** Estimate $I = \int_0^1 x \, dx = \frac{1}{2}$, using a pseudorandom sequence. ($\sigma^2 = \int_0^1 x^2 \, dx - I^2 = \frac{1}{12}$.) The sequence $x_n$ was generated according to the recurrence $x_{n+1} = 5^{17} x_n \bmod (2^{42})$, $x_0 = 1$.

| No. of points | Approximate value of $I$ |
|:---:|:---:|
| $2^1$ | .37 |
| $2^2$ | .52 |
| $2^4$ | .45 |
| $2^8$ | .507 |
| $2^{16}$ | .502 |
| $2^{18}$ | .5008 |

Error at 95% level with $2^{18}$ points is $(1.96\sigma)2^{-9} = .0011$; exact error $= .0008$.

**Example.** Estimate $I = \int_0^1 \cdots \int_0^1 e^{x_1 x_2 x_3 x_4} \, dx_1 \, dx_2 \, dx_3 \, dx_4$. Using a pseudorandom sequence, we computed $I_N = 1/N \sum_{k=1}^N e^{x_{1k} x_{2k} x_{3k} x_{4k}}$. Designate the numbers $x_{11}, x_{21}, x_{31}, x_{41}, x_{12}, x_{22}, x_{32}, x_{42}, \ldots$ by $y_1, y_2, \ldots$. The $y$'s were generated by the recurrence.

$$y_{n+1} = ay_n \bmod (10^{10}), \qquad a = 101203, \qquad y_0 = 9876543211.$$

| $N$ | $I_N$ |
|:---:|:---:|
| 2 | 1.2523 816 |
| 4 | 1.0397 712 |
| 8 | 1.0332 334 |
| 16 | 1.0548 477 |
| 32 | 1.0693 787 |
| 64 | 1.0705 580 |
| 128 | 1.0573 892 |
| 256 | 1.0739 589 |
| 512 | 1.0706 032 |
| 1024 | 1.0741 810 |
| 2048 | 1.0714 488 |
| 4096 | 1.0677 460 |
| 8192 | 1.0695 889 |
| Exact value | 1.0693 9761 |

In this example $\sigma = .09$ and, with $8192 = 2^{13}$ points, the error at the 95% level is $(1.96\sigma)2^{-13/2} = .002$; exact error $= .0002$.

**Example.** Estimate

$$I = 2^{-7} \int_0^1 \cdots \int_0^1 (x_1 + \cdots + x_8)^2 \, dx_1 \cdots dx_8 = 25/192.$$

Pseudorandom numbers were chosen as in the previous example.

| $N$ | $I_N$ |
|---|---|
| 2 | .1118 1381 |
| 4 | .0978 4566 |
| 8 | .1363 5815 |
| 16 | .1279 8534 |
| 32 | .1361 6714 |
| 64 | .1222 1112 |
| 128 | .1290 1039 |
| 256 | .1292 9553 |
| 512 | .1342 6877 |
| 1024 | .1304 3647 |
| 2048 | .1292 0104 |
| 4096 | .1298 9805 |
| 8192 | .1310 6422 |
| Exact value | .1302 0833 |

### 5.9.3  Equidistributed Sequences

DEFINITION.  *A (deterministic) sequence of points $x_1, x_2, \ldots$ in $[a, b]$ is called equidistributed in $[a, b]$ if*

$$\lim_{n \to \infty} \frac{b - a}{n} \sum_{i=1}^{n} f(x_i) = \int_a^b f(x) \, dx \qquad (5.9.3.1)$$

*for all bounded, Riemann-integrable functions $f(x)$.*

The term "equidistributed" comes from the following consideration. Let $[\tau_1, \tau_2]$ be a subinterval of $[a, b]$. Let $N_n[\tau_1, \tau_2] = $ the number of points of $x_1, x_2, \ldots, x_n$ that lie in $[\tau_1, \tau_2]$. Then

$$\lim_{n \to \infty} \frac{N_n}{n} = \frac{\tau_2 - \tau_1}{b - a}. \qquad (5.9.3.2)$$

To show (5.9.3.2) merely select $f(x) \equiv 1$ on $[\tau_1, \tau_2]$ and $f(x) \equiv 0$ elsewhere in the interval $[a, b]$ and use (5.9.3.1). Thus, the fraction of points of an equidistributed sequence that lie in any interval is asymptotically proportional to the length of the interval. This property may also be used as a definition of equidistribution.

We next exhibit a sequence that is equidistributed. Let $(\xi)$ designate the fractional part of $\xi$, that is,

$$(\xi) = \xi - [\xi], \tag{5.9.3.3}$$

where $[\xi]$ is the largest integer $\leqslant \xi$.

THEOREM.    *If $\theta$ is an irrational number, then the sequence*

$$x_n = (n\theta), \qquad n = 1, 2, \ldots, \tag{5.9.3.4}$$

*is equidistributed in* $[0, 1]$.

*Proof.*    We give only an indication of a proof. The details can be found in Davis [6, p. 357]. Since

$$e^{2\pi i k x_j} = e^{2\pi i k(j\theta - [j\theta])} = e^{2\pi i k j\theta},$$

$$\frac{1}{n} [e^{2\pi i k x_1} + e^{2\pi i k x_2} + \cdots + e^{2\pi i k x_n}]$$

$$= \frac{1}{n} [e^{2\pi i k\theta} + (e^{2\pi i k\theta})^2 + \cdots + (e^{2\pi i k\theta})^n] = \frac{1}{n} e^{2\pi i k\theta} \frac{e^{2\pi i k n\theta} - 1}{e^{2\pi i k\theta} - 1}.$$

Hence for $k = \pm 1, \pm 2, \ldots,$

$$\lim_{n \to \infty} \frac{1}{n} [e^{2\pi i k x_1} + \cdots + e^{2\pi i k x_n}] = \int_0^1 e^{2\pi i k x}\, dx. \tag{5.9.3.5}$$

For $k = 0$, (5.9.3.5) holds trivially. The proof is completed by approximating a Riemann-integrable function by the functions $e^{2\pi i k x}$, $k = 0, \pm 1, \ldots$.

While equidistribution is a property of random sequences, there are certain statistical features of random sequences that the sequence (5.9.3.4) does not have. For example, designate by prob $(x_n > x_{n+1})$ the limit (if it exists)

$$\text{prob}\,(x_n > x_{n+1}) = \lim_{N \to \infty} \frac{1}{N} \sum_{\substack{x_n > x_{n+1}, \\ 1 \leqslant n \leqslant N}} 1. \tag{5.9.3.6}$$

For a random sequence, we would require that prob $(x_n > x_{n+1}) = \frac{1}{2}$. Now, if $0 < \theta < 1$, then $x_n > x_{n+1}$ if and only if $1 - \theta \leqslant x_n < 1$. The probability of this last event is, by equidistribution, $\theta$. Hence, prob $(x_n > x_{n+1}) \neq \frac{1}{2}$.

The interest in the sequences $(n\theta)$ for multidimensional integration lies in two facts. In the first place, suppose that $\theta_1, \theta_2, \ldots, \theta_d$ are $d$ irrational numbers that are *linearly independent over the rational numbers*, that is, $\alpha_1\theta_1 + \cdots + \alpha_d\theta_d \neq 0$ for rational $\alpha_i$. Then it can be shown that the points

$$P_n: ((n\theta_1), (n\theta_2), \ldots, (n\theta_d)), \qquad n = 1, 2, \ldots, \tag{5.9.3.7}$$

*are equidistributed over the hypercube* $0 \leqslant x_i \leqslant 1, i = 1, 2, \ldots, d$. This means that

$$\lim_{N \to \infty} I_N = \lim_{n \to \infty} \frac{1}{N} \sum_{n=1}^{N} f((n\theta_1), \ldots, (n\theta_d))$$

$$= \int_0^1 \cdots \int_0^1 f \, dx_1 \, dx_2 \cdots dx_d \qquad (5.9.3.8)$$

for any bounded Riemann-integrable function $f$.

In the second place, truncation error estimates can be obtained which are better than the $N^{-1/2}$ error provided by statistical theory. We shall show how this comes about in the one-dimensional case.

Let $f(x)$ be defined in $0 \leqslant x \leqslant 1, f(0) = f(1)$, and be sufficiently smooth there. Then we have the absolutely and uniformly convergent Fourier series

$$f(x) = \sum_{k=-\infty}^{\infty} a_k e^{2\pi i k x}, \qquad a_{-k} = a_k, \qquad a_0 = \int_0^1 f(x) \, dx. \qquad (5.9.3.9)$$

Therefore, by periodicity, we have

$$f((n\theta)) = \sum_{k=-\infty}^{\infty} a_k e^{2\pi i k (n\theta)} = \sum_{k=-\infty}^{\infty} a_k e^{2\pi i k n\theta}. \qquad (5.9.3.10)$$

Summing, we obtain

$$\frac{1}{N} \sum_{n=1}^{N} f((n\theta)) = \sum_{k=-\infty}^{\infty} a_k \frac{1}{N} \sum_{n=1}^{N} e^{2\pi i k n\theta}$$

$$= \sum_{k=-\infty}^{\infty} a_k \frac{1}{N} \frac{e^{2\pi i N k\theta} - 1}{e^{2\pi i k\theta} - 1}. \qquad (5.9.3.11)$$

Therefore,

$$\frac{1}{N} \sum_{n=1}^{N} f((n\theta)) - \int_0^1 f(x) \, dx = \frac{1}{N} \sum_{k=-\infty}^{\infty}{}' a_k \frac{e^{2\pi i N k\theta} - 1}{e^{2\pi i k\theta} - 1}. \qquad (5.9.3.12)$$

The prime on the summation sign indicates that the term corresponding to $k = 0$ is omitted from the sum. Hence

$$\left| \frac{1}{N} \sum_{n=1}^{N} f((n\theta)) - \int_0^1 f(x) \, dx \right| \leqslant \frac{1}{N} \sum_{k=-\infty}^{\infty}{}' |a_k| \left| \frac{e^{2\pi i N k\theta} - 1}{e^{2\pi i k\theta} - 1} \right|. \qquad (5.9.3.13)$$

Since

$$|e^{iu} - 1| = |\cos u + i \sin u - 1| = (2(1 - \cos u))^{1/2} = 2 \left| \sin \frac{u}{2} \right|, \qquad (5.9.3.14)$$

it follows that

$$\left| \frac{e^{2\pi i N k\theta} - 1}{e^{2\pi i k\theta} - 1} \right| = \left| \frac{\sin \pi N k\theta}{\sin \pi k\theta} \right|. \qquad (5.9.3.15)$$

Now, $|\sin \pi Nk\theta| \leqslant 1$. To obtain a lower bound for the denominator, observe the inequalities $\sin \pi x \geqslant 2x$ in $0 \leqslant x \leqslant \frac{1}{2}$ and $\sin \pi x \geqslant 2(1 - x)$ in $\frac{1}{2} \leqslant x \leqslant 1$. Hence, in general, we have

$$|\sin \pi x| \geqslant 2 |x - \langle x \rangle|, \qquad (5.9.3.16)$$

where $\langle x \rangle$ designates the nearest integer to $x$. Combining these inequalities, we obtain

$$\left| \frac{1}{N} \sum_{n=1}^{N} f((n\theta)) - \int_{0}^{1} f(x) \, dx \right| \leqslant \frac{1}{2N} \sum_{k=-\infty}^{\infty}{}' |a_k| \frac{1}{|k\theta - \langle k\theta \rangle|}. \qquad (5.9.3.17)$$

LEMMA (Liouville).   *Let $\alpha$ be the root of a polynomial of degree n that has integer coefficients and is irreducible over the rationals. Then there exists a constant $c > 0$ such that, for every pair of integers $p, q$ with $q > 0$,*

$$\left| \alpha - \frac{p}{q} \right| \geqslant \frac{c}{q^n}. \qquad (5.9.3.18)$$

*Proof.*   Let

$$f(x) = a_0 x^n + a_1 x^{n-1} + \cdots + a_n,$$

where $a_i$ are integers and $a_0 > 0$. Write

$$f(x) = a_0(x - \alpha)(x - \alpha_2) \cdots (x - \alpha_n).$$

Then,

$$q^n f(p/q) = a_0 p^n + a_1 p^{n-1} q + \cdots + a_n q^n.$$

Therefore, $q^n f(p/q)$ is an integer. It is not 0, for otherwise $f$ would have a factor $x - (p/q)$ and would be reducible. Hence, it follows that

$$|q^n f(p/q)| \geqslant 1. \qquad (5.9.3.19)$$

Now,

$$\frac{f(x)}{a_0(x - \alpha)} = \prod_{k=2}^{n} (x - \alpha_k).$$

Therefore, we have

$$\frac{p}{q} - \alpha = \frac{q^n f(p/q)}{a_0 q^n \prod_{k=2}^{n} (p/q - \alpha_k)}$$

and

$$\left| \frac{p}{q} - \alpha \right| = \frac{|q^n f(p/q)|}{a_0 q^n \prod_{k=2}^{n} |p/q - \alpha_k|} \geqslant \frac{1}{a_0 q^n \prod_{k=2}^{n} |p/q - \alpha_k|}. \qquad (5.9.3.20)$$

Set

$$\beta = \max \left( |\alpha|, |\alpha_2|, \ldots, |\alpha_n| \right), \tag{5.9.3.21}$$

and consider the following two cases.

*Case I.* $|p/q| > 2\beta$. Now

$$\left| \frac{p}{q} - \alpha \right| \geq \left| \frac{p}{q} \right| - |\alpha| > 2\beta - |\alpha| = \beta + (\beta - |\alpha|) \geq \frac{\beta}{q^2}$$

since $q \geq 1$.

*Case II.* $|p/q| \leq 2\beta$. Then

$$\left| \frac{p}{q} - \alpha_k \right| \leq \left| \frac{p}{q} \right| + |\alpha_k| \leq 2\beta + \beta = 3\beta.$$

Therefore, by (5.9.3.20), we have

$$\left| \frac{p}{q} - \alpha \right| \geq \frac{1}{a_0 q^n \prod_{k=2}^{n} (3\beta)} = \frac{1}{a_0 q^n (3\beta)^{n-1}}.$$

If we now set

$$c = \min \left( \beta, \frac{1}{a_0 (3\beta)^{n-1}} \right), \tag{5.9.3.22}$$

then (5.9.3.18) follows.

COROLLARY. *If $\theta$ is a quadratic irrational number, then we can find a constant $c > 0$ such that for all integers $k$,*

$$\frac{1}{|k\theta - \langle k\theta \rangle|} \leq \frac{|k|}{c}. \tag{5.9.3.23}$$

*Proof*

$$|k\theta - \langle k\theta \rangle| = |k| \left| \theta - \frac{\langle k\theta \rangle}{k} \right| \geq |k| \frac{c}{|k|^2}.$$

This follows from (5.9.3.18), with $n = 2$. Taking reciprocals, we obtain (5.9.3.23).

THEOREM. *Let $f(x)$ be periodic in $[0, 1]$ and be of class $C^3[0, 1]$ so that we have $f(0) = f(1)$, $f'(0) = f'(1)$, $f''(0) = f''(1)$. Let $\theta$ be a quadratic irrational number. Then*

$$\left| \frac{1}{N} \sum_{n=1}^{N} f((n\theta)) - \int_0^1 f(x) \, dx \right| \leq \frac{c}{N}. \tag{5.9.3.24}$$

*Proof.* We have

$$f(x) = \sum_{k=-\infty}^{\infty} a_k e^{2\pi i k x} \quad \text{with} \quad a_k = \int_0^1 f(x) e^{-2\pi i k x} \, dx.$$

Integrating by parts, we have, for $k \neq 0$,

$$a_k = \frac{f(x) e^{-2\pi i k x}}{-2\pi i k} \bigg|_0^1 + \frac{1}{2\pi i k} \int_0^1 f' e^{-2\pi i k x} \, dx = \frac{1}{2\pi i k} \int_0^1 f' e^{-2\pi i k x} \, dx.$$

Integrating by parts twice more, we have

$$a_k = \frac{1}{(2\pi i k)^3} \int_0^1 f''' e^{-2\pi i k x} \, dx.$$

Therefore

$$|a_k| \leq \frac{c_1}{k^3},$$

where

$$c_1 = \frac{1}{(2\pi)^3} \int_0^1 |f'''(x)| \, dx.$$

From (5.9.3.23), we have

$$\frac{1}{|k\theta - \langle k\theta \rangle|} \leq \frac{k}{c_2}$$

and, hence, by (5.9.3.17)

$$\left| \frac{1}{N} \sum_{k=1}^N f((n\theta)) - \int_0^1 f(x) \, dx \right| \leq \frac{1}{Nc_2} \sum_{k=-\infty}^{\infty}{}' |a_k| \, k \leq \frac{c_1}{Nc_2} \sum_{k=-\infty}^{\infty}{}' \frac{k}{k^3} = \frac{c}{N}.$$

Even if $f(x)$ does not fulfill the stringent conditions of this theorem, the convergence may be more rapid than $N^{-1/2}$. There is, for example, the Hardy–Littlewood–Ostrowski Theorem: *Let $\theta$ be a positive irrational number whose continued fraction expansion*

$$\theta = a_0 + \cfrac{1}{a_1 + \cfrac{1}{a_2 + \cdots}}$$

*satisfies $0 < a_i \leq A$ (this will be the case if $\theta$ is, for example, a quadratic irrationality). Then*

$$\left| \frac{1}{N} \sum_{n=1}^N (n\theta) - \int_0^1 x \, dx \right| \leq \frac{3}{2} A \frac{\log N}{N}. \tag{5.9.3.25}$$

Thus, we have a rate of convergence which is more rapid than $N^{-1/2}$ but somewhat less than $N^{-1}$.

Richtmeyer has extended this theorem to higher dimensions. Let $\theta_1$, $\theta_2 \ldots$, $\theta_d$ be $d$ irrational numbers that are linearly independent over the rationals. Then, under conditions on $f$ that are analogous to those in the previous theorem, we have

$$\left| \int_0^1 \cdots \int_0^1 f \, dV - \frac{1}{N} \sum_{n=1}^{N} f((n\theta_1), \ldots, (n\theta_d)) \right| \leqslant \frac{c}{N}. \quad (5.9.3.26)$$

References.   Davis [6, pp. 354–357], J. Franklin [1], Hlawka [2], Koksma [1], Korobov [1], LeVeque [1], Ostrowski [1], Richtmeyer [1], [2], Richtmeyer, Devaney, and Metropolis [1], Roth [1].

Example.    Compute $\int_0^1 \cdots \int_0^1 e^{x_1 x_2 x_3 x_4} \, dx_1 \, dx_2 \, dx_3 \, dx_4$, using an equidistributed sequence of points. Select $\theta_1 = \sqrt{2}$, $\theta_2 = \sqrt{3}$, $\theta_3 = \frac{1}{3}\sqrt{6}$, $\theta_4 = \sqrt{10}$.

| $N$ | $I_N$ |
|---|---|
| 2 | 1.0556 385 |
| 4 | 1.0646 192 |
| 8 | 1.0592 766 |
| 16 | 1.0615 566 |
| 32 | 1.0626 119 |
| 64 | 1.0586 261 |
| 128 | 1.0657 314 |
| 256 | 1.0673 119 |
| 512 | 1.0668 403 |
| 1024 | 1.0681 500 |
| 2048 | 1.0685 418 |
| 4096 | 1.0685 545 |
| 8192 | 1.0688 021 |
| Exact value | 1.0693 9761 |

### 5.9.4   Method of Averaging

The intimate relationship that exists between the theory of equidistribution and the theory of Fourier series suggests that it might be possible to apply summability methods (that is, averaging) to speed up the convergence of results obtained from equidistributed sequences. This lies at the basis of a theory which was worked out by Haselgrove and of which we can give only the barest description.

Let us assume that $f(x_1, x_2, \ldots, x_d)$ is a function of period 2 in each variable and that its Fourier expansion is

$$f(x_1, x_2, \ldots, x_d) = \sum_{-\infty}^{\infty} a_{n_1, n_2, \ldots, n_d} \exp\left[i\pi(n_1 x_1 + n_2 x_2 + \cdots + n_d x_d)\right].$$
(5.9.4.1)

Assume, further, that the Fourier coefficients satisfy an inequality of the form

$$\left|a_{n_1, n_2, \ldots, n_d}\right| \leqslant M \left|n_1 n_2 \cdots n_d\right|^{-2}.$$
(5.9.4.2)

In (5.9.4.2), $M$ is a constant and if any $n_i = 0$, the inequality is to hold with the zero factor omitted from the denominator on the right-hand side. This condition is equivalent to a smoothness condition on the derivatives of $f$.

Let $\alpha_1, \alpha_2, \ldots, \alpha_d$ be $d$ irrational numbers that are linearly independent over the rationals. Set

$$S_1 = S_1(N) = \sum_{m=-N}^{N} f(2m\alpha_1, 2m\alpha_2, \ldots, 2m\alpha_d),$$
(5.9.4.3)

$$S_2 = S_2(N) = \sum_{p=0}^{N} S_1(p),$$
(5.9.4.4)

$$s_1(N) = \frac{1}{2N+1} S_1(N),$$
(5.9.4.5)

$$s_2(N) = \frac{1}{(N+1)^2} S_2(N).$$
(5.9.4.6)

The quantity $s_2(N)$ is the Cesàro mean of the sequence of values

$$f(2m\alpha_1, \ldots, 2m\alpha_d).$$

If

$$I = 2^{-d} \int_{-1}^{1} \cdots \int_{-1}^{1} f(x_1, x_2, \ldots, x_d)\, dx_1\, dx_2 \cdots dx_d,$$
(5.9.4.7)

then it can be shown by an analysis similar to the one given in Section 5.9.3 that under the above conditions there exist numbers $\alpha_1, \ldots, \alpha_d$ such that

$$|I - s_1(N)| \leqslant \frac{\text{const}}{N}$$
(5.9.4.8)

and

$$|I - s_2(N)| \leqslant \frac{\text{const}}{N^{2-\varepsilon}}, \qquad \varepsilon > 0.$$
(5.9.4.9)

If the integrand is not periodic, it must be reduced to the periodic case. Consider, for example,

$$J = \int_0^1 \cdots \int_0^1 F(x_1, x_2, \ldots, x_d)\, dx_1, dx_2 \cdots dx_d. \qquad (5.9.4.10)$$

Then it follows that

$$J = 2^{-d} \int_{-1}^1 \cdots \int_{-1}^1 F(|x_1|, |x_2|, \ldots, |x_d|)\, dx_1\, dx_2 \cdots dx_d. \qquad (5.9.4.11)$$

The function

$$f(x_1, x_2, \ldots, x_d) = F(|x_1|, |x_2|, \ldots, |x_d|)$$

will then be periodic in $x_1, \ldots, x_d$.

Haselgrove tabulates good values of $\alpha$ to use for $d \leqslant 8$.

**Example** (Haselgrove)

$$I = \int_0^1 \cdots \int_0^1 e^{-x_1 x_2 \cdots x_5}\, dx_1\, dx_2 \cdots dx_5 = .9706\,5719.$$

| $N$ | $s_1(N)$ | $s_2(N)$ | Monte Carlo |
|---|---|---|---|
| 1000 | .9706 2392 | .9706 2580 | .9676 3166 |
| 2000 | .9708 2902 | .9706 3927 | .9687 0265 |
| 3000 | .9705 4070 | .9706 6765 | .9688 5258 |
| 4000 | .9706 8153 | .9706 6383 | .9694 4396 |
| 5000 | .9706 5925 | .9706 5630 | .9695 0137 |
| 6000 | .9706 1983 | .9706 5761 | .9699 0269 |
| 7000 | .9706 8925 | .9706 5639 | .9701 8578 |
| 8000 | .9706 4881 | .9706 5632 | .9703 0504 |
| 9000 | .9706 3833 | .9706 5706 | .9703 8771 |
| 10000 | .9706 6307 | .9706 5854 | .9703 2729 |
| 11000 | .9706 5947 | .9706 5860 | .9702 9480 |
| 12000 | .9706 7426 | .9706 5744 | .9704 8290 |

The "Monte Carlo" column refers to computations carried out with pseudo-random points. Notice that at $N = 12{,}000$, $s_2$ achieves twice the number of significant figures as the Monte Carlo computation.

**Reference.** Haselgrove [1].

CHAPTER 6

# AUTOMATIC
# INTEGRATION

## 6.1  The Goals of Automatic Integration

The aim of an automatic integration scheme is to relieve the person who has to compute an integral of any need to think. By an *automatic integrator* we mean a program for numerical integration with the following features. The user inserts (1) the limits of integration, (2) a routine for computing $f(x)$, (3) a tolerance $\varepsilon$, and (4) an upper bound $N$ on the number of functional evaluations. The program then exits either

(a) with a value $I$ of the integral, which is allegedly correct to within the tolerance, that is,

$$\left| I - \int_a^b f(x)\, dx \right| \leqslant \varepsilon \qquad \text{or} \qquad \frac{\left| I - \int_a^b f(x)\, dx \right|}{\int_a^b |f(x)|\, dx} \leqslant \varepsilon,$$

or (b) with a statement that the upper bound $N$ has been achieved but not the tolerance $\varepsilon$, and the statement may include the "best" value of the integral determined in the process.

An automatic integrator is a program intended to be used "blind," that is, without any theoretical analysis of the situation either before the problem is placed on the machine or after it comes off the machine. The results of the automatic integration are often utilized or combined in further computation.

The following two general exit criteria are commonly employed.

(1) A sequence of rules, $R_1(f), R_2(f), \ldots$, which is known to be convergent (for a wide class of functions) is applied to the integrand $f$. The question is then asked: Is $|R_{n+1}(f) - R_n(f)| \leqslant \varepsilon$? If the answer is yes, the program exits and prints out the value $R_n(f)$. If the upper bound $N$ is achieved without

a "yes" to the question, the program selects the value of $n$ for which

$$|R_{n+1}(f) - R_n(f)| = d_n$$

is minimum, and prints out both $R_n(f)$ and the difference $d_n$.

While it is possible to use any sequence of rules which is convergent, in practice the rules proceed from $n$ to $n + 1$ by halving the basic interval. In this way, the information gathered at the $n$th stage is not discarded but is used in forming the $(n + 1)$th stage.

(2) A sequence of equidistant rules is used. For a first rule $R_1$, the error committed in the numerical integration is appraised by use of a difference of appropriate order [for example, if Simpson's rule is used, the fourth difference is computed, following (2.2.1) and (4.5.1)]. If this error appraisal is $\leqslant \varepsilon$, then the machine prints out $R_1(f)$ and stops. If the error appraisal is exceeded, an interval size $h$ is computed, which on the basis of the difference information obtained will be sufficiently small to obtain an appraisal $\leqslant \varepsilon$. This process is then iterated.

The attractiveness of an automatic integrator should be plain to anyone who has ever been confronted with the job of carrying out many integrations of complicated integrands. Furthermore, experience has shown that if the tolerance ($\varepsilon$) requirements are modest, such a program can do a reasonable job.

But it is important for a proper understanding of the situation to formulate a number of objections and cautionary remarks. On the theoretical side, no estimate of the accuracy of an approximate integral based on a finite amount of functional information has any validity *in the absence of theoretical information about the function such as theoretically accurate bounds on derivatives, etc.* To clarify this, we can say that no condition of the form

$$\left| \sum_{k=1}^{m} b_k f(y_k) \right| \leqslant \varepsilon \tag{6.1.1}$$

can imply that

$$\left| \int_a^b f(x)\, dx - \sum_{k=1}^{n} w_k f(x_k) \right| \leqslant \varepsilon, \tag{6.1.2}$$

where the $w_k$ and the $b_k$ are *constants that are independent of $f$*. Note that this covers the automatic integrators just discussed. It is possible to find a continuous function (in fact even a polynomial function) for which (6.1.1) will hold and for which

$$R(f) = \sum_{k=1}^{n} w_k f(x_k)$$

differs from $\int_a^b f(x)$ by any preassigned quantity. To obtain such a function, merely define $f$ to be 0 on $\{x_k\}$ and $\{y_k\}$ and adjust its values elsewhere so that $\int_a^b f(x)\, dx$ is large.

This implies several pitfalls as far as the practical working of such programs is concerned. The tolerance $\varepsilon$ may be chosen so small that it is found impossible to meet, and the program exits having reached the maximum allowable number of functional evaluations. Or it is possible that the tolerance condition is met, but the accepted value is quite unsatisfactory. Some striking examples of the latter, with rather innocent-looking integrands, were given by Clenshaw and Curtis.

The integral

$$I = \int_{-1}^{+1} \left(\tfrac{23}{25} \cosh x - \cos x\right) dx$$

leads to the following numerical evaluation ($S$ = Simpson):

$$1 \times S: \quad .4795546,$$
$$2 \times S: \quad .4795551.$$

The difference is                      .0000005.

But we know that          $I$:          .4794282,

so that accepting $2 \times S$ would have led to an error of

.0001269,

which is 200 times the tolerance.

The integral

$$J = \int_{-1}^{1} \frac{dx}{x^4 + x^2 + .9}$$

leads to the following evaluations ($G$ = Gauss):

$$G_3: \quad 1.585026,$$
$$G_4: \quad 1.585060.$$

The difference is                      .000034.

But we know that          $J$:          1.582233;

thus accepting $G_4$ would lead to an error of .0028, or 100 times the tolerance.

Yet we should realize that, in principle, an automatic integrator does nothing that might not reasonably be done by a programmer forced to work in the absence of any theoretical analysis of his integral. A series of printouts, monitored either by eye or by the machine, leads him squarely and surely to the same dilemma: What faith can he put in the alleged value? There is no answer other than to build up experience and set modest goals.

**References.**  Clenshaw and Curtis [1].

### 6.2 Some Automatic Integrators

Automatic integration schemes can be classified as *adaptive* or *nonadaptive* and *iterative* or *noniterative*. In adaptive integration, the points at which the integrand is evaluated are chosen in a way that depends on the nature of the integrand. In nonadaptive integration, the sequence of integration points is chosen according to a fixed scheme independent of the nature of the integrand. In an iterative scheme, successive approximations to the integral are computed until there is agreement to within the given tolerance. In a noniterative scheme, information from a first approximation is used to generate a second approximation, which is then taken as the final answer.

A simple nonadaptive iterative scheme has been widely published. It compares an $n \times S$ with a $2n \times S$, $n = 1, 2, \ldots$, until the difference is less than a fixed $\varepsilon$ times the absolute value of $n \times S$. We shall now give some more sophisticated approaches.

**References.** Higman [1], McCormick and Salvadori [1, pp. 312–315], Noble [1, p. 239], Pennington, [1 pp. 204–205].

### 6.2.1 An Adaptive Noniterative Scheme for Automatic Integration Based on the Midpoint Rule

The input to this scheme is $a, b, \varepsilon, n, f$. The output is $I \approx \int_a^b f(x)\, dx$, with the error hopefully less than $\varepsilon$; $n$ is the number of intervals initially chosen. The method used is as follows: Let $h = (b - a)/n$. Compute $f(x)$ at

$$x_i = a + [(2i - 1)/2n]\, h, \qquad i = 1, \ldots, n,$$

and use as first approximation to $I$ the sum $h \sum_{i=1}^n f_i$, where $f_i = f(x_i)$. Then $D_i$ is computed for $i = 1, \ldots, n$, where

$$D_1 = f_1 - 2f_2 + f_3, \qquad D_n = f_n - 2f_{n-1} + f_{n-2},$$

$$D_i = f_{i-1} - 2f_i + f_{i+1}, \qquad i = 2, \ldots, n - 1.$$

If $|D_i|\, h/24 < \varepsilon/n$, we accept the value $h f_i$ for that panel and go on to $i + 1$; otherwise

$$\bar{h} = h \bigg/ \left( \frac{|D_i|}{24} \frac{h}{\varepsilon} n \right)^{1/2}$$

is computed and $h_i$ is chosen such that $h_i < \bar{h}$ and $h_i$ divides $h$: $h = n_i h_i$. The value for that panel is then $h_i \sum_{j=1}^{n_i} f(x_{ij})$, where

$$x_{ij} = a + (i - 1)\, h + \frac{2j - 1}{2n_i} h_i, \qquad j = 1, \ldots, n_i;$$

$I$ is then taken as the sum of the values for the $n$ panels.

The theoretical background for this method is the fact that the error term in the midpoint rule

$$\int_{x_0}^{x_0 + h} f(x)\, dx \approx hf(x_0 + h/2)$$

is $h^3 f''(\xi)/24$, $x_0 < \xi < x_0 + h$. Hence, if we assume that $D_i \approx h^2 f''(\xi_i)$ and that we want the error term in each panel to be less than $\varepsilon/n$, we choose $h_i$ as above. The total error will then be less than $\varepsilon$. A FORTRAN program for this method is given in the Appendix.

This method is a noniterative adaptive scheme. This means that the number of functional evaluations in each interval depends on the behavior of the integrand in that interval. It is not iterative because, after choosing the $h_i$, it does not check whether the new approximation satisfies the error criteria. The method was tested on various functions and gave the results listed in the table that follows.

**Reference.**    Russell [1].

**Examples**

| Function | $\int_0^1 f(x)\, dx$ | $\varepsilon$ | $n$ | Computed value | Number of evaluations |
|---|---|---|---|---|---|
| $x^{1/2}$ | .6666 6667 | .001 | 5 | .6678 3588 | 11 |
| | | | 20 | .6668 9109 | 24 |
| | | .0000 01 | 5 | .6666 7952 | 205 |
| | | | 20 | .6666 6964 | 276 |
| $x^{3/2}$ | .4000 0000 | .001 | 5 | .3997 4105 | 15 |
| | | | 20 | .3998 5290 | 20 |
| | | .0000 01 | 5 | .3999 9823 | 219 |
| | | | 20 | .3999 9848 | 276 |
| $x^{-1/2}$ | 2.0000 0000 | .001 | 5 | 1.8975 480 | 23 |
| | | | 20 | 1.9546 326 | 48 |
| | | .0000 01 | 5 | 1.9807 263 | 599 |
| | | | 20 | 1.9919 003 | 1134 |
| $1/(1 + x^4)$ | .8669 7299 | .001 | 5 | .8671 5831 | 15 |
| | | | 20 | .8670 7717 | 20 |
| | | .0000 01 | 5 | .8669 7346 | 257 |
| | | | 20 | .8669 7378 | 212 |
| $2/(2 + \sin 10\pi x)$ | 1.1547 005 | .001 | 5 | .9999 9999 | 5 |
| | | | 20 | 1.1547 004 | 140 |
| | | .0000 01 | 5 | .9999 9999 | 5 |
| | | | 20 | 1.1546 989 | 3700 |

These results demonstrate several weaknesses of this method. In the first place there is no assurance that the final answer will be correct to within the tolerance $\varepsilon$. In the second place, the number of evaluations of the integrand tends to be excessive for small $\varepsilon$. Finally, the last example is a case where the initial value of $n$ was too small and there was no further computation of the integrand because the error test was satisfied at all the integration points.

### 6.2.2   An Example of an Adaptive Iterative Integration Based on Simpson's Rule

A routine of this type has been given by Villars. It has an input $a$, $b$, $\varepsilon$, and possibly $h_0$; otherwise $h_0 = (b - a)/4$. It computes over the interval $[x_i, x_i + 4h_i]$ with $2 \times S$. The error corresponding to the 4th difference is compared with the pro-rata part of the total allowable error $\varepsilon$. If the 4th difference error is too large, the working interval $h_i$ is halved and the calculation is repeated. If it is too small, that is, if it is less than $\frac{1}{16}$ of the pro-rata error, the interval size $h_i$ is doubled for the next increment. Whenever a value for a given interval is accepted, the error calculated from the 4th difference is subtracted out. If $h$ is reduced too much, the program exits with an error indication. When $h$ is reduced, previously computed values of the integrand go to waste.

A similar routine, which is more sophisticated, has been given by Kuncir. Its input includes a parameter $N$, which limits the step size to $\geq (b - a)/2^N$. In case the step size has to be reduced further, the routine exits with two numbers $i$ and $I$, where $i$ is the location on the $x$-axis at which the integration was terminated and $I$ is the integral from $a$ to $i$. In the case where the integration is successful, $i = b$ and $I$ is the integral desired. In this routine there are no superfluous evaluations of the integrand. On the other hand, it does not subtract out the 4th difference error. There is no need to double the integration intervals, for this is done automatically.

**References.**   Henriksson [A1], Kuncir [A1], Villars [1], [2].

### 6.2.3   Adaptive Newton–Cotes Integration

This scheme is a generalized version of the previous one with the following different features. The algorithms are written in recursive form. However, the special adaptive Simpson's rule integrator has been given in nonrecursive form, and a FORTRAN version of it is given in the Appendix. This latter routine has been tested extensively and some results are given in the next table. The adaptive Simpson's rule has also been used successfully in integrating $|x|^{-1/2}$ through zero, ignoring the singularity. The general algorithm is written to work with the first seven Newton–Cotes rules, using two to eight points. The input is $f$, $x$, $a$, $b$, $n - 1$, $\varepsilon$. The function $f$ may be a function of several variables; $x$ is the variable of integration and is included to facilitate iterated integration. For a fixed $n$-point rule, the interval is divided into $n$ subintervals and an $n$-point Newton–Cotes integration is performed over each subinterval and compared with the value over the entire interval. That is, $n \times NC_n$ is compared with $NC_n$. If

$$|NC_n - n \times NC_n| < \varepsilon(n \times NC_n(|F|)),$$

we accept the answer. Otherwise, we treat each subinterval as the original interval, using as comparison $\varepsilon/\sqrt{n}$ rather than $\varepsilon/n$ since the latter proves too strict in practice. Each subinterval is subdivided as many times as necessary for agreement, with the number of subdivisions bounded by $100/n$. If there is no agreement at this stage, the last result is nevertheless accepted for that small subinterval, and the integration proceeds. Thus, there is no error exit to this procedure.

**References.**    McKeeman [A1], [A3], [1], McKeeman and Tesler [A1].

| Function $f(x)$ | Exact value of $\int_0^1 f(x)\,dx$ | Romberg value for $\varepsilon = 10^{-3}, 10^{-6}$ | Number of points* | Adaptive Simpson value for $\varepsilon = 10^{-3}, 10^{-6}$ | Number of points† |
|---|---|---|---|---|---|
| $x^{1/2}$ | .6666 6667 | .6665 3263 | 65 | .6666 5866 | 55 |
|  |  | .6666 6633 | 4097 | .6666 6655 | 199 |
| $x^{3/2}$ | .4000 0000 | .4000 0854 | 17 | .4000 1016 | 19 |
|  |  | .3999 9995 | 129 | .3999 9992 | 91 |
| $\dfrac{1}{1+x}$ | .6931 4718 | .6931 4739 | 9 | .6931 4743 | 19 |
|  |  | .6931 4706 | 33 | .6931 4711 | 55 |
| $\dfrac{1}{1+x^4}$ | .8669 7299 | .8669 7292 | 17 | .8669 7326 | 19 |
|  |  | .8669 7300 | 65 | .8669 7293 | 67 |
| $\dfrac{1}{1+e^x}$ | .3798 8551 | .3798 8544 | 9 | .3798 8543 | 19 |
|  |  | .3798 8546 | 17 | .3798 8543 | 19 |
| $\dfrac{x}{e^x-1}$ | .7775 0463 | .7775 0448 | 9 | .7775 0459 | 19 |
|  |  | .7775 0453 | 17 | .7775 0459 | 19 |
| $\dfrac{2}{2+\sin 10\pi x}$ | 1.1547 005 | 1.1547 003 | 65 | 1.1546 288 | 163 |
|  |  | 1.1547 004 | 257 | 1.1547 002 | 883 |

\* The minimum number of points is 9 and the number of points is always of the form $2^m + 1$.
† The minimum number of points is 19 and the number of points is always of the form $7 + 12k$.

## 6.3 Romberg Integration

Romberg integration is essentially an application of Richardson's extrapolation procedure to the Euler–Maclaurin sum formula. Romberg's name has been attached to it because he was the first to describe the algorithm in recursive form. A nonrecursive treatment of Richardson extrapolation is given in Henrici. A complete discussion of the theory of Romberg integration is given in the paper by Bauer, Rutishauser, and Stiefel. We shall describe the main features of the classical algorithm and give some of its modifications.

Let $f(x)$ be a bounded, Riemann-integrable function on $[0, 1]$ and set $I = \int_0^1 f(x)\, dx$. Let

$$T_0^{(k)} = h \sum_{j=0}^{2^k}{}'' f(hj), \qquad h = 2^{-k}, \tag{6.3.1}$$

be trapezoidal sums. The double prime indicates that the first and last terms are to be multiplied by $\frac{1}{2}$. Then, from the Euler–Maclaurin sum formula, assuming that $f(x)$ is sufficiently differentiable, we obtain

$$I - T_0^{(k)} = C_1 h^2 + C_2 h^4 + \cdots = C_1 2^{-2k} + C_2 2^{-4k} + \cdots, \tag{6.3.2}$$

where the constants $C_i$ depend on $f$ but are independent of $h$. Now let

$$T_m^{(k)} = \frac{4^m T_{m-1}^{(k+1)} - T_{m-1}^{(k)}}{4^m - 1}.$$

This enables us to construct the following triangular array, which we call *the T-table*.

$$
\begin{array}{llll}
T_0^{(0)} & & & \\
T_0^{(1)} & T_1^{(0)} & & \\
T_0^{(2)} & T_1^{(1)} & T_2^{(0)} & \\
\vdots & & & \ddots
\end{array}
$$

Each application of $T_m^{(k)}$ knocks out the term with $h^{2m}$ in the expansion of the error. The values $T_1^{(k)}$ turn out to be exactly those obtained by use of Simpson's rule. The following properties of the $T$-table have been proved.

1. The columns and diagonals of the $T$-table converge to $I$.
2. If $f \in C^{2m+2}$, then

$$\left| T_m^{(k)} - I \right| \leqslant \left| \frac{4^{-k(m+1)} B_{2m+2} f^{(m+2)}(\xi)}{2^{m(m+1)}(2m+2)!} \right|, \qquad 0 \leqslant \xi \leqslant 1.$$

3. If $f(z)$ is analytic in a region containing $[0, 1]$, then any diagonal converges *superlinearly*, that is, asymptotically faster than any geometric series.

4. If we write

$$T_m^{(k)} = h \sum_{j=0}^{2^{m+k}} {}'' d_j^{(m)} f(jh), \qquad h = 2^{-(m+k)},$$

then

$$.48 < d_j^{(m)} < 1.46.$$

ALGOL procedures for classical Romberg integration are given in Bauer and by others listed in the Appendix. A FORTRAN program by Dunkl appears in the Appendix. This program was used to integrate the functions given in the table that follows as well as the table in Section 6.2.3.

The classical Romberg scheme proceeds by successively halving the interval. The advantage of this is that it uses all functional values computed at each stage. On the other hand, the number of values computed goes up exponentially. Hence, variations of the Romberg method have been proposed, based on the following result. Let $\{n_k\}$ be a sequence of integers such that $n_{k+1}/n_k > c > 1$. Let

$$T_0^{(k)} = h_k \sum_{j=0}^{n_k} {}'' f(jh_k), \qquad h_k = \frac{1}{n_k}.$$

Form a $T$-table with

$$T_m^{(k)} = \frac{h_k^2 T_{m-1}^{(k+1)} - h_{k+m}^2 T_{m-1}^{(k)}}{h_k^2 - h_{k+m}^2}; \qquad (6.3.4)$$

then the columns and diagonals converge to $I$. Bauer *et al.* have worked out the formulas where $\{n_k\} = \{1, 2, 3, 6, 9, 18, 27, 54, \ldots\}$. In this case, the $T_m^{(k)}$ are given by

$$T_m^{(k)} = \begin{cases} \dfrac{3^m T_{m-1}^{(k+1)} - T_{m-1}^{(k)}}{3^m - 1}, & m \text{ even}, \\[2ex] \dfrac{4 \cdot 3^m T_{m-1}^{(k+1)} - 3 T_{m-1}^{(k)}}{4 \cdot 3^m - 3}, & m \text{ odd}, k \text{ even}, \\[2ex] \dfrac{3 \cdot 3^m T_{m-1}^{(k+1)} - 4 T_{m-1}^{(k)}}{3 \cdot 3^m - 4}, & m \text{ odd}, k \text{ odd}. \end{cases} \qquad (6.3.5)$$

**Example.** The convergence (that is, shutoff) criterion used in computing the values below was that three successive values along the main diagonal of the $T$-table agree within $\varepsilon = .001$; $n$ is the number of functional evaluations needed to achieve convergence.

| Function | $\int_0^1 f(x)\,dx$ | Classical Romberg | $n$ | Modified Romberg | $n$ |
|---|---|---|---|---|---|
| $x^{1/2}$ | 6666 6667 | .6665 3263 | 65 | .6667 6597 | 163 |
| $x^{3/2}$ | .4000 0000 | .4000 0854 | 17 | .3999 0517 | 55 |
| $1/(1 + x)$ | .6931 4718 | .6931 4739 | 9 | .6932 5864 | 37 |
| $1/(1 + x^4)$ | .8669 7299 | .8669 7292 | 17 | .8670 3917 | 55 |
| $1/(1 + e^x)$ | .3798 8551 | .3798 8544 | 9 | .3796 2453 | 7 |
| $x/(e^x - 1)$ | .7775 0463 | .7775 0448 | 9 | .7774 0864 | 19 |
| $2/(2 + \sin 10\pi x)$ | 1.1547 005 | 1.1547 003 | 65 | 1.1547 015 | 37 |

Two other sequences have been suggested. One is $n_k = k + 1$, which does not satisfy the condition mentioned above but which nevertheless yields a $T$-table that converges, provided that $m \leqslant 15$. Here there may be numerical instability due to roundoff. The other is $\{n_k\} = \{1, 2, 3, 4, 6, 8, 12 \ldots\}$, which has been recommended highly by Bulirsch as optimal in the sense of giving the best accuracy with the least amount of roundoff for a fixed amount of computation.

The midpoint rule has an error expansion similar to that of the trapezoidal rule. If we have

$$M_0^{(k)} = h \sum_{j=1}^{2^k} f((j - \tfrac{1}{2})h), \qquad h = 2^{-k}, \tag{6.3.6}$$

then it follows that

$$I - M_0^{(k)} = -\tfrac{1}{2}C_1 h^2 - \tfrac{7}{8}C_2 h^4 - \tfrac{31}{32}C_2 h^6 - \cdots, \tag{6.3.7}$$

where the $C_i$ are the same as in (6.3.2).

Hence we can build up a corresponding $M$-table.

$$M_0^{(0)}$$
$$M_0^{(1)} \quad M_1^{(0)}$$
$$M_0^{(2)} \quad M_1^{(1)} \quad M_2^{(0)}$$
$$\vdots \qquad\qquad \ddots$$

Its properties are similar to those of the $T$-table.

Since, in general, $T_0^{(k+1)}$ is computed as $\tfrac{1}{2}(T_0^{(k)} + M_0^{(k)})$, there is very little extra work involved in generating the $M$-table. Furthermore, we have

$$T_m^{(k)} = \tfrac{1}{2}(T_m^{(k-1)} + M_m^{(k-1)}) \tag{6.3.8}$$

and, in addition,

$$T_m^{(k)} = M_{m-1}^{(k)} + \frac{(2 \cdot 4^{m-1} - 1)(T_{m-1}^{(k)} - M_{m-1}^{(k)})}{4^{m-1} - 1}. \tag{6.3.9}$$

These relations enable us to generate the values of $T_m^{(k)}$ from $T_0^{(0)}$ and the values $M_0^{(0)}, M_1^{(0)}, \ldots$ without forming the $T_k^{(0)}$ explicitly; this saves a round-off, which can be troublesome in Romberg integration.

In the case where the $T$-table is computed, the criterion of convergence is agreement to within $\varepsilon$ of three successive values along the main diagonal. In the extended case, the criterion is agreement to within $\varepsilon$ of $T_m^{(0)}$ and $M_m^{(0)}$. This usually occurs sooner than in the previous case and, when it does, the final value of the integral is taken as $\frac{1}{2}(T_m^{(0)} + M_m^{(0)}) = T_m^{(1)}$.

Although the Romberg scheme converges whenever the trapezoidal rule does, nevertheless, for functions of the form

$$f(x) = x^\beta \phi(x), \qquad \phi(x) \text{ analytic}, \qquad 0 < \beta < 1,$$

convergence will be rather slow (see $x^{1/2}$ in the table in Section 6.2.3). Bulirsch gives two devices by which convergence can be speeded up. First, the $T_0^{(k)}$ column is modified to yield

$$\hat{T}_0^{(k)} = T_0^{(k)} + G(\beta)f\left(\frac{h_k G(1 + \beta)}{G(\beta)}\right) h_k^{1+\beta} \tag{6.3.10}$$

with

$$G(\beta) = \sin\frac{\pi}{2} \, \frac{\beta\Gamma(1 + \beta)\zeta(1 + \beta)}{|\pi^{1+\beta}2^\beta} = -\zeta(-\beta), \tag{6.3.11}$$

where $\zeta$ is the Riemann zeta function (see Section 3.4). Then the $T_m^{(k)}$ are computed by

$$T_m^{(k)} = \frac{h_k^{1+\beta}T_{m-1}^{(k+1)} - h_{k+m}^{1+\beta}T_{m-1}^{(k)}}{h_k^{1+\beta} - h_{k+m}^{1+\beta}}. \tag{6.3.12}$$

In a similar fashion, Rutishauser gives the following scheme for

$$f(x) = x^{-1/2}\phi(x),$$

$\phi(x)$ analytic. Let

$$T_2^{(k)} = h\left\{\alpha_1 f(\alpha_2 h) + \sum_{j=1}^{2^k - 1} f(jh) + \tfrac{1}{2}f(1)\right\}, \qquad h = 2^{-k}, \tag{6.3.13}$$

where

$$\alpha_1 = (\zeta(-\tfrac{1}{2})\zeta(\tfrac{1}{2}))^{1/2} = .5509\ 8782\ 8,$$

$$\tag{6.3.14}$$

$$\alpha_2 = \frac{\zeta(-\tfrac{1}{2})}{\zeta(\tfrac{1}{2})} = .1423\ 5326\ 0.$$

Then

$$T^{(k)}_{3m} = \frac{4^m T^{(k+1)}_{3m-1} - T^{(k)}_{3m-1}}{4^m - 1},$$

$$T^{(k)}_{3m+1} = \frac{4^{m+1} T^{(k+1)}_{3m} - \sqrt{8}\, T^{(k)}_{3m}}{4^{m+1} - \sqrt{8}}, \qquad m = 1, 2, 3, \ldots, \qquad (6.3.15)$$

$$T^{(k)}_{3m+2} = \frac{4^{m+1} T^{(k+1)}_{3m+1} - \sqrt{2}\, T^{(k)}_{3m+1}}{4^{m+1} - \sqrt{2}}$$

yield the desired $T$-table.

Romberg integration, an iterative nonadaptive scheme for automatic integration, has proved successful in practice and, as can be seen from the table in Section 6.2, is competitive with the adaptive Simpson's rule. It is automatic in that the number of functional evaluations depends on the behavior of the integrand over the entire interval of integration. It is nonadaptive in that it evaluates the integrand at a fixed set of points, for in adaptive schemes, the set of points at which the integrand is evaluated depends on the integrand itself. In general, this leads to greater efficiency for the adaptive schemes in terms of functional evaluations. However, the fixed set of points used in Romberg integration is advantageous when we wish to integrate a function $f(\alpha, x)$ depending on a parameter $\alpha$ for various values of the parameter. In many cases, $f(\alpha, x)$ can be written as $g(x)h(\alpha, x)$ or it contains subexpressions depending only on $x$. In these cases, the parts depending only on $x$ can be computed only once as they are needed, stored in a proper sequence, and used again and again.

Prager has given an adaptive Romberg scheme which works as follows. The input consists of $a, b, h$, and $n$. A $T$-table is set up for the interval $[a, a + h]$ with $k$ not greater than 4. If $T^{(0)}_k$ agrees with $T^{(0)}_{k-1}$ to $n$ figures, the build-up of the $T$-table ceases and $T^{(0)}_k$ is accepted as the integral over the interval. If agreement occurs with $k = 1$, $h$ is increased to $1.5h$. If it occurs with $k = 4$, $h$ is decreased to $.6h$; otherwise $h$ remains the same. In all cases, integration then proceeds over the next interval. If $T^{(0)}_4$ does not agree with $T^{(0)}_3$ to $n$ figures, $h$ is decreased to $.6h$, and integration over the shortened interval is attempted. There is an error exit when the number of intervals over which integration is performed exceeds $8(b - a)/h$. Examples of the use of this scheme are given in Sections 2.12.1 and 3.2.

References.  Bauer [1], [A1], Bauer, Rutishauser, and Stiefel [1], Bulirsch [1], Dunkl [1], Filippi [2], Gram [A1], Henrici [2], Krasun and Prager [1], Kubik [A1], Prager [1], Rabinowitz [2], Romberg [1], Rutishauser [2], Stiefel [1], [2], Stiefel and Rutishauser [1], Thacher [4].

### 6.4  Automatic Integration, Using Tschebyscheff Polynomials

Clenshaw and Curtis suggest approximating the integrand $f(x)$ by a series of Tschebyscheff polynomials $\sum_{i=0}^{N} a_i T_i(x)$ and then integrating this expansion to get a second Tschebyscheff expansion $\sum_{i=0}^{N+1} b_i T_i(x)$ for the indefinite integral $F(x) = \int_{-1}^{x} f(t) \, dt$ as well as a value for the definite integral $F(1) = 2(b_1 + b_3 + b_5 + \cdots)$. If the last three values of $b_i$ in the expansion of either $F(x)$ or $F(1)$ are small, the sum is accepted. Otherwise, $N$ is replaced by $2N$ and the computations are repeated, using previously computed results, until the error criterion is satisfied. Theoretically, we do not have to double the number of terms each time but can use any ascending sequence of integers for successive approximation. However, doubling has computational advantages. Since we shall discuss a modification of this method which is similar to it accurate, we refer the reader to the original paper for further details about but more the original method (see Section 2.13.1).

Filippi modifies this approach by approximating not $f(x)$ but $F(x)$ as a Tschebyscheff series. Let

$$F(x) = \frac{A_0}{2} + A_1 T_1(x) + \cdots, \qquad (6.4.1)$$

where

$$A_n = \frac{2}{\pi} \int_{-1}^{1} F(x) T_n(x)(1 - x^2)^{-1/2} \, dx, \qquad n = 0, 1, 2, \ldots . \qquad (6.4.2)$$

Now

$$T_n(x)(1 - x^2)^{-1/2} = -\frac{1}{n^2} \frac{d}{dx} \left((1 - x^2)^{1/2} T_n'(x)\right) \qquad (n > 1), \qquad (6.4.3)$$

so that making use of $F'(x) = f(x)$, we obtain

$$A_n = \frac{2}{\pi n^2} \int_{-1}^{1} f(x) T_n'(x)(1 - x^2)^{1/2} \, dx \qquad (n \geqslant 1). \qquad (6.4.4)$$

The functions

$$T_n'(x) = n \frac{\sin (n \arccos x)}{\sin (\arccos x)}$$

form an orthogonal set with respect to the weight $(1 - x^2)^{1/2}$. Hence the coefficients $A_n$ are the Fourier coefficients in the expansion

$$f(x) = A_1 + A_2 T_2'(x) + \cdots + A_n T_n'(x) + \cdots. \qquad (6.4.5)$$

The partial sums

$$q_{N-1}(x) = A_1 + A_2 T_2'(x) + \cdots + A_N T_N'(x)$$

are not necessarily the best approximations to $f(x)$. They are characterized instead by the condition

$$\int_{-1}^{1} [f(x) - q_{N-1}(x)]^2 (1 - x^2)^{1/2} \, dx = \min \tag{6.4.6}$$

for all $N$th-degree polynomials. The Lagrange interpolation polynomial $\bar{q}_{N-1}(x)$ to $f(x)$ with interpolation points $t_r = r\pi/(N + 1)$, the zeros of $T'_{N+1}$, is an optimal approximation to $q_{N+1}(x)$. Hence, if we write

$$\bar{q}_{N-1}(x) = a_1 + a_2 T'_2(x) + \cdots + a_N T'_N(x), \tag{6.4.7}$$

then we obtain

$$F(x) \sim \bar{Q}_N(x) = \frac{a_0}{2} + a_1 T_1(x) + \cdots + a_N T_N(x), \tag{6.4.8}$$

where

$$a_n = \frac{2}{n(N + 1)} \sum_{r=1}^{N} f(\cos t_r) \sin t_r \sin n t_r \qquad (n = 1, 2, \ldots, N) \tag{6.4.9}$$

and

$$\frac{a_0}{2} = a_1 - a_2 + a_3 - \cdots + (-1)^{N+1} a_N. \tag{6.4.10}$$

The value of the definite integral is given by

$$\int_{-1}^{+1} f(x) \, dx = 2(a_1 + a_3 + a_5 \cdots). \tag{6.4.11}$$

The computation of $a_n$ proceeds as follows: Let $z_{N+1} = z_{N+2} = 0$. Compute $z_N, z_{N-1}, \ldots, z_1$ by the recurrence relation

$$z_r = 2z_{r+1} \cos t_n - z_{r+2} + f(\cos t_r) \sin t_r.$$

Then $a_n = 2z_1 \sin t_n / n(N + 1)$.

For automatic integration we start with $N = N_1$ and check the last three coefficients $a_N, a_{N-1}, a_{N-2}$. If they are less than a given $\varepsilon$, we have finished. Otherwise, we take $N = 2N_1 + 1$, which enables us to use the previously computed values of $f(\cos t_r) \sin t_r$ and proceed as before, stopping when we reach $N$ max.

**References.**  Clenshaw and Curtis [1], Filippi [1].

### 6.5  *Automatic Integration in Several Variables*

In a certain sense, multiple integration by sampling is an automatic integration procedure. The input consists of the integrand, the region, a tolerance $\varepsilon$, and possibly an upper bound $N$ on the number of functional evaluations permitted. The output consists of the value of the integral, hopefully correct to within $\varepsilon$, unless convergence was not achieved within $N$ evaluations. In such a case, the routine will indicate this. Convergence is taken to occur when many successive approximations to the integral agree to within $\varepsilon$.

Other attempts at automatic integration in several variables include a generalization of Romberg integration to two dimensions, proposed by Laurent, and the previously mentioned work by Lyness and McHugh on Richardson extrapolation. A rather expensive automatic integration procedure results when we apply one of the automatic integration procedures in one dimension to the iterated form of a multiple integral. Such integration procedures are usually written in recursive form in that the integrand can be an integral and, hence, the procedure calls upon itself. Thus the adaptive Newton–Cotes integration procedure mentioned in Section 6.7.3 can be used for the integration of an iterated integral.

Another example of the recursive algorithm is "Multiple Integral," of McKeeman. This assumes the availability of a procedure for integrating in one dimension. Although the procedure requires that the region be a hyper-rectangle, Cadwell has shown this is not necessary.

**Example** (Cadwell). The one-dimensional integration rule used in this example is an iterative nonadaptive Simpson's rule employing at least 5 points. The symbol $\varepsilon$ designates the one-dimensional tolerance.

$$\int_V e^{-x_1^2 - x_2^2 - x_3^2 - x_4^2} \, dV = \frac{\pi^2}{16} (1 - 2e^{-1}) = .16300,$$

where $V$ is the region $x_i \geqslant 0$, $\sum x_i^2 \leqslant 1$.

| $\varepsilon$ | Number of points | Approximate integral |
|---|---|---|
| .01 | 625 | .16125 |
| .001 | 3345 | .16281 |
| .0001 | 69113 | .16298 |

**References.** Cadwell [1], Freeman [A1], Laurent [1], Lyness and McHugh [1], McKeeman [A2], [A3], Thacher [2].

## 6.6 Concluding Remarks

At the present stage of computer technology and practice, automatic integrators are generally recommended for integrating functions of one variable over a finite interval. If the programmer is confronted with an isolated (that is, a one-shot) integral, an adaptive Simpson's program seems best. If he has an integral which he must compute for various values of the parameter it contains, Romberg integration in any of its forms is indicated. For indefinite integration, Tschebyscheff polynomials may be used. If vast amounts of computation are required, automatic integration can become expensive, and preliminary analysis leading to the use of classical procedures may result in considerable savings. This would be the case, for example, if a multiple integral of dimension $d \geqslant 3$ is computed as an iterated automated integral.

Automatic integrations are not useful in the following situations: integration of data, solution of integral equations, or other situations where $N$ functional evaluations lead to a system of equations in $N$ unknowns. Integrals with special difficulties such as infinite ranges of integration, singularities, highly oscillatory integrands should be treated in a special way, and there is some tendency to develop automatic routines tailored for each sort of difficulty. The programmer will therefore be in the position of the sportsman who has given up worms but now must know which fly to use to catch his fish.

# ON THE PRACTICAL EVALUATION
# OF INTEGRALS†

*Milton Abramowitz*

Someone has recently defined an applied mathematician as an individual enclosed in a small office and engaged in the study of mathematical problems which interest him personally; he waits for someone to stick his head in the door and introduce himself by saying, "I've got a problem." Usually the person coming for help may be a physicist, engineer, meteorologist, statistician, or chemist who has suddenly reached a point in his investigation where he encounters a mathematical problem calling for an unusual or nonstandard technique for its solution. It is of considerable importance for the mathematician to be able to provide practical answers to such questions. By a practical answer one does not mean a result which is obtained after months of detailed analysis but, rather, a solution or explanation obtained in a minimum of time. The reply to questions presented to him may require analysis or merely the ability to furnish a reference to where one can find the particular topic discussed. The range of mathematical topics from which queries may arise is all-inclusive. However, a topic which arises frequently enough to merit some discussion is one which particularizes the statement "I've got a problem," to "I've got an integral." We propose to discuss here some typical questions along this line which have arisen in the experience of the writer. It is difficult to give a general classification of the integrals which might be encountered, and for the purposes of this article it is best to give illustrations by selected examples.

Before proceeding to the special problem it is important to mention other

† © Society for Industrial and Applied Mathematics 1954. All Rights Reserved. Reprinted by permission from the Journal of the Society for Industrial and Applied Mathematics, Volume 2, 1954.

aspects of providing practical assistance. There is no doubt that mathematically rigorous or precisely derived results are both desirable and necessary. However, in trying to provide useful results to research workers in other fields the mathematician should avoid such niceties at the outset. Furthermore, one should not try at first to answer questions in all completeness. When one is asked for a solution with special characteristics as required by the physical problem, the course of the investigation should be guided by these requirements. A rough-and-ready reply is often of much more value than a solution obtained with precise attention to rigor. The epsilons and deltas can come later.

The integrals to be discussed will in general be functions of one or more parameters. In attempting to evaluate a particular integral one should try as soon as possible to decide whether to obtain an analytic solution or settle for a numerical quadrature. However, prior to undertaking any work it is advisable to study the integrals from the following points of view:

(1) Confirm the existence of the integral,
(2) Ascertain the important ranges of the parameters involved,
(3) Reduce the integral to its simplest form,
(4) Determine the essential parameters which are involved,
(5) Determine the accuracy to which numerical values (if desired) are to be given.

The fourth item mentioned above is of considerable importance. The integral will arise in a physical problem where many parameters are often involved. The research worker will very often overlook the fact that these quantities may be combined in some way to yield a smaller number of parameters. In analyzing the integral such a reduction is highly desirable. Furthermore, the manner in which the parameters combine is usually of some physical significance so that the mathematical analysis may bring to light additional important information. As an example consider the integral

$$\int_0^\infty e^{-(ax^2 + bx)}\, dx,$$

whose value is known. Here it would appear that from the point of view of evaluating the integral, $a$ and $b$ are essentially distinct. However, we write successively

$$\int_0^\infty e^{-(ax^2 + bx)}\, dx = e^{b^2/4a} \int_0^\infty e^{-(ax^2 + bx + b^2/4a)}\, dx = e^{b^2/4a} \int_0^\infty e^{-(\sqrt{a}x + b/2\sqrt{a})^2}\, dx$$

$$= \frac{e^{b^2/4a}}{\sqrt{a}} \int_{b/2\sqrt{a}}^\infty e^{-u^2}\, du = \frac{e^{b^2/4a}}{\sqrt{a}} \operatorname{erfc} \frac{b}{2\sqrt{a}},$$

and thus the essential quantity in evaluating the integral is $b/2\sqrt{a}$.

If the particular integrand in question involves functions which have been adequately tabulated, a numerical integration may not only furnish an adequate solution but may be the simplest method of computation. Naturally, if one wishes to exhibit a specific property of the integral representation of a transcendental function which describes the behavior of a physical system, a numerical table may not be satisfactory and analysis will be necessary.

Although the kinds of integrals which one encounters are too varied to classify, the questions one might ask about a particular integral are predominantly of the following type.

(1) What are the numerical values of the integral when the parameters involved are assigned definite values? Here one may wish a particular value, a graph, or a table of values.

(2) What are the series expansions for the integral in terms of the parameters? One need not necessarily be limited to power series. Furthermore, since power series usually have limited ranges of utility, other representations may be desirable.

(3) What is the asymptotic behavior of the integral in terms of the parameter involved? (For example, $\Gamma(x + 1) = \int_0^\infty e^{-t} t^x \, dt \sim \sqrt{2\pi x} \, x^x e^{-x}$, when $x$ is large.)

(4) What is the complete asymptotic expansion of the integral in terms of the parameters involved?

$$(\Gamma(x + 1) \sim \sqrt{2\pi x} \, x^x e^{-x} \{1 + 1/12x + 1/288x^2 - \cdots\}).$$

Let us now illustrate some procedures which have been employed in specific instances and which one might follow. The most natural course, if one cannot find the integral in a table, is to identify it in terms of integrals which are already known.

**Example 1. Reduction to a Known Form.** The following integral arose in the theory of radiation:

$$f(a) = \int_{-1}^{+1} \frac{u^3}{\sqrt{1 - u^2}} \sin au \, du.$$

The presence of the factor $(\sin au)/\sqrt{1 - u^2}$ in the integrand suggests the possibility of a transformation which will yield a representation in terms of Bessel functions. This suggests the transformation $u = \sin t$, and one gets

$$f(a) = \int_{-\pi/2}^{+\pi/2} \sin^3 t \sin (a \sin t) \, dt$$

$$= 2 \int_0^{+\pi/2} \sin^3 t \sin (a \sin t) \, dt.$$

Now with the help of the formula $4 \sin^3 t = 3 \sin t - \sin 3t$ and the known integral representation for the Bessel functions,

$$J_{2n+1}(a) = (2/\pi) \int_0^{\pi/2} \sin(a \sin t) \sin(2n+1)t \, dt,$$

we find

$$f(a) = (\pi/4)\{3J_1(a) - J_3(a)\}.$$

**Example 2. Evaluation by a Limiting Procedure.** Sometimes the integral under consideration may not be in a form which can be found in the tables, and some modification may be required to make use of known results. For example, it may be possible to introduce a factor depending on a parameter and then obtain the desired evaluation by a limiting process with respect to the parameter. A case in point is the integral

$$I = \int_0^\infty J_0(t) \, dt.$$

From the known result for the Laplace transform of $J_0(t)$ we have

$$\int_0^\infty e^{-pt} J_0(t) \, dt = \frac{1}{\sqrt{1 + p^2}}.$$

This integral is defined for $R(p) > 0$, and in the limit as $p \to 0$ it may be shown to be defined. Thus if we let $p \to 0$ in the right member, we get $I = 1$. In using this technique one must always make certain of the existence of the limiting integral. For if one starts with the integral

$$\int_0^\infty e^{-pt} \sin t \, dt = \frac{1}{p^2 + 1},$$

although the limit of the right member as $p \to 0$ is unity, the integral does not exist for $p = 0$.

**Example 3. Use of Functional Relationships.** Sometimes one is able to make use of functional relationships involving the higher transcendental functions to obtain not an approximation to the particular integral but the complete expansion. The usefulness of such results is dependent on the adequate tabulation of the functions involved. An example of this technique provided by the integral which arises in an electrical circuit problem with time-varying capacitance is [1]

$$E(a, x) = \int_{-\infty}^x e^{(t + a \cos t)} \, dt,$$

where $-1 < a < 1$. Here one makes use of the known inversion of the relation

$$y = \tau - a \sin \tau$$

in terms of the Bessel functions $J_n(y)$, namely

$$\tau = y + \sum_{n=1}^{\infty} \frac{2}{n} J_n(na) \sin ny.$$

After making the substitution $t = (\pi/2) + \tau$, the integral becomes

$$e^{\pi/2} \int_{-\infty}^{x-\pi/2} e^{t - a \sin t} \, d\tau = e^{\pi/2} \int_{-\infty}^{Y} e^y \frac{d\tau}{dy} \, dy,$$

where $Y = x - \pi/2 + a \cos x$. Differentiating the preceding expansion and substituting for $d\tau/dy$, we then obtain, by termwise integration of the series, the expansion

$$E(a, x) = e^{(x + a \cos x)} \left\{ 1 + 2 \sum_{n=1}^{\infty} J_n(na) \frac{n \sin nY \cos nY}{n^2 + 1} \right\}.$$

Thus the procedure has reduced the problem to the evaluation of a rapidly convergent series of adequately tabulated functions.

**Example 4. The Combined Use of Functional Relationships and Termwise Integration.** An example of an integral [2] which arises in the theory of cooperative phenomena and where functional relationships turn out to be particularly useful is given by

$$I(b) = \frac{1}{\pi^3} \int_0^{\pi} \int_0^{\pi} \int_0^{\pi} \frac{dx \, dy \, dz}{3b - (\cos x + \cos y + \cos z)}.$$

Integrating with respect to $z$, we get for $b > 1$,

$$I(b) = \frac{1}{\pi^2} \int_0^{\pi} \int_0^{\pi} \frac{dx \, dy}{[(3b - \cos x - \cos y)^2 - 1]^{1/2}}.$$

To determine a series expansion for this integral, let us write

$$u = \frac{2}{3b - \cos x},$$

$$t = \cos y,$$

and obtain

$$I(b) = \frac{1}{\pi^2} \int_0^\pi \int_{-1}^{+1} \frac{dt\, dx}{\{[(2/u - t)^2 - 1][1 - t^2]\}^{1/2}}.$$

The integral with respect to $t$ may now be transformed into the normal form of the elliptic integral $K(u)$, namely

$$K(u) = \int_0^1 \frac{ds}{\{(1 - s)(1 - u^2 s^2)\}^{1/2}}.$$

To achieve this, we make the change of variable

$$t = \frac{As^2 + B}{Cs^2 + D},$$

and, since there are only three essential constants in this transformation, we may choose $D = 1$. In order that we have the correspondence $t = 1 \to s = 1$, $t = -1 \to s = 0$, we find $B = -1$ and $A = C + 2$, so that

$$t = \frac{(C + 2)s^2 - 1}{Cs^2 + 1}.$$

Carrying out the indicated substitution, we obtain

$$I(b) = \frac{1}{\pi^2} \int_0^\pi \int_0^1 \frac{2\sqrt{C + 1}\, ds\, dx}{\sqrt{(1 - s^2)R_4(s)}},$$

where $R_4(s) = \{2/u(s + 1) - [(C + 2)s^2 - 1]\}^2 - (Cs^2 + 1)^2$.

Now in order that $R_4(s)$ shall be a quadratic, the coefficient of $s^4$ must vanish, and we get the condition for $C$ as

$$\frac{4}{u^2} C^2 + (C + 2)^2 - \frac{4}{u} C(C + 2) - C^2 = 0.$$

Solving for $C$, we get $C = u$ and $C = u/(1 - u)$. It can be shown that the condition $b > 1$ leads to rejection of the second value of $C$. Substituting $C = u$, we find

$$I(b) = \frac{1}{\pi^2} \int_0^\pi \int_0^1 \frac{u\, ds\, dx}{\sqrt{(1 - s^2)(1 - u^2 s^2)}}$$

$$= \frac{1}{\pi^2} \int_0^\pi uK(u)\, dx.$$

This form can now be used to obtain an expansion for $I(b)$ which converges rapidly except in the neighborhood of $b = 1$. To this end one makes use of the series expansion for $K(u)$, namely

$$K(u) = \frac{\pi}{2}\left\{1 + \sum_{m=1}^{\infty}\left[\frac{1\cdot 3\cdot 5\cdots(2m-1)}{2\cdot 4\cdot 6\cdots 2m}\right]^2 u^{2m}\right\}.$$

Substituting this series for the integral and integrating termwise, we obtain

$$I(b) = \frac{1}{\sqrt{9b^2-1}} + \sum_{m=1}^{\infty}\left[\frac{1\cdot 3\cdot 5\cdots(2m-1)}{2\cdot 4\cdot 6\cdots 2m}\right]^2 \frac{2^{2m}g_{2m}}{(2m)!},$$

where

$$g_n = \left[\frac{d^n}{d(3b)^n}\{9b^2-1\}^{-1/2}\right],$$

as shown below, and satisfies the recurrence relation

$$(9b^2-1)g_{n+1} + 3b(2n+1)g_n + n^2g_{n-1} = 0.$$

The evaluation of the quantities $g_{2n}$ is of interest and we may show† that they may be expressed in terms of the Legendre polynomial $P_n(z)$. We have

$$\int_0^\pi u^{2n+1}\,dx = 2^{2n+1}\int_0^\pi \frac{dx}{(3b-\cos x)^{2n+1}} = 2^{2n+1}g_{2n}.$$

For $n = 0$ the integral may be evaluated by elementary methods (or reference to a table of integrals) and the result is $\pi(9b^2-1)^{-1/2}$. For $n > 0$ the integrals are obtained by differentiation with respect to the parameter $3b$. However, from the known integral [3] for $P_n(z)$,

$$P_n(z) = \frac{1}{\pi}\int_0^\pi \{z - \sqrt{z^2-1}\cos\phi\}^n\,d\phi,$$

and from the relation $P_{-n-1}(z) = P_n(z)$ we get for $z = 3b/\sqrt{9b^2-1}$,

$$g_{2n} = \frac{(2n)!}{\pi}(9b^2-1)^{-(n+1)/2}P_{2n}\left(\frac{3b}{\sqrt{9b^2-1}}\right).$$

The recurrence relation for the $g_n$ can now be found readily from the known recurrence relation for the Legendre polynomials,

$$(n+1)P_{n+1} - (2n+1)zP_n + nP_{n-1} = 0.$$

We note that, when $b = 1$, the integral is improper due to the singularity at $x = 0$. In the region of $b = 1$ the integral can be evaluated efficiently by

† The author wishes to thank Dr. P. Henrici for pointing this out.

extracting the contributions from the singularity while for $b = 1$ the value is known [4]. The technique involved in extracting the singularity is complicated and we illustrate it by the following simpler example.

**Example 5. Extraction of Singular Part.**   Consider

$$I(q) = \int_0^q \frac{e^{-x} \, dx}{1 - x}, \qquad 0 \leq q \leq 1.$$

We note that the integrand has a pole at $x = 1$ and $I(1) = \infty$. However, in the neighborhood of $x = 1$, $e^{-x}(1 - x)^{-1}$ behaves like $e^{-1}(1 - x)^{-1}$, so that we may write $I(q)$ as

$$I(q) = e^{-1} \int_0^q \frac{dx}{1 - x} + \int_0^q \left( \frac{e^{-x}}{1 - x} - \frac{e^{-1}}{1 - x} \right) dx$$

$$= -e^{-1} \log (1 - q) + \int_0^q \left( \frac{e^{-x}}{1 - x} - \frac{e^{-1}}{1 - x} \right) dx.$$

Now the second integral has no singularity in the neighborhood of $q = 1$ and may be evaluated quite easily by quadratures. Thus, the fundamental notion here is to modify the integrand by subtracting from it an expression (integrable in closed form) which eliminates the singularity and yields a form which can be integrated numerically. This matter has been discussed in some detail in [5].

**Example 6. Reduction to a Differential Equation.**   The infinite integral [6] which arises in the determination of the response of a detector to a random noise voltage having a narrow spectrum,

$$f(x) = \int_0^\infty \frac{e^{-u^2} \, du}{x + u},$$

provides an interesting illustration of some methods available for evaluating integrals. To obtain an expression useful for large values of $x$ is simple. One merely expresses $1/(x + u)$ as a geometric progression in $(x/u)$ and integrates term by term. The result is an asymptotic series of the form

$$f(x) = \frac{1}{2} \sum_{r=0}^{n-1} \frac{(-1)^r}{x^{r+1}} \Gamma\left( \frac{r + 1}{2} \right) + R_n,$$

where the remainder can be shown to be smaller than the next term neglected. This is an asymptotic expansion which actually diverges, but by keeping $n$ fixed and letting $x$ increase we can make the error arbitrarily small. However, if $x$ is fixed, the terms in the series will decrease up to a certain value, from which they will start to increase. Thus, to obtain the smallest error one must stop the calculation just before the smallest term. To obtain an expansion valid for $x$ in the neighborhood of $x = 0$, Goodwin and Staton [6] show that the integral satisfies the differential equation

$$\frac{df}{dx} + 2xf = \sqrt{\pi} - \frac{1}{x}.$$

From this equation one sees that $f$ behaves like $-\log x$ as $x \to 0$ so that the limit as $x \to 0$ of $(f + \log x)$ must be found. By considering the limit

$$\lim_{x \to 0} \left\{ \int_0^\infty \frac{e^{-u^2}}{u + x} du - \int_0^\infty \frac{du}{(u^2 + 1)(u + x)} \right\} = \int_0^\infty \left[ \frac{e^{-u^2}}{u} - \frac{1}{u(1 + u^2)} \right] du,$$

where the second integral of the left member has the value $[\log x - \frac{1}{2}\pi x]/(1 + x^2)$ and the right member has the value $-\gamma/2$ ($\gamma$ being Euler's constant), it then follows immediately that $f(x) + \log x \to -\frac{1}{2}\gamma$. The ascending series can now be obtained from the differential equation above. It is to be noted that there is no standard procedure which can be used to form the second integral of the left member.

If we write $y = f(x) + e^{-x^2} \log x$, the differential equation becomes

$$y' + 2xy = \sqrt{\pi} - \frac{1 - e^{-x^2}}{x} = \sqrt{\pi} + \sum_{n=1}^\infty \frac{(-1)^n x^{2n-1}}{n!},$$

and now from the theory of differential equations we know that a series for $y$ can be determined in the form

$$y = \sum_{n=0}^\infty a_n x^n$$

with

$$a_0 = -\tfrac{1}{2}\gamma, \qquad \gamma = \text{Euler's constant}.$$

If a table of the function $f(x)$ were required, alternative methods of calculation with the series, which are effective, are either a numerical integration of the differential equation or a direct evaluation by numerical quadrature of the integral.

**Example 7. Method of Laplace Transformation.** Instead of employing the foregoing method for determining the ascending series, it is possible to use the Laplace transform to obtain the result in more direct fashion. The Laplace transform is defined as

$$L\{g(t)\} = \int_0^\infty e^{-tp} g(t)\, dt.$$

If we make the substitution $u = xv$ in the integral for $f(x)$, we get

$$g(t) = \int_0^\infty \frac{e^{-tv^2}}{1 + v} \, dv. \qquad t = x^2.$$

The transform of $g(t)$ with respect to $t$ is

$$\int_0^\infty \frac{dv}{(1 + v)(p + v^2)} = \frac{\pi}{2\sqrt{p}(p + 1)} + \frac{1}{2} \frac{\log p}{(p + 1)}.$$

Now from the known transforms [16]

$$L^{-1}\left\{\frac{1}{\sqrt{p}(p + 1)}\right\} = \frac{2e^{-t}}{\sqrt{\pi}} \int_0^{\sqrt{t}} e^{u^2} \, du, \qquad L^{-1}\left\{\frac{\log p}{(p + 1)}\right\} = -e^{-t}Ei(t),$$

where $Ei(t)$ is the exponential integral, we obtain by inversion of the Laplace transform (here this merely involves reference to a table of Laplace transforms) the following expression for $f(x)$:

$$f(x) = \sqrt{\pi}e^{-x^2} \int_0^x e^{u^2} \, du - \tfrac{1}{2}e^{-x^2} Ei(x^2).$$

Actually one could also obtain the power series for $f(x)$ by expanding the transform in a series of $1/p$ and inverting the transform termwise. However, the above method [7] gives us a result which expresses $f(x)$ in terms of a function which has been already tabulated.

**Example 8. Saddle-Point Approximation, Improvement by Method of Differential Equations.** Another method of particular value is the saddle-point method. As an example of this technique we take the integral [8]

$$f(x) = \int_0^\infty e^{-u^2 - x/u} \, du,$$

arising in the theory of absorption coefficients for thermal neutrons. We shall find an approximation to this integral useful for large values of $x$. The fundamental idea to be employed here is the assumption that the principal contribution to the integral comes in the neighborhood of $u = u_0$, where $g(u) = u^2 + x/u$ has a minimum value. The point $u_0$ which is the saddle-point is determined from the condition that $g'(u_0) = 0$. However, it is convenient to make the following change of variable,

$$u = vt, \qquad t = (x/2)^{1/3},$$

and thus obtain

$$t \int_0^\infty e^{-t^2(v^2 + 2/v)} \, dv.$$

Now $h(v) = v^2 + 2/v$ has a minimum at $v = 1$, and from Taylor's theorem we have

$$h(v) = h(1) + (v - 1)h'(1) + \frac{(v - 1)^2}{2!} h''(1) \cdots$$

in the neighborhood of $v = 1$. Since $h(1) = 3$, $h'(1) = 0$, $h''(1) = 6$, the integral may be approximated by

$$te^{-3t^2} \int_0^\infty e^{-3t^2(v - 1)^2} \, dv.$$

To evaluate the integral we now set $\sqrt{3}t(v - 1) = s$ and obtain

$$f(x) \cong \frac{e^{-3t^2}}{\sqrt{3}} \int_{-\sqrt{3}t}^\infty e^{-s^2} \, ds.$$

Now, since $x$ and therefore $t$ is large, we can assume that the lower limit in the integral can be extended to infinity without introducing any appreciable error. We thus have

$$f(x) \cong \frac{e^{-3t^2}}{\sqrt{3}} \int_{-\infty}^\infty e^{-s^2} \, ds = \sqrt{\frac{\pi}{3}} e^{-3t^2}, \qquad t = \left(\frac{x}{2}\right)^{1/3}.$$

This represents an asymptotic approximation to the integral and for most purposes would prove adequate. However, should it be necessary to obtain an improvement to this result, the following technique is recommended. First, it can be shown that the original integral satisfies the differential equation

$$xf''' + f'' + 2f = 0.$$

Secondly, in the asymptotic result obtained earlier the variable $x$ appears in the form $3(x/2)^{2/3} = z$, say. This suggests introducing $z$ as a new variable on the assumption that the complete asymptotic expansion is a function of $z$. If we then carry out this substitution, we get the differential equation

$$\frac{d^3f}{dz^3} + \frac{1}{4z^2} \frac{df}{dz} + f = 0.$$

Now, on the basis of the previous result we can write $f(z) = \sqrt{\pi/3} \, e^{-z}U(z)$, where $U(\infty) = 1$, and obtain a differential equation for $U$:

$$\frac{d^3U}{dz^3} - 3\frac{d^2U}{dz^2} + \left[3 + \frac{1}{4z^2}\right] \frac{dU}{dz} - \left(\frac{1}{4z^2}\right)U = 0.$$

From the theory of ordinary differential equations we can now obtain a solution to this equation in the form

$$U = 1 + \frac{a_1}{z} + \frac{a_2}{z^2} \cdots,$$

where the coefficients $a_i$ can be obtained by substituting this expression in the previous equation. We stress the fact that all the steps mentioned here are of an elementary character. From the practical point of view, the determination of the differential equation for $f(x)$ may call for some ingenuity, but all the subsequent steps are straightforward.

**Example 9. Inversion of Order of Integration using Contour Integrals.** As a final example let us consider the modified Airy integral

$$A(x) = \int_0^\infty e^{-t^3 - xt} \, dt.$$

The fundamental idea to be demonstrated is the replacement of some part or all of the integrand by an equivalent definite integral and inversion of the order of integration. In addition, we shall employ the notion of the Mellin–Barnes type integral to obtain both the power series in $x$ and an asymptotic expansion in $1/x$. Although these results can be obtained here from the integral directly, the method serves to illustrate the technique.

It can be shown [9] that

$$e^{-s} = \frac{1}{2\pi i} \int_{-a-i\infty}^{-a+i\infty} \Gamma(-z)(s)^z \, dz,$$

where $a$ is real and positive and the path of integration is a straight line parallel to the imaginary axis. Thus, if we substitute for $e^{-xt}$ in the integral for $A(x)$, we get

$$A(x) = \int_0^\infty e^{-t^3} \left[ \frac{1}{2\pi i} \int_{-a-i\infty}^{-a+i\infty} \Gamma(-z)(xt)^z \, dz \right] dt$$

$$= \frac{1}{2\pi i} \int_{-a-i\infty}^{-a+i\infty} \Gamma(-z)(x)^z \left[ \int_0^\infty e^{-t^3} t^z \, dt \right] dz$$

$$= \frac{1}{3} \frac{1}{2\pi i} \int_{-a-i\infty}^{-a+i\infty} \Gamma(-z)\Gamma\left(\frac{z+1}{3}\right)(x)^z \, dz.$$

Now we consider the paths of integration composed of the line $R(z) = -a$, where $0 < a < 1$, and that part of the circle $|z| = m + \frac{1}{2}$ to the left or right of this line where $m$ is an integer. The value of $a$ must be chosen so as to separate the poles of $\Gamma(-z)$ from those of $\Gamma[(z + 1)/3]$. It can then be shown that the contribution from the line-integral around either circular arc vanishes

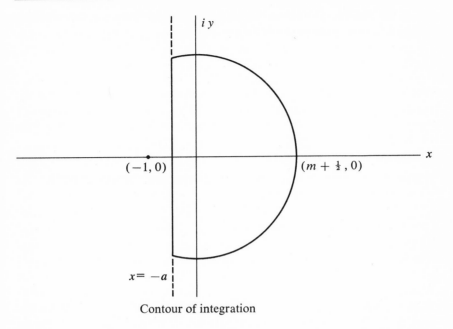

Contour of integration

as $m \to \infty$, and the value of the integral will be obtained as the sum of the residues resulting from the poles enclosed by the closed contour. Furthermore, we note that two different expansions can be derived, depending on whether the circular arc is drawn to the right or the left of the imaginary axis. Let us first consider the region as fixed by the circle to the right. The poles of the integrand are those arising from $\Gamma(-z)$, namely $z = n$ ($n$ a positive integer). The residue of $\Gamma(-z)$ is $(-1)^n/n!$; thus, if $m \to \infty$, the ascending series is

$$A(x) = \frac{1}{3} \sum_{n=0}^{\infty} \frac{\Gamma[(n + 1)/3](-x)^n}{n!}.$$

If we now take the circle to the left of the imaginary axis, the poles are now those resulting from $\Gamma[(z + 1)/3]$, namely when $(z + 1)/3$ is zero or a negative integer, that is, when $z = -3n - 1$. The residue of $\Gamma[(z + 1)/3]$ is thus $3(-1)^n/\Gamma(n + 1)$, and the contribution to the integral at each pole is $(x)^{-3n-1}$ $\Gamma(3n + 1)/\Gamma(n + 1)$. It can be shown that the series so obtained actually diverges but that, if one keeps only a finite number of terms, the remainder is smaller than the first term neglected. We thus obtain

$$A(x) \sim \sum_{n=0}^{\infty} \frac{(-1)^n \Gamma(3n + 1)}{\Gamma(n + 1)x^{3n+1}},$$

where the symbol $\sim$ is written to indicate the fact that the series is an asymptotic expansion. We have omitted a discussion of the convergence and the remainder terms in these expansions for reasons of space.

It seems worthwhile to summarize some suggested methods which might be tried in making an investigation of a particular integral:

(1) Try to recognize the integral or find it listed in existing tables of integrals. Here one should also refer to tables of transforms such as Laplace transforms, Fourier transforms, Mellin transforms, and Hankel transforms. For the convenience of the reader a short list of tables is given in references [13] to [19]. A useful device is to differentiate with respect to one or more parameters and thereby obtain a known integral. One may also replace an appropriate constant by a parameter and then apply this technique.

(2) Try the method of integration by parts. This procedure is relatively simple and in very many cases yields at least one expansion for the integral. For example, in the case of the exponential integral $Ei(t) = \int_0^\infty e^{-ut} \, du/u$ one can derive the asymptotic expansion for large values of $t$ immediately. The technique of exponentializing the integrand [10], namely writing the integral in the form $\int_a^b e^{p(x)} \, dx$ and integrating by parts successively, is very useful.

(3) Modify the integrand by subtracting out a singular function which can be integrated and reduces the integrand to a regular function.

(4) Evaluate the integral by numerical quadrature to produce a table. The integrand may possess a singularity and therefore require some modification before the quadrature can be effected. Even in those cases where the integral can be evaluated in closed form it may be worth using numerical integration in preference to any of the techniques suggested. In fact one may know the value of the integral and still use quadratures rather than the explicit value.

(5) Substitute for part or all of the integrand the equivalent power series expansion and integrate term by term. In the case of the Airy integral discussed earlier, expansion of the exponent $e^{-xt}$ and termwise integration yield the ascending power series while expansion of the part $e^{-t^3}$ gives the descending series.

(6) Use some functional relation satisfied by a part or all of the integrand. As an illustration of this we may cite the integral discussed by Henrici, in which he uses an expansion in terms of a series of Bessel functions.

(7) Substitute an equivalent definite integral for a part or all of the integrand and invert the order of integration.

(8) Find the transform (e.g., Laplace transform) of the particular integral. The resulting transformed integral may be simplified to the extent where the integration may be carried out explicitly and the desired expression may be obtained by inversion.

(9) Determine the differential equation satisfied by the integral or a modification of the integral in order to employ the methods made available by the theory of differential equations.

(10) Employ an appropriate complex integral taken along a suitably chosen contour. A well-known example of this technique is the integral

$$\int_0^\infty \frac{\cos mx}{x^2 + a^2}\, dx,$$

where one evaluates the line integral

$$\int \frac{\exp(imz)}{z^2 + a^2}\, dz$$

along an appropriate path. This subject is discussed in all of the standard works on complex variables.

(11) Approximate the integrand in the region where the principal contribution to the integral is obtained by functions whose integration can then be effected. Approximation in terms of orthogonal functions may be useful.

(12) Use the saddle-point method to find an asymptotic representation for the integral. When the differential equation satisfied by the integral is known, the technique discussed earlier may be used.

(13) Use the method of steepest descent to determine an asymptotic representation for the integral. A comprehensive discussion of this subject may be found in the report [11] of the British Admiralty.

It should be emphasized again that the list of methods outlined can not be considered exhaustive. In addition to the foregoing types of integrals, which arise mainly in physical applications, mention might also be made of the endless variety that are met in a field such as mathematical statistics. In fact, the essential difficulty in many problems involving probability distributions is simply the evaluation of certain integrals. An example of such an integral, in which a combination of integration by parts and differentiation with respect to a parameter yielded a known integral, may be found in [21].

In closing this discussion we note that it is often possible to handle a particular integral in several ways. In the case of the integral

$$\int_0^\infty \frac{\sin x}{x}\, dx$$

there are a variety of ways [20] in which it can be evaluated. In the article mentioned, five distinct methods are discussed while reference to others is given. The attack made on any particular integral depends on the tools one has at hand. It is hoped that the foregoing discussion will provide the reader with an introduction to some useful techniques. It is not intended to be a comprehensive study, and all questions of mathematical rigor have been omitted. Finally, the author wishes to thank J. Todd, P. Henrici, and H. Antosiewicz for their suggestions during the preparation of this report.

## REFERENCES

1. HENRICI, P., *Weitere Bermerkung zu* $\int e^{b(x + a\cos x)} dx$, Zeitschrift für angewandte Mathematik und Physik, vol. III (1952).

2. TIKSON, M., *Tabulation of an integral arising in cooperative phenomena*, Journal of Research of National Bureau of Standards, vol. 50 (1953) March.

3. MACROBERT, T. M., *Spherical Harmonics*, Dover (1948), p. 101.

4. OBERHETTINGER, F., and MAGNUS, W., *Anwendung der Elliptischen Funktionen in Physik und Technik*, p. 8.

5. HARTREE, D. R., *Numerical Analysis*, p. 106, 1952.

6. GOODWIN, E. T., and STATON, J., *Table of* $\int_0^\infty \dfrac{e^{-u^2}}{u + x} du$, Quarterly Journal of Mechanics and Applied Math. (1) (1948), p. 319.

7. RITCHIE, O. H., *On a definite integral*, Mathematical Tables and Other Aids to Computation, (1950), 4, p. 26.

8. ABRAMOWITZ, M., *Evaluation of the Integral*, $\int_0^\infty e^{-u^2 - x/u} du$, Journal of Math. and Phys., July (1953).

9. MACROBERT, T. M., *Functions of a Complex Variable*, Macmillan, p. 151, 1950.

10. SALZER, H. E., *Coefficients in an Asymptotic Expansion for* $\int_a^b e^{p(u)} du$, Mathematical Tables and Other Aids to Computation, October (1946), p. 188.

11. COPSON, E. T., *The Asymptotic Expansion of a Function Defined by a Definite Integral or Contour Integral*, Admiralty Computing Service, 1946.

12. ANTOSIEWICZ, H. A., *On a Certain Integral involving Bessel Functions*, NBS Report.

13. ERDÉLYI, A., MAGNUS, W., OBERHETTINGER, F., and TRICOMI, F. G., *Higher Transcendental Functions*, vol. 1 and 2, McGraw-Hill, 1953.

14. GRÖBNER, W., and HOFREITER, N., *Integraltafel*, Springer, Berlin, 1949.

15. DWIGHT, H. B., *Tables of Integrals*, Macmillan, 1951.

16. DOETSCH, G., *Tabellen zur Laplace-Transformation und Einleitung zum Gebrauch*, Springer, Berlin, 1947.

17. MACLACHLAN, N. W., and HUMBERT, P., *Formulaire pour le calcul symbolique*, Mémorial des Sciences Mathématiques, Fascicule C, Gauthier-Villars, Paris, 1941.

18. DE HAAN, B., *Nouvelles Tables d'Intégrales Définies*, Leiden, 1867.

19. CAMPBELL, G. A., and FOSTER, R. M., *Fourier Integrals for Practical Application*, Van Nostrand, New York, 1951.

20. HARDY, G. H., *The Integral* $\int_0^\infty \dfrac{\sin x}{x} dx$, Math. Gazette 5, No. 80 (1909), p. 98.

21. LIEBLEIN, J., *On the Exact Evaluation of the Variances and Covariances of Order Statistics in Samples from the Extreme-Value Distribution*, The Annals of Mathematical Statistics, Vol. 24 (1953), No. 2.

NATIONAL BUREAU OF STANDARDS
WASHINGTON, D.C.

# FORTRAN PROGRAMS

## GAUSS

Gauss (p. 192) is an all-purpose integration program to be used when the number of integration abscissas, their values, and the values of the corresponding weights are known in advance. GAUSS can be used for compound Gauss, Newton–Cotes, Lobatto, Radau, etc. integration over a finite interval and for Laguerre, generalized Laguerre, and Hermite integration over semi-infinite and infinite intervals. It can also be used for any simple integration formula where all the abscissas and weights are given. The parameters are $X$, $W$, $N$, FUN, KEY, $A$, $B$, $M$; $X$ and $W$ are the names of two arrays containing the abscissas and weights, respectively, of a particular $N$-point integration rule. KEY indicates the type of rule as explained below, $A$ and $B$ are the end points for the case of integration over a finite interval, and $M$ is the number of subintervals into which $[A, B]$ is divided. In the Laguerre case, we permit integrals of the form $\int_a^\infty e^{-x} f(x)\, dx$, and $A$ is the value of $a$.

KEY = 1 for a composite symmetric rule such as that of Gauss. The abscissas and weights are assumed to be normalized over the interval $[-1, 1]$. Only the nonnegative abscissas and their corresponding weights are to be stored in $X$ and $W$, respectively, and these are to be given in ascending order of the abscissas.

KEY = 2 for a composite nonsymmetric rule such as that of Radau. Abscissas and weights are assumed to be normalized over $[-1, 1]$ and can be given in any order.

KEY = 3 for a composite symmetric rule such as that of closed Newton–Cotes or Lobatto, which includes the end points of the interval of integration among the abscissas. Abscissas and weights are to be given as for KEY = 1.

KEY = 4 for a symmetric rule over $(-\infty, \infty)$, such as Hermite, or for any simple symmetric rule where the exact abscissas and weights are given. Abscissas and weights are to be given only for nonnegative abscissas in ascending order.

KEY = 5 for $\int_a^\infty e^{-x} f(x)\, dx$, using Laguerre integration. Abscissas and weights can be given in any order.

KEY = 6 for any approximate integration such as generalized Laguerre integration, where the integral is approximated by $\sum_{i=1}^N w_i f(x_i)$ and the $N$-values of $w_i$ and $x_i$ are given.

A program FUNCTION FUN $(X)$ must be supplied by the user for whatever name is substituted for FUN in the call of GAUSS.

```
          FUNCTION GAUSS(N,X,W,FUN,KEY,A,B,M)
          DIMENSION X(N),W(N)
          L=(N+1)/2
          K=2*L-N+1
          SUM=0.
          IF (KEY - 5) 7,5,6
7         IF (KEY - 4)8,4,11
8         EM=M
          H1=(B-A)/EM,
          A0=A
          H=H1*.5
          GO TO (1,2,3        ),KEY
C         KEY=1,M*SYMMETRIC RULE,E.G. GAUSS
1         DO 10 M1=1,M
          A1=A0+H
          IF(K-1)11,12,13
11        STOP
13        SUM=SUM+W(1)*FUN(A1)
12        DO 15 I=K,L
          H2=H*X(I)
15        SUM=SUM+W(I)*(FUN(A1+H2)+FUN(A1-H2))
10        A0=A0+H1
16        GAUSS=H*SUM
          RETURN
C         KEY=2,M*NON-SYMMETRIC RULE, E.G. RADAU
2         DO 20 M1=1,M
          DO 21 I=1,N
21        SUM=SUM+W(I)*FUN(A0+H+H *X(I))
20        A0=A0+H1
          GO TO 16
C         KEY=3,M*SYMMETRIC RULE WITH END POINT 1,E.G. LOBATTO
3         SUM=     W(L)*(FUN(B)-FUN(A))
          W1=2*W(L)
          L1=L-1
          DO 30 M1=1,M
          A1=A0+H
          IF(K-1)11,32,33
33        SUM=SUM+W(1)*FUN(A1)
32        DO 35 I=K,L1
          H2=H*X(I)
35        SUM=SUM+W(I)*(FUN(A1+H2)+FUN(A1-H2))
          SUM=SUM+W1*FUN(A0)
30        A0=A0+H1
          GO TO 16
C         KEY=4,INFINITE SYMMETRIC RULE,E.G. HERMITE
4         IF(K-1)11,42,43
43        SUM=SUM+W(1)*FUN(X(1))
42        DO 44 I=K,M
44        SUM=SUM+W(I)*(FUN(X(I))+FUN(-X(I)))
45        GAUSS=SUM
          RETURN
C         KEY=5,LAGUERRE INTEGRATION FROM A TO INFINITY
5         DO 50 I=1,N
50        SUM=SUM+W(I)*FUN(X(I)+A)
          GAUSS=EXPF(-A)*SUM
          RETURN
C         KEY=6 PURE INNER PRODUCT,E.G. GENERALIZED LAGUERRE
6         DO 60 I=1,N
60        SUM=SUM+W(I)*FUN(X(I))
          GO TO 45
          END
```

*AVINT* (*see Section 2.3*)

This program computes $\int_{XLO}^{XUP} y(x)\, dx$. $X$, $Y$ are $N$-dimensional arrays containing the abscissas $x_i$ and the ordinates $y_i$, respectively. The $x_i$ are usually unequally spaced and must be given in ascending order. The $y_i$ are usually data. $XLO$ must be less than $XUP$, but otherwise there are no restrictions on $XLO$ and $XUP$ except, of course, that of accuracy which requires that if $XLO$ is less than $x_1$, it be close to $x_1$, and if $XUP$ is greater than $x_N$, it be close to $x_N$. AVINT is adapted from P. E. Hennion [A1], Algorithm 77, CACM 5, 1962, p. 96.

```
      FUNCTION AVINT(X,Y,N,XLO,XUP)
      DIMENSION X(N),Y(N)
      SUM=0.
      SYL=XLO
      J=N
      IB=2
      DO 1 I=1,N
      IF(X(I)-XLO)1,17,17
1     IB=IB+1
17    DO 2 I=1,N
      IF(XUP-X(J)) 2,18,18
2     J=J-1
18    J=J-1
      DO 3 JM=IB,J
      X1=X(JM-1)
      X2=X(JM)
      X3=X(JM+1)
      TERM1=Y(JM-1)/((X1-X2)*(X1-X3))
      TERM2=Y(JM)/((X2-X1)*(X2-X3))
      TERM3=Y(JM+1)/((X3-X1)*(X3-X2))
      A=TERM1+TERM2+TERM3
      B=-(X2+X3)*TERM1-(X1+X3)*TERM2-(X1+X2)*TERM3
      C=X2*X3*TERM1+X1*X3*TERM2+X1*X2*TERM3
      IF(JM-IB)14,4,14
4     CA=A
      CB=B
      CC=C
      GO TO 15
14    CA=.5*(A+CA)
      CB=.5*(B+CB)
      CC=.5*(C+CC)
15    SYU=X(JM)
      SUM=SUM+CA*(SYU**3-SYL**3)/3.+CB*.5*(SYU**2-SYL**2)+CC*(SYU-SYL)
      CA=A
      CB=B
      CC=C
3     SYL=SYU
      AVINT=SUM+CA*(XUP**3-SYL**3)/3.+CB*.5*(XUP**2-SYL**2)+CC*(XUP-SYL)
      RETURN
      END
```

*FILONT* (*see Section 2.10.2*)

This program computes $\int_A^B F(x) \cos Tx \, dx$ if KEY = 1 and $\int_A^B F(x) \sin Tx \, dx$ if KEY = 2, using Filon's method. $F(x)$ is assumed to be given as a table of functional values in the array $F$ at $M$ equidistant points from $A$ to $B$. A similar program can be constructed for the case where $F$ is the name of a function to be computed. Just replace $F(1)$ by $F(A)$, $F(M)$ by $F(B)$, and $F(I)$ and $F(I\text{-}1)$ by $F(A1)$ wherever the former appear in FILONT.

```
       FUNCTION FILONT(F,T,A,B,M,KEY)
       DIMENSION F(M)
       N=M-1
       H=(B-A)/FLOATF(N)
       TH=T*H
       S=SINF(TH)
       C=COSF(TH)
       AL=1./TH+S*C/TH**2-2.*S*S/TH**3
       BE=(2.+2.*C*C-4.*S*C/TH)/TH**2
       GA=4.*(S/TH-C)/TH**2
       SUM=0.0
       F1=F(1)
       F2=F(M)
       S1=SINF(A*T)
       S2=SINF(B*T)
       C1=COSF(A*T)
       C2=COSF(B*T)
       A1=A+H
       GO TO (1,2) KEY
1      SU=F2*S2-F1*S1
       SU1=-.5*(F2*C2-F1*C1)
       DO 3 I=2,N,2
       SUM=SUM+F(I-1)*COSF(A1*T)
       A1=A1+H
       SU1=SU1+F(I)*COSF(A1*T)
3      A1=A1+H
       GO TO 4
2      SU=F2*C2-F1*C1
       SU1=-.5*(F2*S2-F1*S1)
       DO 5 I=2,N,2
       SUM=SUM+F(I-1)*SINF(A1*T)
       A1=A1+H
       SU1=SU1+F(I)*S1NF(A1*T)
5      A1=A1+H
4      FILON=H*(AL*SU+BE*SU1+GA*SUM)
       RETURN
       END
```

*SUM* (*see Section 5.6*)

This program is used to compute the $N$-dimensional integral of FUN($x$) over a product region $B$, using a product rule. $B$ may be a product of any combination of finite, semi-infinite, or infinite intervals. For each factor in $B$, it is assumed that an integration rule is given and, hence, $B$ is defined implicitly by the integration rules. The number of points in the $i$th rule is given in $N1(I)$. The abscissas and weights of the $i$th rule are given in the $i$th columns of the two-dimensional arrays $X$ and $W$, respectively. The dimensions of $X$ and $W$ are ($N$MAX, $N$), where $N$MAX is the maximum number of points in any of the $N$ rules. A program FUNCTION FUN($X$, $N$) must be supplied by the user for whatever name is substituted for FUN in the call of SUM. This latter program computes the value of the function of $N$ variables, FUN, at the point in $N$ dimensions whose co-ordinates are stored in the array $Z$. $Z$ and $M$ are $N$-dimensional arrays for temporary storage needed by SUM.

```
      FUNCTION SUM(X,W,N1,N,NMAX,FUN)
      DIMENSION X(NMAX,N),W(NMAX,N),Z(N),M(N),N1(N)
      DO 1 J=1,N
1     M(I)=1
      N2=N+1
      SUM=0.
6     K=1
      W1=1.
      DO 2 I=1,N
      M1=M(I)
      Z(I)=X(M1,I)
2     W1=W1*W(M1,I)
      SUM=SUM+W1*FUN(Z,N)
8     IF(M(K)-N1(K)) 3,4,5
5     STOP
3     M(K)=M(K)+1
      GO TO 6
4     M(K)=1
      K=K+1
      IF(K-N2) 8,7,5
7     RETURN
      END
```

**P5** (*see Section 5.7*)

This program computes a precision 5 approximation to the *N*-dimensional integral of *F(x)* over a hyperrectangle, *R*, whose center is given in the array O. The values of half the length of each side of *R* are given in the array *H*. Both arrays have dimension *N*. A program FUNCTION *F(X, N)* must be supplied by the user for whatever name is substituted for *F* in the call of P5. This latter program computes the value of the function of *N* variables, *F*, at the point in *N* dimensions whose coordinates are stored in the array *X*.

```
      FUNCTION P5(F,N,O,H)
      DIMENSION O(N),H(N),X(N)
      NN=N-1
      A2=25./324.
      A=SQRTF(.6)
      EN=N
      A0=(25.*EN*EN-115.*EN+162.)/162.
      A1=(70.-25.*EN)/162.
      H1=1.
      DO 14 I=1,N
14    H1=2.*H1*H(I)
      DO 1 I=1,N
1     X(I)=O(I)
      S=A0*F(X,N)
      S1=0.
      DO 2 I=1,N
      X(I)=O(I)+A*H(I)
      S1=S1+F(X,N)
      X(I)=O(I)-A*H(I)
      S1=S1+F(X,N)
2     X(I)=O(I)
      S2=0.
      B=A
5     DO 12 I=1,NN
      X(I)=O(I)+B*H(I)
      C=A
      I1=I+1
6     DO 3 J=I1,N
      X(J)=O(J)+C*H(J)
      S2=S2+F(X,N)
3     X(J)=O(J)
         C=-C
      IF(C) 6,4,12
4     STOP
12    X(I)=O(I)
      B=-B
      IF(B) 5,4,7
7     P5   =H1*(S+A1*S1+A2*S2)
      RETURN
      END
```

**RIEMAN** (*see Section 6.2.1*)

This program by D. L. Russell [1] (courtesy SHARE Installation AN, Argonne National Laboratory, Argonne, Illinois) computes an approximation to $\int_{A1}^{A2} \text{FUN}(x)\, dx$ which is hopefully correct to within *EPS*, by an adaptive, non-iterative integration scheme based on the midpoint rule. $N$ is the number of intervals into which the interval $[A1, A2]$ is subdivided and should reflect the variability of the integrand. A program FUNCTION FUN($X$) must be supplied by the user for whatever name is substituted for FUN in the call of RIEMAN.

```
        FUNCTION RIEMAN(A1,A2,N,EPS,FUN)
        DIMENSION A(3),F(3)
        EN=N
100     DIVA=(A2-A1)/EN
101     DO 103 I=1,3
102     A(I)=A1+(FLOATF(2*I-1)/2.0)*DIVA
103     F(I)=  FUN(A(I))
104     END=A1
105     RIEMAN=0.0
199     DO 233 I=1,N
1991    RESULT=0.0
200     ERROR=(((F(3)-2.0*F(2)+F(1))*DIVA)/24.0)*EN
201     ERR=ABSF(ERROR/EPS)
202     IF(ERR-1.0)218,218,203
203     K=SQRTF(ERR)+1.0
204     L=K/2
        PRINT 1,I,L,ERROR,ERR
1       FORMAT (2I4,2E20.8)
205     K=2*L+1
206     DIVR=DIVA/FLOATF(K)
207     DIVR2=DIVR/2.0
208     DO 211 J=1,L
209     ADD=  FUN(END+DIVR2    )*DIVR
210     RESULT=RESULT+ADD
211     END=END+DIVR
212     END=END+DIVR
213     DO 216 J=1,L
214     ADD=  FUN(END+DIVR2    )*DIVR
215     RESULT=RESULT+ADD
216     END=END+DIVR
217     GO TO 220
218     END=END+DIVA
219     DIVR=DIVA
220     IF(I-1) 222,222,221
221     IF(I-(N-1)) 224,230,232
222     RESULT=RESULT+F(1)*DIVR
223     GO TO 233
224     RESULT=RESULT+F(2)*DIVR
225     F(1)=F(2)
226     F(2)=F(3)
227     F(3)=  FUN(END+1.5*DIVA)
228     GO TO 233
230     RESULT=RESULT+F(2)*DIVR
231     GO TO 233
232     RESULT=RESULT+F(3)*DIVR
233     RIEMAN=RIEMAN+RESULT
234     RETURN
        END
```

**SIMP** (*see Section 6.2.3*)

This program is a FORTRAN adaptation from W. M. McKeeman and L. Tesler, [A1] Algorithm 182, CACM 6, 1963, p. 315. It computes an approximation to $\int_{A_1}^{B} \text{FUN}(x)\,dx$ to within the tolerance *EP* except for exceptional situations. A program FUNCTION FUN($X$) must be supplied by the user for whatever name is substituted for FUN in the call of SIMP.

```
      FUNCTION SIMP(A1,B,EP,FUN)
C     NONRECURSIVE ADAPTIVE INTEGRATION
C     ALGORITHM 182 CACM 6 (1963) 315
      DIMENSION DX(30),EPSP(30),X2(30),X3(30),F2(30),F3(30),F4(30),
     1FMP(30),FBP(30),EST2(30),EST3(30),PVAL(30,3),NRTR(30)
      COMMON PVAL,SUM,LVL,L1
C     THE PARAMETER SETUP FOR THE INITIAL CALL
      A=A1
      EPS=EP
      LVL=0
      ABSAR  =0.
      EST=0.
      DA=B-A
      FA=FUN(A)
      FM=4.*FUN ((A+B)*.5)
      FB=FUN(B)
C     1=RECUR
1     LVL=LVL+1
      DX(LVL)=DA/3.
      SX=DX(LVL)/6.
      F1=4.*FUN(.5*DX(LVL)+A)
      X2(LVL)=A+DX(LVL)
      F2(LVL)=FUN(X2(LVL))
      X3(LVL)=X2(LVL)+DX(LVL)
      F3(LVL)=FUN(X3(LVL))
      EPSP(LVL)=EPS
      F4(LVL)=4.*FUN    ( DX(LVL)*.5+X3(LVL))
      FMP(LVL)=FM
      EST1=SX*(FA+F1+F2(LVL))
      FBP(LVL)=FB
      EST2(LVL)=SX*(F2(LVL)+F3(LVL)+FM)
      EST3(LVL)=SX*(F3(LVL)+F4(LVL)+FB)
      SUM=EST1+EST2(LVL)+EST3(LVL)
      ABSAR  =ABSAR  -ABSF(EST)+ABSF(EST1)+ABSF(EST2(LVL))+ABSF(EST3(LVL
     1))
      IF(ABSF(EST-SUM)-EPSP(LVL)*ABSAR  ) 2,2,3
3     IF(LVL-30) 4,2,2
C     2=UP
2     LVL=LVL-1
      L=NRTR(LVL)
      PVAL(LVL,L)=SUM
      GO TO (11,12,13)L
C     11=R1,12=R2,13=R3
4     NRTR(LVL)=1
      EST=EST1
      FM=F1
      FB=F2(LVL)
7     EPS=EPSP(LVL)/1.7
      DA=DX(LVL)
      GO TO 1
11    NRTR(LVL)=2
      FA=F2(LVL)
      FM=FMP(LVL)
      FB=F3(LVL)
      EST=EST2(LVL)
      A=X2(LVL)
      GO TO 7
12    NRTR(LVL)=3
      FA=F3(LVL)
      FM=F4(LVL)
      FB=FBP(LVL)
      EST=EST3(LVL)
      A=X3(LVL)
      GO TO 7
13    SUM=PVAL(LVL,1)+PVAL(LVL,2)+PVAL(LVL,3)
      IF(LVL-1) 5,5,2
5     SIMP   =SUM
      RETURN
```

**QUAD** (*see Section 6.3*)

This program is used to approximate $I = \int_A^B \text{FUN}(x)\, dx$ by Romberg integration and was written by Dunkl [1] (courtesy SHARE Installation TY, University of Toronto, Toronto, Ontario, Canada). The maximum number of steps taken is fifteen and, if convergence is not achieved by then, the final value computed is taken as the approximation to the integral. The parameters *EPS* and *ETA* are error tolerances and the result QUAD hopefully satisfies the less restrictive of the following two conditions:

(i) $|QUAD - I| < EPS$ (absolute error),

(ii) $QUAD = \int_A^B \{1 + y(x)\}\, \text{FUN}(x)\, dx$, where $|y(x)| < ETA + 2^{-26}$ (relative error).

In case (ii), if $\text{FUN}(x)$ does not change the sign for any $x$ between $A$ and $B$, then $|QUAD - I|/|I| < ETA + 2^{-26}$.

The parameter *MIN* indicates at what step in the integration procedure we start to check for convergence; $3 < MIN < 15$. A program FUNCTION FUN($X$) must be supplied by the user for whatever name is substituted for FUN in the call of QUAD.

```
      FUNCTION QUAD(A,B,FUN,EPS,ETA,MIN)
C     ROMBERG INTEGRATION
      DIMENSION Q(16)
1     H=B-A
      FCNA=FUN(A)
      FCNB=FUN(B)
      TABS=ABSF(H)*(ABSF(FCNA)+ABSF(FCNB))/2.
      T=H*(FCNA+FCNB)/2.
      NX=1
      DO 12 N=1,15
      H=H/2.
      SUM=0
      SCORR=0
      SUMABS=0
      DO 2 I=1,NX
      XI=2.*FLOATF(I)-1.
      FCNXI=FUN(A+XI*H)
      SUMABS=SUMABS+ABSF(FCNXI)
      FCNXI=FCNXI+SCORR
      SS=SUM+FCNXI
      SCORR=(SUM-SS)+FCNXI
2     SUM=SS
      T=T/2.+H*SUM
      TABS=TABS/2.+ABSF(H)*SUMABS
      Q(N)=2.*(T+H*SUM)/3.
      IF(N-2) 10,3,3
3     F=4.
      DO 4 J=2,N
      I=N+1-J
      F=F*4.
4     Q(I)=Q(I+1)+(Q(I+1)-Q(I))/(F-1.)
      IF(N-3) 9,5,5
5     IF(N-MIN) 9,6,6
6     X=ABSF(Q(1)-QX2)+ABSF(QX2-QX1)
      IF(TABS) 7,8,7
7     IF(X/TABS-3.*(ABSF(ETA)+0.14901161E-7))11,11,8
8     IF(X-3.*ABSF(EPS))11,11,9
9     QX1=QX2
10    QX2=Q(1)
12    NX=NX*2
11    QUAD=Q(1)
      RETURN
      END
```

# BIBLIOGRAPHY OF
# ALGOL PROCEDURES

BAUER, F. L.

A1. "Algorithm 60, Romberg Integration," *CACM*,† *4*, 1961, p. 255. See also *CACM*, *5*, 1962, p. 168.

BULIRSCH, R.

A1. Romberg–Neville Integration, romnevint, in Bulirsch [1, pp. 15–16].

FREEMAN, R. D., JR.

A1. "Algorithm 32, MULTINT." *CACM*, *4*, 1961, p. 106. See also *CACM*, *6*, 1963, p. 69.

GRAM, C.

A1. ALGOL Programming, Contribution No. 8, "Definite Integral by Romberg's Method. ALGOL Procedure." *BIT*,‡ *4*, 1964, pp. 54–60. See also *BIT. 4*: 1964, pp. 118–120.

HENNION, P. E.

A1. "Algorithm 77, Interpolation, Differentiation, and Integration." *CACM. 5*: 1962, p. 96. See also *CACM*, *5*, 1962, p. 348, and *CACM*, *6*, 1963, pp. 446–447, 663.

A2. "Algorithm 84, Simpson's Integration." *CACM*, *5*, 1962, p. 208. See also *CACM*, *5*, 1962, pp. 392, 440.

HENRIKSSON, S.

A1. "ALGOL Programming, Contribution No. 2, Simpson Numerical Integration with Variable Length of Step." *BIT*, *1*, 1961, p. 290.

HERBOLD, R. J.

A1. "Algorithm 1, Quad I." *CACM*, *3*, 1960, p. 74.

KUBIK, R. N.

A1. "Algorithm 257, Havie Integrator." *CACM*, *8*, 1965, p. 381.

† *CACM* = Communications of the Association for Computing Machinery.
‡ *BIT* = Nordisk Tidskrift for Informationsbehandling.

KUNCIR, G. F.

A1. "Algorithm 103, Simpson's Rule Integrator." *CACM*, *5*, 1962, p. 347.

McKEEMAN, W. M.

A1. "Algorithm 145, Adaptive Numerical Integration by Simpson's Rule." *CACM*, *5*, 1962, p. 604. See also *CACM*, *6*, 1963, p. 167, and *CACM*, *8*, 1965, p. 171.

A2. "Algorithm 146, Multiple Integration." *CACM*, *5*, 1962, pp. 604–605. See also, *CACM*, *7*, 1964, p. 296.

A3. "Algorithm 198, Adaptive Integration and Multiple Integration." *CACM*, *6*, 1963, pp. 443–444.

McKEEMAN, W. M., and Tesler, L.

A1. "Algorithm 182, Nonrecursive Adaptive Integration." *CACM*, *6*, 1963, p. 315. See also, *CACM*, *7*, 1964, p. 244.

OLYNYK, F.

A1. "Algorithm 233, Simpson's Rule for Multiple Integration." *CACM*, *7*, 1964, pp. 348–349.

PFALZ, J. L.

A1. "Algorithm 98, Evaluation of Definite Complex Line Integrals." *CACM*, *5*, 1962, p. 345.

RUTISHAUSER, H.

A1. "Algorithm 125, Weightcoeff." *CACM*, *5*, 1962, pp. 510–511.

TEIJELO, L.

A1. "Algorithm 255, Computation of Fourier Coefficients." *CACM*, *8*, 1965, p. 279.

# BIBLIOGRAPHY OF TABLES

Of making many tables there is no end. This is true even when the tables are restricted to the weights and abscissas of integration rules and even after several authors (Hamming, Rutishauser) have published algorithms for generating integration rules to suit one's needs. Tables continue to appear in large numbers and a bibliography of such tables would be obsolete almost immediately. We shall, therefore, content ourselves with the following.

1. A listing of the section headings in Fletcher, Miller, Rosenhead, and Comrie's "Index of Mathematical Tables", which deal with numerical integration.

2. A description of the tables and formulas on integration in the NBS Handbook of Mathematical Functions.

3. A description of the tables in the comprehensive book of Gaussian integration rules by Stroud and Secrest.

4. A description of some tables of unusual interest.

For the rest we refer the reader to the pages of the journal "Mathematics of Computation" and its predecessor "Mathematical Tables and Other Aids to Computation" (MTAC) both for countless tables of integration rules and for reviews of other such tables, published and unpublished, as well as for errata in published tables.

## 4.1 Section Headings in the "Index of Mathematical Tables"

(See Fletcher, Miller, Rosenhead, and Comrie, *An Index of Mathematical Tables*, Addison-Wesley, Reading, Mass.)

23.5     Numerical Integration, using Ordinates (pp. 584–591)
.51      Cotes' Formulae
.512     Sard's Formulae
.515     Other Formulae with Equal Intervals
.518     Integration of Linear Sums of Exponential Functions
.52      Partial-Range Formulae, etc.
.53      Formulae for Forward Integration

.54     Steffensen's Formulae
.55     Maclaurin's Formulae
.56     Filon's Formulae
.57     Chebyshev's Formulae
.575    Other Formulae with Equal Coefficients
.58     Formulae with Unequal Intervals and Coefficients
.581    Gaussian Quadrature Formulae
.5815   Radau's Quadrature Formulae
.582    Gauss–Laguerre Quadrature Formulae
.583    Generalized Gauss–Laguerre Quadrature Formulae
.584    Gauss–Hermite Quadrature Formulae
.585    Other Quadrature Formulae with Unequal Intervals and Coefficients
.588    A Formula for Repeated Integration
.59     Lagrangian Integration Polynomials
23.6    Integration and Summation, using Differences (pp. 591–593)
.61     Single Integrals Anywhere in the Interval
.62     Repeated Integrals Anywhere in the Interval
.67     Osculatory Quadrature Formulae
.68     $J = \dfrac{1}{nw} \displaystyle\int_0^{nw} f(x)\, dx$ in Terms of Differences
.69     Lubbock Coefficients
.695    Summation of Slowly Convergent Series
23.7    Double Integrals, etc. (page 593)

### 4.2 Tables and Formulas for Integration in the NBS Handbook

1. Newton–Cotes Formulas (Closed Type), $n = 2(1)11$,     pp. 886–887.
2. Newton–Cotes Formulas (Open Type), $n = 2(1)7$,     p. 887.
3. Lagrangian Integration Coefficients,

$$\int_{x_m}^{x_{m+1}} f(x)\, dx \approx \frac{1}{h} \sum_k A_k(m) f(x_k), \qquad n = 3(1)10, \quad \text{p. 915.}$$

4. Abscissas and Weight Factors for Gaussian Integration, $n = 2(1)12(4)24(8)48(16)96$,     pp. 916–919.
5. Abscissas for Equal Weight Chebyshev Integration

$$\int_{-1}^{1} f(x)\, dx \approx \frac{2}{n} \sum_{i=1}^{n} f(x_i), \qquad n = 2(1)7, 9, \quad \text{p. 920.}$$

6. Abscissas and Weight Factors for Lobatto Integration, $n = 3(1)10$,     p. 920.

7. Abscissas and Weight Factors for Gaussian Integration for Integrands with a Logarithmic Singularity, $n = 2(1)4$,     p. 920.

8. Abscissas and Weight Factors for Gaussian Integration of
   Moments

$$\int_0^1 x^k f(x)\, dx \approx \sum_{i=1}^{n} w_i f(x_i), \qquad k = 0(1)5, \quad n = 1(1)8, \qquad \text{pp. 921–922.}$$

9. Abscissas and Weight Factors for Laguerre Integration,
   $n = 2(1)10, 12, 15,$                                                    p. 923.
10. Abscissas and Weight Factors for Hermite Integration,
    $n = 2(1)10, 12, 16, 20,$                                               p. 924.
11. Coefficients for Filon's Quadrature Formula,                           p. 924.
    $n = $ number of points in formula.


### 4.3   Tables of Gaussian Type Integration Formulas in Stroud and Secrest "Gaussian Quadrature Formulas"

All integration formulas to thirty significant figures.

1. $\displaystyle\int_{-1}^1 f(x)\, dx \approx \sum_{i=1}^{N} A_i f(x_i)$   (Gauss),   $N = 2(1)64(4)96(8)168, 256, 384, 512$

2. $\displaystyle\int_{-1}^1 (1 - x^2)^\alpha f(x)\, dx \approx \sum_{i=1}^{N} A_i f(x_i),$   $N = 2(1)20,$   $\alpha = -\frac{1}{2}, \frac{1}{2}, 1, \frac{3}{2}$

3. $\displaystyle\int_{-1}^1 (1 + x)^\beta f(x)\, dx \approx \sum_{i=1}^{N} A_i f(x_i),$   $\begin{array}{l}\beta = 1, \\ \beta = 2, 3, 4,\end{array}$   $\begin{array}{l}N = 2(1)30 \\ N = 2(1)20\end{array}$

4. $\displaystyle\int_{-1}^1 |x|^\alpha f(x)\, dx \approx \sum_{i=1}^{N} A_i f(x_i),$   $N = 2(1)20,$   $\alpha = 1, 2, 3, 4$

5. $\displaystyle\int_{-\infty}^\infty e^{-x^2} f(x)\, dx \approx \sum_{i=1}^{N} A_i f(x_i)$   (Hermite),   $N = 2(1)64(4)96(8)136$

6. $\displaystyle\int_0^\infty e^{-x} f(x)\, dx \approx \sum_{i=1}^{N} A_i f(x_i)$   (Laguerre),   $N = 2(1)32(4)68$

7. $\displaystyle\int_{-\infty}^\infty |x|^\alpha e^{-x^2} f(x)\, dx \approx \sum_{i=1}^{N} A_i f(x_i),$   $N = 2(1)20,$   $\alpha = 1, 2, 3$

8. $\displaystyle\int_{-\infty}^\infty |x|^\alpha e^{-|x|} f(x)\, dx \approx \sum_{i=1}^{N} A_i f(x_i),$   $N = 2(1)20,$   $\alpha = 1, 2, 3$

9. $\displaystyle\int_0^1 \ln\left(\frac{1}{x}\right) f(x)\, dx \approx \sum_{i=1}^{N} A_i f(x_i),$   $N = 2(1)16$

10. $\displaystyle\frac{1}{2\pi i} \int_{c-i\infty}^{c+i\infty} p^{-1} e^p F(p)\, dp \approx \sum_{i=1}^{N} A_i F(p_i),$   $N = 2(1)24.$

11. $\displaystyle\int_{-1}^1 f(x)\, dx \approx A f(-1) + \sum_{i=1}^{N} A_i f(x_i) + A f(+1)$   (Lobatto),
    $$N = 2(1)32(4)96.$$

12. $\displaystyle\int_{-1}^{1} f(x)\,dx \approx Af(-1) + \sum_{i=1}^{N} A_i f(x_i)$     (Radau),     $N = 2(1)19(4)47$.

13. $\displaystyle\int_{-1}^{1} f(x)\,dx \approx \sum_{i=1}^{N} A_i f(x_i) + \sum_{k=0}^{M} B_{2k} f^{(2k)}(0)$,     $N = 2(2)16$,   $M = 1, 2, 3$.

14. $\displaystyle\int_{-\infty}^{\infty} e^{-x^2} f(x)\,dx \approx \sum_{i=1}^{N} A_i f(x_i) + \sum_{k=0}^{M} B_{2k} f^{(2k)}(0)$,   $N = 2(2)16$,   $M = 1, 2, 3$.

### 4.4   Tables of Unusual Interest

1. J. C. P. Miller, "Quadrature in Terms of Equally Spaced Function Values" (91 pages) contains almost every formula ever developed which expresses an integral as a weighted sum of equally spaced values of the integrand. Miller gives both finite difference formulas and formulas in terms of equally spaced function values. He also gives a number of special formulas. In many formulas, the coefficients are given both as exact fractions and in decimal form. Error coefficients are given both for truncation errors and rounding errors.

2. Krylov, Lugin, and Ianovich, "Tables for the Numerical Integration of Functions with Power Singularities" (434 pages) gives abscissas and weights to 8 S (significant figures) for the integration

$$\int_{0}^{1} x^\beta (1 - x)^\alpha f(x)\,dx, \qquad \alpha, \beta = -.9(.1)3, \quad \beta < \alpha, \quad n = 1\text{-}8.$$

3. Aizenshtat, Krylov, and Metleskii, "Tables for Calculating Laplace Transforms and Integrals of the Form $\int_0^\infty x^s e^{-x} f(x)\,dx$" (378 pages) gives $x_i$, $w_i$, and $w_i e^{x_i}$ for $s = -.9(.02)0$, $.55(.05)3$, $-\frac{3}{4}$, $-\frac{1}{4}$, $m + k/3$, $m = -1(1)2$, $k = 1, 2$, $n = 1(1)15$, 8 S.

4. Shao, Chen, and Frank, "Tables of Zeros and Gaussian Weights of Certain Associated Laguerre Polynomials and the Related Generalized Hermite Polynomials" (311 pages) gives $x_i$, $w_i$ for generalized Laguerre integration for $s = -.5(.5)10$, $n = 4, 8(8)32(16)64(32)128$ and for generalized Hermite integration for $s = 0(1)10$, $n = 8(8)32(16)64(32)128(64)256$ to 25 S.

5. Skoblja, "Tables for the Numerical Inversion of the Laplace Transform

$$f(x) = \frac{1}{2\pi i} \int_{c-i\infty}^{c+i\infty} e^{xp} F(p)\,dp\text{"}$$

(44 pages) give $w_k$ and $x_k$ occurring in the integration formula

$$\frac{1}{2\pi i} \int_{c-i\infty}^{c+i\infty} e^p p^{-s} \phi(p)\,dp \approx \sum_{k=1}^{n} w_k \phi(x_k),$$

which is exact for $\phi(p) = p^{-j}$, $j = 0, 1, \ldots, 2n - 1$. Here $w_k$ are given to 7 S and $s_k$ to 8 S for $n = 1(1)10$, $s = .1(.1)3$.

6. Kruglikova, "Tables for the Numerical Fourier Transform" (31 pages) gives $w_k$ and $x_k$ occurring in the integration formulas

$$\int_0^\infty \left(1 + \frac{\sin x}{\cos x}\right) f(x)\, dx \approx \sum_{k=1}^{n} w_k f(x_k),$$

which is exact for $f(x) = (1 + x)^{-s-i}$, $i = 0, 1, \ldots, 2n - 1$. Here $x_k$ are given to 10–14 S and $w_k$ to 5–14 S for $s = r + \frac{1}{4}$, $r + \frac{1}{3}$, $r + \frac{1}{2}$, $r + \frac{2}{3}$, $r + \frac{3}{4}$, $r + 1$ ($r = 1, 2, 3$) and for $n = 1(1)8$.

**References.** Fletcher, Rosenhead, Miller, and Comrie [1], NBS Handbook [1], Stroud and Secrest [2], Miller [1], Shao, Chen, and Frank [1], Krylov, Lugin, and Ianovich [1], Aizenshtat, Krylov, and Metleskii [1], Skoblja [1], Kruglikova [1], Hamming [1, Ch. 10], Rutishauser [A1].

# BIBLIOGRAPHY OF BOOKS AND ARTICLES

ABRAMOWITZ, M.
1. "On the Practical Evaluation of Integrals." *J. Soc. Ind. App. Math.*, *2* (1954), pp. 20–35.

ABRAMOWITZ, M., and I. A. STEGUN (Eds.)
1. *Handbook of Mathematical Functions.* National Bureau of Standards, Applied Math. Series No. 55, Government Printing Office, Washington, 1964.

AIZENSHTAT, V. S., V. I. KRYLOV, and A. S. METLESKII
1. *Tables for Calculating Laplace Transforms and Integrals of the Form* $\int_0^\infty x^s e^{-x} f(x) \, dx$. Minsk, 1962.

ALBRECHT, J., and L. COLLATZ.
1. "Zur numerischen Auswertung mehrdimensionaler Integrale." *Z. Ang. Math. Mech.*, *38* (1958), pp. 1–15.

ALDER, B., S. FERNBACH, and M. ROTENBERG (Eds.)
1. *Methods in Computational Physics*, 2. New York: Academic Press, 1963.

ANDERSEN, D. G.
1. "Gaussian Quadrature Formulae for $\int_0^1 - \ln (x) f(x) \, dx$." *Math. Comp.*, *19*, (1965), pp. 477–481.

BAREISS, E. H., and C. P. NEUMAN
1. "Singular Integrals and Singular Integral Equations with a Cauchy Kernel and the Method of Symmetric Pairing." *Argonne Nat'l Lab. Report 6988*, 1965.

BARNHILL, R. E.
1. "The Convergence of Quadratures on Complex Contours," *J. SIAM Numer. Anal. Ser. B*, *2* (1965), pp. 321–336.

207

BAUER, F. L.
1. "La méthode d'intégration numérique de Romberg." *Colloque sur l'analyse numérique*, 22–24 mars 1961 à Mons, pp. 119–129.

BAUER, F. L., H. RUTISHAUER, and E. STIEFEL
1. "New Aspects in Numerical Quadrature." In: *Experimental Arithmetic, High Speed Computing, and Mathematics*. Providence: American Mathematical Society, 1963, pp. 199–218.

BELL, D. A.
1. "Approximations in Fourier Transforms." *Computer J.*, *6* (1963/64), pp. 244–247.

BIRKHOFF, G., and D. YOUNG
1. "Numerical Quadrature of Analytic and Harmonic Functions." *J. Math. and Phys.*, *29* (1950), pp. 217–221.

BLANC, C., and W. LINIGER
1. "Stochastische Fehlerauswertung bei numerischen Methoden." *Z. Ang. Math. Mech.*, *35* (1955), pp. 121–130.

BUCK, R. C.
1. *Advanced Calculus*, New York: McGraw-Hill, 1956.

BULIRSCH, R.
1. "Bemerkungen zur Romberg—Integration." *Num. Math.*, *6* (1964), pp. 6–16.

BURGOYNE, F. D.
1. "Quadrature Formulas over Infinite Intervals in Terms of Differences." *Math. Comp.*, *17* (1963), pp. 298–301.

BUYST, L., and L. SCHOTSMANS
1. "A Method of Gaussian Type for the Numerical Integration of Oscillating Functions." *ICC Bulletin*, *3* (1964), pp. 210–214.

CADWELL, J. H.
1. "A Recursive Program for the General $n$-Dimensional Integral." *Comm. ACM*, *6* (1963), pp. 35–36.

CHAI, A. S., and H. J. WERTZ
1. "Some Considerations in Practical Computation." *MRC Technical Summary Report 469* (1964), Madison, Wisconsin.

CLARK, M., and K. F. HANSEN
1. *Numerical Methods of Reactor Analysis*. New York: Academic Press, 1964.

CLENSHAW, C. W.
1. "Chebyshev Series for Mathemetical Functions." *Math. Tables Volume 5*. National Physical Laboratory, London: H.M.S.O., 1962.

CLENSHAW, C. W., and A. R. CURTIS
1. "A Method for Numerical Integration on an Automatic Computer." *Num. Math., 2* (1960), pp. 197–205.

CONCUS, P., D. CASSATT, G. JAEHNIG, and E. MELBY
1. "Tables for the Evaluation of $\int_0^\infty x^\beta e^{-x} f(x) \, dx$ by Gauss–Laguerre Quadrature." *Math. Comp., 17* (1963), pp. 245–256.

COWDREY, D. R., and C. M. REEVES
1. "An Application of the Monte Carlo Method to the Evaluation of Some Molecular Integrals." *Computer J., 6* (1963/64), pp. 277–286.

DAVIS, P. J.
1. "Errors of Numerical Approximation for Analytic Functions." *J. Rational Mech. Anal., 2* (1953), pp. 303–313.
2. "On Simple Quadratures." *Proc. Am. Math. Soc., 4* (1953), pp. 127–136.
3. "On a Problem in the Theory of Mechanical Quadratures." *Pacific J. Math., 5* (1955), pp. 669–674.
4. "On the Numerical Integration of Periodic Analytic Functions." In: *On Numerical Approximation*, R. Langer, Ed. Madison: Univ. of Wisconsin Press, 1959, pp. 45–59.
5. "Errors of Numerical Approximation for Analytic Functions." In: *Survey of Numerical Analysis*, J. Todd, Ed. New York: McGraw-Hill, 1962, pp. 468–484.
6. *Interpolation and Approximation.* New York: Blaisdell, 1963.

DAVIS, P. J., and I. POLANSKY
1. "Numerical Interpolation, Differentiation, and Integration." Chapter 25 of *Handbook of Mathematical Functions.* Washington: National Bureau of Standards, 1964, pp. 875–924.

DAVIS, P. J., and P. RABINOWITZ
1. "On the Estimation of Quadrature Errors for Analytic Functions." *MTAC, 8* (1954), pp. 193–203.
2. "Some Monte Carlo Experiments in Computing Multiple Integrals." *MTAC, 10* (1956), pp. 1–8.
3. "Abscissas and Weights for Gaussian Quadratures of High Order." *J. Res. Natl. Bur. Std., 56* (1956), pp. 35–37.
4. "Additional Abscissas and Weights for Gaussian Quadratures of High Order: Values for $n = 64, 80,$ and 96." *J. Res. Natl. Bur. Std., 60* (1958), pp. 613–614.
5. "Advances in Orthonormalizing Computation." *Advances in Computers, 2,* F. L. Alt, Ed. New York: Academic Press, 1961, pp. 55–133.
6. "Some Geometrical Theorems for Abscissas and Weights of Gauss Type." *J. Math. Anal. Appl., 2* (1961), pp. 428–437.
7. "Ignoring the Singularity in Numerical Integration." *J. SIAM Ser. B. Numer. Anal., 2* (1965), pp. 367–383.

DUNKL, C. F.
1. "Romberg Quadrature to Prescribed Accuracy." SHARE File Number 7090-1481 TYQUAD.

ERDÉLYI, A.
1. *Asymptotic Expansions.* Pasadena: Department of Mathematics, California Institute of Technology, 1955.

ERDÉLYI, A., *et al.*
1. *Higher Transcendental Functions*, 3 vols. New York: McGraw-Hill, 1953.
2. *Tables of Integral Transforms*, 2 vols. New York: McGraw-Hill, 1954.

FARRINGTON, C. C.
1. "Numerical Quadrature of Discontinuous Functions." Preprints of papers presented at the 16th National Meeting of the ACM, Los Angeles, Sept. 5-8, 1961, New York: ACM.

FEJÉR, L.
1. "Mechanische Quadraturen mit positiven Cotesschen Zahlen." *Math. Z., 37* (1933), pp. 287-309.

FELDHEIM, E.
1. "Théorie de la convergence des procédés d'interpolation et de quadrature mécanique." *Mémor. Sci. Math., 95* (1939), pp. 1-90.

FETTIS, H. E.
1. "Numerical Calculation of Certain Definite Integrals by Poisson's Summation Formula." *MTAC, 9* (1955), pp. 85-92.
2. "Further Remarks Concerning the Relative Accuracy of Simpson's and the Trapezoidal Rule for a Certain Class of Functions." *Z. Ang. Math. Mech., 38* (1958), pp. 159-160.

FILIPPI, S.
1. "Angenäherte Tschebyscheff-Approximation einer Stammfunction—eine Modifikation des Verfahrens von Clenshaw und Curtis." *Num. Math., 6* (1964), pp. 320-328.
2. Das Verfahren von Romberg–Stiefel–Bauer als Spezialfall des allgemeinen Prinzips von Richardson, Zeit. moderne Rechentechnik und Automation (MTW), 11 (1964), I. Teil, pp. 49-54, II. Teil, pp. 98-100.

FILON, L. N. G.
1. "On a Quadrature Formula for Trigonometric Integrals." *Proc. Roy. Soc. Edinburgh, 49* (1928), pp. 38-47.

FISHMAN, H.
1. "Numerical Integration Constants." *MTAC, 11* (1957), pp. 1-9.

FLETCHER, A., J. C. P. MILLER, L. ROSENHEAD, and L. J. COMRIE
1. *An Index of Mathematical Tables 1*, 2nd ed., Reading, Mass.: Addison-Wesley, 1962.

FLETCHER, R., and C. M. REEVES
1. "A Mechanization of Algebraic Differentiation and the Automatic Generation of Formulae for Molecular Integrals of Gaussian Orbitals." *Computer J.*, 6 (1963/64), pp. 287–292.

FLINN, E. A.
1. "A Modification of Filon's Method of Numerical Integration." *J. Assoc. Comp. Mach.*, 7 (1960), pp. 181–184.

FORSYTHE, G. E.
1. "Singularity and Near Singularity in Numerical Analysis." *Am. Math. Monthly*, 65 (1958), pp. 229–240.

FRANKLIN, J. N.
1. "Deterministic Simulation of Random Processes." *Math. Comp.*, 17 (1963), pp. 28–59.

FRANKLIN, P.
1. *A Treatise on Advanced Calculus.* New York: Wiley, 1940.

FRASER, D. A. S.
1. *Statistics: An Introduction.* New York: Wiley, 1958.

FRÖBERG, C.-E.
1. *Introduction to Numerical Analysis.* Reading, Mass.: Addison-Wesley, 1965.

GATES, L. D., JR.
1. "Numerical Solution of Differential Equations by Repeated Quadratures." *SIAM Review*, 6 (1964), pp. 134–147.

GHIZETTI, A.
1. "Sulle formule di quadratura." *Rend. Sem. Mat. Fis. Milano*, 26 (1954–1955), pp. 1–16, or, *Consiglio Naz. Ricerche. Pubbl. Ist. Appl. Calcolo no. 434* (1956).
2. "Sulla convergenza dei procedimenti di calcolo, degli integrali definiti, fornati dalle formule di quadratura." *Rend. Sem. Mat. Univ. Padova*, 26 (1956), pp. 201–222.

GOLDBERG, R. R.
1. *Methods of Real Analysis.* New York: Blaisdell, 1964.

GOLOMB, M., and H. F. WEINBERGER
1. "Optimal Approximation and Error Bounds." In: *On Numerical Approximation*, R. Langer, Ed. Madison: University of Wisconsin Press, 1959, pp. 117–190.

GOODWIN, E. T.
1. "The Evaluation of Integrals of the Form $\int_{-\infty}^{\infty} f(x)e^{-x^2}\,dx$. *Proc. Camb. Phil. Soc.*, 45 (1949), pp. 241–245.

GREENWOOD, R. E., P. D. M. CARNAHAN, and J. W. NOLLEY.
1. "Numerical Integration Formulas for Use with Weight Functions $x^2$ and $x/\sqrt{1 - x^2}$. *Math. Comp.*, 13 (1959), pp. 37–40.

GRÖBNER, W., and N. HOFREITER
1. *Integraltafel*, 2 vols. Vienna: Springer-Verlag, 1961.

HABER, S.
1. "A Note on Some Quadrature Formulas for the Interval $(-\infty, \infty)$." *Math. Comp.*, *18* (1964), pp. 313–314.

HALTON, J. H.
1. "On the Efficiency of Certain Quasi-random Sequences of Points in Evaluating Multi-dimensional Integrals." *Num. Math.*, *2* (1960), pp. 84–90.

HALTON, J. H., and D. C. HANDSCOMB
1. "A Method for Increasing the Efficiency of Monte Carlo Integration." *J. Assoc. Comp. Mach.*, *4* (1957), pp. 329–340.

HAMMER, P. C.
1. "The Midpoint Method of Numerical Integration." *Math. Magazine*, *31* (1957–58), pp. 193–195.
2. "Numerical Evaluation of Multiple Integrals." In: *On Numerical Approximation*, R. Langer, Ed. Madison: Univ. of Wisconsin Press, 1959, pp. 99–115.

HAMMER, P. C., O. J. MARLOWE, and A. H. STROUD
1. "Numerical Integration over Simplexes and Cones." *MTAC*, *10* (1956), pp. 130–137.

HAMMER, P. C., and A. H. STROUD
1. "Numerical Integration over Simplexes." *MTAC*, *10* (1956), pp. 137–139.
2. "Numerical Evaluation of Multiple Integrals II." *MTAC*, *12* (1958), pp. 272–280.

HAMMER, P. C., and H. H. WICKE
1. "Quadrature Formulas Involving Derivatives of the Integrand." *Math. Comp.*, *14* (1960), pp. 3–7.

HAMMER, P. C., and A. W. WYMORE
1. "Numerical Evaluation of Multiple Integrals I." *MTAC*, *11* (1957), pp. 59–67.

HÄMMERLIN, G.
1. "Zur numerischen Integration periodischer Funktionen." *Z. Ang. Math. Mech.*, *39* (1959), pp. 80–82.
2. Über ableitungsfreie Schranken für Quadraturfehler," *Num. Math.*, *5* (1963), pp. 226–233.
3. Über ableitungsfreie Schranken für Quadraturfehler II. Ergänzungen und Möglichkeiten zur Verbesserung." *Num. Math.*, *7* (1965), pp. 232–237.

HAMMERSLEY, J. M., and D. C. HANDSCOMB
1. *Monte Carlo Methods*. London: Methuen, 1964.

HAMMING, R. W.
1. *Numerical Methods for Scientists and Engineers*. New York: McGraw-Hill, 1962.

HANDSCOMB, D. C.
1. "Remarks on a Monte Carlo Integration Method." *Num. Math.*, 6 (1964), pp. 261–268.

HARPER, W. M.
1. "Quadrature Formulas for Infinite Integrals." *Math. Comp.*, 16 (1962), pp. 170–175.

HARTREE, D. R.
1. "The Evaluation of a Diffraction Integral." *Proc. Camb. Phil. Soc.*, 50 (1954), pp. 567–574.
2. *Numerical Analysis*. 2nd ed. London: Oxford Univ. Press, 1958.

HASELGROVE, C. B.
1. "A Method for Numerical Integration." *Math. Comp.*, 15 (1961), pp. 323–337.

HENRICI, P.
1. *Discrete Variable Methods in Ordinary Differential Equations*. New York: Wiley, 1962.
2. *Elements of Numerical Analysis*. New York: Wiley, 1964.

HETHERINGTON, R. G.
1. "Numerical Integration over Hypershells." Ph.D. Thesis, University of Wisconsin, Numerical Analysis Department, Madison, 1961.

HIGMAN, B.
1. "What EVERYBODY should know about ALGOL." *Computer J.*, 6 (1963/64), pp. 50–56.

HILDEBRAND, F. B.
1. *Introduction to Numerical Analysis*. New York: McGraw-Hill, 1956.

HLAWKA, E.
1. "Zur angenäherten Berechnung mehrfacher Integrale." *Monat. Math.*, 66 (1962), pp. 140–151.
2. "Uniform Distribution Modulo 1 and Numerical Analysis." *Compositio Mathematica*, 16 (1964), pp. 92–105.

HOBSON, E. W.
1. *The Theory of Functions of a Real Variable*, Vol. I. Cambridge: University Press, 1927.

HOFSOMMER, D. J.
1. Note on the Computation of the Zeros of Functions Satisfying a Second Order Differential Equation." *MTAC*, 12 (1958), pp. 58–60.

HULL, T. E., and A. R. DOBELL
1. "Random Number Generators." *SIAM Review.*, *4* (1962), pp. 230–254.

HUNTER, D. B.
1. "The Calculation of Certain Bessel Functions." *Math. Comp.*, *18* (1964), pp. 123–128.

HURWITZ, H., JR., R. A. PFEIFFER, and P. F. ZWEIFEL
1. "Numerical Quadrature of Fourier Transform Integrals II." *MTAC*, *13* (1959), pp. 87–90.

HURWITZ, H., JR., and P. F. ZWEIFEL
1. "Numerical Quadrature of Fourier Transform Integrals." *MTAC*, *10* (1956), pp. 140–149.

IBM
1. Reference Manual C 20-8011. Random Number Generation and Testing.

IMHOF, J. P.
1. "Remarks on Quadrature Formulas," *J. Soc. Ind. App. Math*, *11* (1963), pp. 336–341.

JACKSON, D.
1. *The Theory of Approximation*, New York: Amer. Math. Soc. 1930.

KAHN, H.
1. *Applications of Monte Carlo*. Research Memorandum RM-1237-AEC, Rand Corporation, Santa Monica, California, Revised Edition, 1956.
2. "Multiple Quadrature by Monte Carlo Methods." In: *Mathematical Methods for Digital Computers*, A. Ralston and H. S. Wilf, Eds. New York: Wiley, 1960, pp. 249–257.

KAPLAN, E. L.
1. "Numerical Integration Near a Singularity," *J. Math. and Phys.*, *31* (1952), pp. 1–28.

KING, R.
1. "Runge-Kutta Methods with Constrained Minimum Error Bounds," to appear.

KNOPP, K.
1. *Theory and Application of Infinite Series*. London: Blackie and Son, 1951.

KOKSMA, J. F.
1. "The Theory of Asymptotic Distribution Modulo 1," *Compositio Math.*, *16* (1964), pp. 1–22.

KOPAL, Z.
1. *Numerical Analysis*. 2nd Ed., New York: Wiley, 1961.

KOROBOV, N. M.
1. *Teoretikochislovie Metodi v Priblizhennom Analize.* Moscow: GIFL, 1963.

KOROVKIN, P. P.
1. *Linear Operators and Approximation Theory.* Delhi: Hindustan, 1960.

KOWALEWSKI, G.
1. *Interpolation und Genäherte Quadratur.* Leipzig: Teubner, 1932.

KRAFT, R., and C. J. WENSRICH
1. *Monte Carlo Bibliography.* Report UCRL-6581, University of California, Radiation Laboratory, Livermore, 1961.

KRASUN, A. M., and W. PRAGER
1. "Remark on Romberg Quadrature." *Comm. ACM, 8* (1965), pp. 236–237.

KRUGLIKOVA, L.
1. *Tables for the Numerical Fourier Transform.* Minsk, 1964.

KRYLOV, V. I.
1. *Approximate Calculation of Integrals,* trans. by A. H. Stroud. New York: Macmillan, 1962.

KRYLOV, V. I., V. V. LUGIN, and L. A. IANOVICH
1. *Tables for the Numerical Integration of Functions with Power Singularities.* Minsk: 1963.

KUNZ, K. S.
1. *Numerical Analysis.* New York: McGraw-Hill, 1957.

LAMBERT, J. D., and A. R. MITCHELL
1. "The Use of Higher Derivatives in Quadrature Formulae." *Computer J.*, 5 (1962/63), pp. 322–327.

LANCE, G. N.
1. *Numerical Methods for High Speed Computers.* London: Iliffe, 1960.

LANCZOS, C.
1. Introduction to: *Tables of Chebyshev Polynomials.* Washington: National Bureau of Standards, Applied Math. Series, vol. 9, 1952.
2. *Applied Analysis.* Englewood Cliffs: Prentice-Hall, 1956.

LAUFFER, R.
1. "Interpolation mehrfacher Integrale," *Arch. Math.*, 6 (1955), pp. 159–164.

LAURENT, P.-J.
1. "Formules de Quadrature Approchée sur Domaines Rectangulaires Convergentes pour toute Fonction Intégrable Riemann." *Compt. Rend.*, *258* (1964), pp. 798–801.

LEVEQUE, W. J.
1. *Topics in Number Theory*, 2. Reading, Mass: Addison-Wesley, 1956.

Lo, Y. T., S. W. Lee, and B. Sun
1. "On Davis' Method of Estimating Quadrature Errors." *Math. Comp.*, *19* (1965), pp. 133–138.

Lohmann, W.
1. "Numerische Auswertung von Integralen über eine volle Periode von periodischen Integrandenfunktionen mit der 'Rechteckregel'." *Z. Ang. Math. Mech.*, *36* (1956), pp. 464–465.

Longman, I. M.
1. "Note on a Method for Computing Infinite Integrals of Oscillatory Functions." *Proc. Camb. Phil. Soc.*, *52* (1956), pp. 764–768.
2. "Tables for the Rapid and Accurate Numerical Evaluation of Certain Infinite Integrals Involving Bessel Functions." *MTAC*, *11* (1957), pp. 166–180.
3. "On the Numerical Evaluation of Cauchy Principal Values of Integrals." *MTAC*, *12* (1958), pp. 205–207.
4. "A Method for the Numerical Evaluation of Finite Integrals of Oscillatory Functions." *Math. Comp.*, *14* (1960), pp. 53–59.

Lotkin, M.
1. "A New Integrating Procedure of High Accuracy." *J. Math. and Phys.*, *31* (1952), pp. 29–34.

Lubkin, S.
1. "A Method of Summing Infinite Series." *J. Res. Natl. Bur. Std.*, *48* (1952), pp. 228–254.

Luke, Y. L.
1. "Mechanical Quadrature Near a Singularity." *MTAC*, *6* (1952), pp. 215–219.
2. "On the Computation of Oscillatory Integrals." *Proc. Camb. Phil. Soc.*, *50* (1954), pp. 269–277.
3. "Evaluation of an Integral Arising in Numerical Integration Near a Logarithmic Singularity." *MTAC*, *10* (1956), pp. 14–21.
4. "Simple Formulas for the Evaluation of Some Higher Transcendental Functions." *J. Math. and Phys.*, *34* (1956), pp. 298–307.

Lyness, J. N.
1. "Symmetric Integration Rules for Hypercubes." *Math. Comp.*, *19* (1965), I. Error Coefficients, pp. 260–276. II. Rule Projection and Rule Extension, pp. 394–407. III. Construction of Integration Rules Using Null Rules, pp. 625–637.

Lyness, J. N., and B. J. J. McHugh
1. "Integration over Multidimensional Hypercubes—I. A Progressive Procedure." *Computer J.*, *6* (1963/64), pp. 264–270.

Macon, N.
1. *Numerical Analysis.* New York: Wiley, 1963.

MEYERS, L. F., and A. SARD
1. "Best Approximate Integration Formulas." *J. Math. and Phys.*, *29* (1950), pp. 118–123.

MICHELS, H. H.
1. "Abscissas and Weight Coefficients for Lobatto Quadrature." *Math. Comp.*, *17* (1963), pp. 237–244.

MILLER, J. C. P.
1. "Quadrature in Terms of Equally-Spaced Function Values." *MRC Technical Summary Report 167*, July, 1960, Madison, Wisconsin.
2. "Numerical Quadrature over a Rectangular Domain in Two or More Dimensions." *MTAC*, *14* (1960). Part 1: pp. 13–20. Part 2: pp. 130–138. Part 3: pp. 240–248.

MILNE, W. E.
1. "The Remainder in Linear Methods of Approximation." *J. Res. Natl. Bur. Std.*, *43* (1949), pp. 501–511.
2. "The Trapezoidal Rule," Unpublished.

MINEUR, H.
1. *Techniques de Calcul Numérique.* Paris and Liège: Béranger, 1952.

MISES, R. V.
1. "Numerische Berechnung mehrdimensionaler Integrale." *Z. Ang. Math. Mech.*, *34* (1954), pp. 201–210.

MOORS, B. P.
1. *Valeur Approximative d'une Intégrale Définie.* Paris: Gauthier-Villars, 1905.

MORAN, P. A. P.
1. "Approximate Relations between Series and Integrals." *MTAC*, *12* (1958), pp. 34–37.

MORRISON, D.
1. "Numerical Quadrature in Many Dimensions." *J. Assoc. Comp. Mach.*, *6* (1959), pp. 219–222.

MORTON, K. W.
1. "On the Treatment of Monte Carlo Methods in Text Books." *MTAC*, *10* (1956), pp. 223–224.

MUSTARD, D.
1. "Numerical Integration Over the *n*-dimensional Spherical Shell." *Math. Comp.*, *18* (1964), pp. 578–589.

MUSTARD, D., J. N. LYNESS, and J. M. BLATT
1. "Numerical Quadrature in *n*-dimensions." *Computer J.*, *6* (1963/64), pp. 75–87.

MCCORMICK, J. M., and M. G. SALVADORI
1. *Numerical Methods in FORTRAN.* Englewood Cliffs: Prentice-Hall, 1964.

MCCRACKEN, D. D., and W. S. DORN
1. *Numerical Methods and Fortran Programming.* New York: Wiley, 1964.

MCKEEMAN, W. M.
1. "Certification of Algorithm 145. Adaptive Numerical Integration by Simpson's Rule." *Comm. ACM, 6* (1963), pp. 167–168.

MCLAREN, A. D.
1. "Optimal Numerical Integration on a Sphere." *Math. Comp., 17* (1963), pp. 361–383

MCNAMEE, J.
1. "Error Bounds for the Evaluation of Integrals by the Euler–Maclaurin Formula and by Gauss-Type Formulae." *Math. Comp., 18* (1964), pp. 368–381.

NATANSON, I. P.
1. *Constructive Function Theory, Vol. I.* New York: Ungar, 1964.

NBS Handbook
1. *Handbook of Mathematical Functions, Applied Math. Series No. 55*, National Bureau of Standards, Washington, D.C., 1964.

NAVOT, I.
1. "An Extension of the Euler–Maclaurin Summation Formula to Functions with a Branch Singularity." *J. Math. and Phys., 40* (1961), pp. 271–276.
2. "A Further Extension of the Euler–Maclaurin Summation Formula." *J. Math. and Phys., 41* (1962), pp. 155–163.
3. "The Euler–Maclaurin Functional for Functions with a Quasi-Step Discontinuity." *Math. Comp., 17* (1963), pp. 337–345.

NIKOLSKY, S. M.
1. *Kvadraturnye Formuli.* Moscow, 1958.

NOBLE, B.
1. *Numerical Methods: 2. Differences, Integration and Differential Equations.* New York: Interscience, 1964.

OHRINGER, L.
1. Newton–Cotes Integration (floating point). Guide General Program Library 9.5.002.

OSTROWSKI, A. M.
1. "Bermerkungen zur Theorie der Diophantischen Approximationen." *Abh. Math. Sem. Univ. Hamburg, 1* (1922), pp. 77–98.

PECK, L. G.
1. "On Uniform Distribution of Algebraic Numbers." *Proc. Amer. Math. Soc. 4* (1953), pp. 440–443.

Peirce, W. H.
1. "Numerical Integration over the Planar Annulus." *J. Soc. Ind. Appl. Math.*, 5 (1957), pp. 66–73.
2. "Numerical Integration over the Spherical Shell." *MTAC*, 11 (1957), pp. 244–249.

Pennington, R. H.
1. *Introductory Computer Methods and Numerical Analysis.* New York: Macmillan, 1965.

Picone, M.
1. "Vedute Generali Sull' Interpolazione e Qualche Loro Conseguenza." *Annali della Scuola Normale Superiore di Pisa Ser. III*, 5 (1951), pp. 193–244.

Pólya, G.
1. "Über die Konvergenz von Quadraturverfahren." *Math. Z.*, 37 (1933), pp. 264–286.

Pólya, G., and Szegö, G.
1. *Aufgaben und Lehrsätze aus der Analysis*, 2 vols. New York: Dover, 1945.

Popoviciu, T.
1. "Sur une généralisation de la formule d'intégration numérique de Gauss." *Acad. R. P. Romîne Fil. Iaşi. Stud. Cerc. Şti.*, 6 (1955), pp. 29–57.

Prager, W.
1. *Introduction to Basic FORTRAN Programming and Numerical Methods.* New York: Blaisdell, 1965.

Price, J. F.
1. Discussion of Quadrature Formulas for Use on Digital Computers, Boeing Scientific Research Labs. Report D1-82-0052, May, 1960.
2. Examples and Notes on Multiple Integration, Boeing Scientific Research Labs., Report D1-82-0231, February, 1963.

Rabinowitz, P.
1. "Abscissas and Weights for Lobatto Quadrature of High Order," *Math. Comp.*, 14 (1960), pp. 47–52.
2. The Automatic Integration of a Function with a Parameter. (To appear.)

Rabinowitz, P., and G. Weiss
1. "Tables of Abscissas and Weights for Numerical Evaluation of Integrals of the Form $\int_0^\infty e^{-x} x^n f(x)\, dx$." *MTAC*, 13 (1959), pp. 285–294.

Radon, J.
1. "Zur mechanischen Kubatur." *Monat. für Math.*, 52 (1948), pp. 286–300.

Rall, L. B.
1. "Numerical Evaluation of Integrals and Solutions of Integral Equations." *SIAM Review*, 7 (1965), pp. 55–64.

RALSTON, A.
1. "A Family of Quadrature Formulas Which Achieve High Accuracy in Composite Rules." *J. Assoc. Comp. Mach.*, 6 (1959), pp. 384–394.
2. "Methods for Numerical Quadrature." In: *Mathematical Methods for Digital Computers*, A. Ralston and H. S. Wilf, Eds. New York: Wiley, 1960, pp. 242–248.
3. *A First Course in Numerical Analysis.* New York: McGraw-Hill, 1965.

RICHTMEYER, R. D.
1. "On the Evaluation of Definite Integrals and a Quasi-Monte Carlo Method Based on Properties of Algebraic Numbers," Report LA-1342 (1952), Los Alamos Scientific Laboratory, Los Alamos, N. M.
2. "A Non-Random Sampling Method, Based on Congruences for Monte Carlo Problems," Report NYO-8674, *Institute of Mathematical Sciences*, New York University (1958).

RICHTMEYER, R. D., M. DEVANEY, and N. METROPOLIS
1. "Continued Fraction Expansions of Algebraic Numbers." *Num. Math.*, 4 (1962), pp. 68–84.

ROBINSON, S. M., and A. H. STROUD
1. "The Approximate Solution of an Integral Equation Using High-Order Gaussian Quadrature Formulas." *Math. Comp.*, 15 (1961), pp. 286–288.

ROMBERG, W.
1. "Vereinfachte numerische Integration." *Norske Vid. Selsk. Forh. Trondheim* 28 (1955), pp. 30–36.

ROSSER, J. B.
1. "Transformations to Speed the Convergence of Series." *J. Res. Natl. Bur. Std.*, 46 (1951), pp. 56–64.

ROTH, K. F.
1. *Rational Approximations to Irrational Numbers.* London: University College, 1962.

ROTHMANN, H. A.
1. "Gaussian Quadrature with Weight Function $x^n$ on the Interval $(-1, 1)$." *Math. Comp.*, 15 (1961), pp. 163–168.

RUBBERT, F. K.
1. "Zur Praxis der numerischen Quadratur." *Z. Ang. Math. u. Mech.*, 29 (1949), pp. 186–188.

RUNGE, C., and F. A. WILLERS
1. "Numerische und graphische Quadratur und Integration gewöhnlicher und partieller Differentialgleichungen." *Encyklopädie der Mathematischen Wissenschaften*, 2, Section 3, pp. 47–176, Leipzig, 1909–1921.

RUSSELL, D. L.
1. "Numerical Integration by Midpoint Procedure with Preferential Interval Placement." SHARE File Number 0704-1017 AND107.

RUTISHAUSER, H.
1. "On a Modification of the QD-Algorithm with Graeffe-Type Convergence." *ZAMP, 13* (1963), pp. 493–496.
2. "Ausdehnung des Rombergschen Prinzips." *Num. Math., 5* (1963), pp. 48–54.

RYSHIK, I. M., and I. S. GRADSTEIN
1. *Tables of Series, Products, and Integrals.* Berlin, 1957.

SACK, R. A.
1. "Newton-Cotes Type Quadrature Formulas with Terminal Corrections." *Computer J., 5* (1962/63), pp. 230–237.

SAG, T. W., and G. Szekeres
1. "Numerical Evaluation of High-Dimensional Integrals." *Math. Comp., 18* (1964), pp. 245–253.

SALZER, H.
1. "Osculatory Quadrature Formulas." *J. Math. and Phys., 34* (1955), pp. 103–112.
2. "Equally Weighted Quadrature Formulas over Semi-Infinite and Infinite Intervals." *J. Math. and Phys., 34* (1955), pp. 54–63.

SALZER, H. E., and N. LEVINE
1. "Table of a Weierstrass Continuous Non-Differentiable Function." *Math. Comp., 15* (1961), pp. 120–130.

SALZER, H. E., D. C. SHOULTZ, and E. D. THOMPSON
1. *Tables of Osculatory Integration Coefficients.* San Diego: Convair, 1960.

SARD, A.
1. "Best Approximate Integration Formulas; Best Approximation Formulas." *Am. J. Math., 71* (1949), pp. 80–91.
2. "Linear Approximation." *Math. Surveys No. 9.* Providence, R.I.: American Math. Soc., 1963.

SCHIFF, B., H. LIFSON, C. L. PEKERIS, and P. RABINOWITZ
1. "The $2^{1,3}p$, $3^{1,3}p$ and $4^{1,3}p$ States of Helium and the $2^1p$ State of Li$^+$." *Phys. Rev. 140* (1965), pp. 1104–1121.

SCHOENBERG, I. J.
1. "On Monosplines of Least Deviation and Best Quadrature Formulas." *J. SIAM, Numer. Anal., Ser. B, 2* (1965), pp. 144–170.

SECREST, D.
1. "Numerical Integration of Arbitrarily Spaced Data and Estimation of Errors," *J. SIAM, Numer. Anal., Ser. B, 2* (1965), pp. 52–68.

SERBIN, H.
1. "Numerical Quadrature of Some Improper Integrals." *Quart. Appl. Math.*, *12* (1954), pp. 188–194.

SHANKS, D.
1. "Non-linear Transformations of Divergent and Slowly Convergent Sequences." *J. Math* and *Phys.*, *34* (1955), pp. 1–42.

SHAO, T. S., T. C. CHEN, and R. M. FRANK
1. "Tables of Zeros and Gaussian Weights of Certain Associated Laguerre Polynomials and the Related Generalized Hermite Polynomials." *IBM Technical Report 00.1100.* Poughkeepsie, New York: IBM Data Systems Division, 1964.
2. "Tables of Zeros and Gaussian Weights of Certain Associated Laguerre Polynomials and the Related Generalized Hermite Polynomials." *Math. Comp.*, *18* (1964), pp. 598–616.

SHAVITT, I.
1. "The Gaussian Function in Calculations of Statistical Mechanics and Quantum Mechanics." In: *Methods in Computational Physics*, vol. II. Alder, Fernbach, Rotenberg, Eds. New York: Academic Press, 1963, pp. 1–44.

SHOHAT, J. A.
1. "On a Certain Formula of Mechanical Quadrature with Non-Equidistant Ordinates." *Trans. Am. Math. Soc.*, *31* (1929), pp. 448–463.
2. "On Mechanical Quadratures, in Particular, with Positive Coefficients." *Trans. Amer. Math. Soc.*, *42* (1937), pp. 461–496.

SIMON, A. H.
1. *Oscillatory Integrals and Contour Integration.* Princeton, N.J.: RCA Laboratories.

SKOBLJA, N.
1. "Tables for the Numerical Inversion of the Laplace Transform $f(x) = \frac{1}{2\pi i} \int_{c-i\infty}^{c+i\infty} e^{xp} F(p)\, dp$," Minsk, 1964.

SLAGLE, J. R.
1. "A Heuristic Program that Solves Symbolic Integration Problems in Freshman Calculus." *J. Assoc. Comp. Mach.*, *10* (1963), pp. 507–520.

SQUIRE, W.
1. "Some Applications of Quadrature by Differentiation." *J. Soc. Ind. Appl. Math.*, *9* (1961), pp. 94–108.

STANCU, D. D.
1. "The Remainder of Certain Linear Approximation Formulas in Two Variables." *J. SIAM Ser. B. Numer. Anal.*, *1* (1964), pp. 137–163.

STANCU, D. D., and A. H. STROUD
  1. "Quadrature Formulas with Simple Gaussian Nodes and Multiple Fixed Nodes." *Math. Comp.*, *17* (1963), pp. 384–394.

STEFFENSEN, J. F.
  1. *Interpolation.* New York: Chelsea, 1950.

STENGER, F.
  1. "Numerical Integration in *n* Dimensions." Master's Thesis, Dept. of Math., University of Alberta, Edmonton, 1963.

STEWART, C. E.
  1. "On the Numerical Evaluation of Singular Integrals of Cauchy Type." *J. Soc. Ind. Appl. Math.*, *8* (1960), pp. 342–353.

STIEFEL, E.
  1. "Altes und Neues über numerische Quadratur." *Z. Ang. Math. Mech.*, *41* (1961), pp. 408–413.
  2. *An Introduction to Numerical Mathematics.* New York: Academic Press, 1963.

STIEFEL, E., and H. RUTISHAUSER
  1. "Remarques concernant l'intégration numérique." *Compt. Rend.*, *252* (1961), pp. 1899–1900.

STROUD, A. H.
  1. "Remarks on the Disposition of Points in Numerical Integration Formulas." *MTAC*, *11* (1957), pp. 257–261.
  2. "Quadrature Methods for Functions of More than One Variable." In: Numerical Properties of Functions of More Than One Independent Variable, H. C. Thacher, Jr., Ed., *Annals of the New York Academy of Sciences*, *86* (1960), pp. 776–791.
  3. "Numerical Integration Formulas of Degree Two." *Math. Comp.*, *14* (1960), pp. 21–26.
  4. "A Bibliography on Approximate Integration." *Math. Comp.*, *15* (1961), pp. 52–80.
  5. "Numerical Integration Formulas of Degree 3 for Product Regions and Cones." *Math. Comp.*, *15* (1961), pp. 143–150.
  6. "Approximate Integration Formulas of Degree 3 for Simplexes." *Math. Comp.*, *18* (1964), pp. 590–597.

STROUD, A. H., and D. SECREST
  1. "Approximate Integration Formulas for Certain Spherically Symmetric Regions." *Math. Comp.*, *17* (1963), pp. 105–135.
  2. *Gaussian Quadrature Formulas.* Englewood Cliffs, N.J.: Prentice-Hall, 1966.

STROUD, A. H., and D. D. STANCU
  1. "Quadrature Formulas with Multiple Gaussian Nodes," *J. SIAM.*, *Ser. B, Numer. Anal.*, *2* (1965), pp. 129–143.

SZEGÖ, G.
1. *Orthogonal Polynomials*. New York: Amer. Math. Soc., 1959.

TAUSSKY, O., and J. TODD.
1. "Generation and Testing of Pseudorandom Numbers." In: *Symposium on Monte Carlo Methods*, H. A. Meyer, Ed. New York: Wiley, 1956, pp. 15–28.

TCHAKALOFF, L.
1. "Formules générales de quadrature mécanique du type de Gauss." *Colloq. Math.*, *5* (1957), pp. 69–73.

TCHAKALOFF, V.
1. "Formules de Cubature Mécaniques à Coefficients Non Négatifs." *Bull. Sci. Math.*, (2), *81* (1957), pp. 123–134.

THACHER, H. C., JR.
1. "Optimum Quadrature Formulas in *s* Dimensions." *MTAC*, *11* (1957), pp. 189–194.
2. "Certification of Algorithm 32, MULTINT." *Comm. ACM*, *6* (1963), p. 69.
3. "An Efficient Composite Formula for Multidimensional Quadrature." *Comm. ACM*, *7* (1964), pp. 23–25.
4. "Remark on Algorithm 60, Romberg Integration." *Comm. ACM*, *7* (1964), pp. 420–421.
5. "An Iterative Method for Quadratures," *Comp. J.*, *5* (1962/63), pp. 228–229.

TIKSON, M.
1. "Tabulation of an Integral Arising in the Theory of Cooperative Phenomena." *J. Res. Natl. Bur. Std.*, 50 (1953), pp. 177–178.

TOCHER, K. D.
1. "The Application of Automatic Computers to Sampling Experiments." *J. Roy. Stat. Soc.*, *Ser. B, 16* (1954), pp. 39–61.

TODD, J.
1. "Classical Numerical Analysis." In: *Survey of Numerical Analysis*, J. Todd, Ed. New York: McGraw-Hill, 1962, pp. 27–118.
2. "The Problem of Error in Digital Computation." In: *Error in Digital Computation*, 1, L. B. Rall, Ed. New York: Wiley, 1965.

TYLER, G. W.
1. "Numerical Integration of Functions of Several Variables." *Can. J. Math.*, *5* (1953), pp. 393–412.

USPENSKY, J. V.
1. "On the Convergence of Quadrature Formulas Related to an Infinite Interval." *Trans. Am. Math. Soc.*, *30* (1928), pp. 542–559.

VALENTIN, R. A.
1. Applications of Functional Analysis to Optimal Numerical Approximations for Analytic Functions, Ph.D. Thesis, Div. of Applied Math., Brown University, Providence, R.I., March, 1965.

VILLARS, D. S.
1. "Use of the IBM 701 Computer for Quantum Mechanical Calculations II. Overlap Integral," NAVORD Report 5257, U.S. Naval Ordnance Test Station, China Lake, Calif., 1956.
2. "Simultaneous Multiple Integration, Floating Point." SHARE File Number 0704-0240 NO SIG.

WACTLAR, H. D., and M. P. BARNETT
1. "Mechanization of Tedious Algebra—the $e$ Coefficients of Theoretical Chemistry." *Comm. ACM*, 7 (1964), pp. 704–710.

WALSH, J. L., and W. E. SEWELL
1. "Note on Degree of Approximation to an Integral by Riemann Sums." *Am. Math. Monthly*, 44 (1937), pp. 155–160.

WEEG, G. P.
1. "Numerical Integration of $\int_0^\infty e^{-x} J_0(\eta x/\xi) J_1(x/\xi) x^{-n}\, dx$." *Math. Comp.*, 13 (1959), pp. 312–313.

WILF, H. S.
1. "Exactness Conditions in Numerical Quadrature." *Num. Math.*, 6 (1964), pp. 315–319.

WILKINSON, J. H.
1. *Rounding Errors in Algebraic Process*. Englewood Cliffs, N.J.: Prentice-Hall, 1963.

WINSTON, C.
1. "On Mechanical Quadrature Formulae Involving the Classical Orthogonal Polynomials." *Ann. Math.*, 35 (1934), pp. 658–677.

WYNN, P.
1. "On a Cubically Convergent Process for Determining the Zeros of Certain Functions." *MTAC*, 10 (1956), pp. 97–100.

YOUNG, A.
1. "Approximate Product-Integration." *Proc. Roy. Soc., London, Ser. A*, 224 (1954), pp. 552–561.

YOUNG, D.
1. "An Error Bound for the Numerical Quadrature of Analytic Functions." *J. Math. and Phys.*, 31 (1952), pp. 42–44.

# INDEX

$A(B)$, 10
Abscissas, 1
  nonequally spaced, 22
Adaptive integration, 162, 164, 173
Airy integral, 186
ALGOL program, 167, 200
Analytic function, 10, 70, 115
Analytical techniques, 3, 176–89
Antithetic variates, 148
Approximate integration, 1
  finite interval, 15
  higher dimensions, 125
  infinite interval, 89
Approximations, 59, 87, 123
Automatic integration, 159–174
  several variables, 172
  Tschebyscheff polynomials, 171
Averaging, method of, 156
AVINT, 193

Bernoulli numbers, 21
Bessel function, 58, 59
Boole's rule, 30

$C[a, b]$, 10
Cartesian product, 130
Cauchy principal value, 7, 77
  interpolatory-type formulas, 79
Cauchy's theorem, 115
Central limit theorem, 144
Change of variable, 11–13, 72, 89, 127–29
Christoffel–Darboux formula, 47
Closed type formulas, 32
$C^1 [a, b]$, 10
$C^n [a, b]$, 10
Compound rule, 20, 24, 141
Continued fractions, 47
Contour integrals, 69, 186
  complex plane, 70
Convolution integral, 88
Cylindrical coordinates, 13

Debye function, 21
Derivative-free error estimates, 116, 121
Differential equation, 40, 182
Differentiation, formal, 2, 114
Dimension effect, 129

Elliptic integral, 22
Equidistributed sequences, 146, 150
Error analysis, 102
Errors, via analytic function theory, 115
  via differences, 113
  via functional analysis, 120
  Gauss integration, 35
  integrands of low continuity, 122
Euler–Maclaurin formula, 52, 92, 166
Euler's transformation, 99
  modified, 66

Filon's method, 62
FILONT, 194
Floating point arithmetic, 103
Formula, closed type, 32
  Lobatto, 33
  MacLaurin type, 33
  midpoint, 15, 33, 162
  open type, 32
  Radau, 33
  singular integrands, 74
FORTRAN program, 141, 163–167, 191–199
Four-point formula (open type), 32
Fourier–Bessel transform, 59
Fourier coefficients, 10, 59
Fourier transform, 59
Fubini's theorem, 9
Function, analytic, 10, 70, 115
  bounded, Riemann-integrable, 10
  continuous, 10
  entire, 10
  nondifferentiable, 27

227

Function—*continued*
  piecewise continuous, 10
  rapidly oscillatory, 37, 59
  smoothness of, 10
  weight, 11
Functional analysis, 3, 120
Fundamental polynomials, 13

GAUSS, 191
Gauss integration rule, 33
  continued fractions, 47
  convergence of, 48, 97
  with derivatives, 42
  infinite interval, 95
  preassigned abscissas, 37
  remainder, 35, 96, 112
  singular integrand, 74
Gram determinant, 43

Hermite formula, 96
Hilbert transform, 79
Hypercube, rules for, 136–140

Ignoring singularities, 76
Importance sampling, 147
Improper integrals, 6, 71–77
Indefinite integration, 80
  via differential equations, 81
  nonequally spaced data, 88
  Tschebyscheff series, 83, 171
Inner product, 33, 46
Integral calculus, fundamental theorem
  of, 6
Integral, contour, 18, 69, 186
  double, 8, 128
  elliptic, 22
  evaluation of, 175
  higher dimensional, 7, 125, 172
  improper, 6, 71
  iterated, 9, 133
    indefinite, 14
  Lebesgue, 9
  multiple, 12, 125
  over $[0, \infty]$, 6, 89
  over $[-\infty, \infty]$, 7, 95
  principal value of, 7, 77
  Riemann, 4, 7
  tables of, 3, 187
Integrands, unbounded, 7, 71

Integration, adaptive, 162–164
  approximate, 1, 15, 89, 125
  automatic, 159, 162
  change of order, 9, 127
  finite interval, 15
  formal, 2
  indefinite, 80, 83, 88, 171
  iterative, 162
  numerical, 1
  by parts, 6
  periodic functions, 53
  rapidly oscillatory functions, 59
  Romberg, 166
  between zeros, 61
Integration rules, derivative data, 42, 52
  Gauss type, 33
    preassigned abscissas, 37
  interpolatory type, 27
  Lobatto, 40
  Newton–Cotes, 29
  open type, 32
  Radau, 39
Interpolation, higher dimensional, 135
  Lagrange, 13
Interpolatory-type rule, 27
  Cauchy principal value, 79
  infinite interval, 94
Iterated integral, 9, 133
Iterative integration, 162

Jacobian, 12, 128
Jacobi polynomials, 34

Lagrange interpolation, 13, 135
Laguerre, formula, 96
  polynomials, 34
Laplace transformation, 183, 187
Laws of large numbers, 143
Legendre, functions, second kind, 119
  polynomials, 34
Linear functional, 108
Lobatto formula, 33, 40, 61

Markoff formulas, 115
Mathematical tables, 3, 187, 202
Mean-value theorem, 5
  double integral, 9
Mechanical quadrature, 1
Mellin–Barnes integral, 186

Midpoint rule, 15, 33, 162
Modulus of continuity, 15
Moments, 10, 46
Monte Carlo method, 126, 142
Multiple integrals, 7, 125
  elementary, 126
  by sampling, 142
  transformation of, 12
Multistep method, 82

Newton–Cotes integration rules, 29, 164
  six-point rule, 30
Newton series, 94
Norm, 121
Numerical integration, 1
  appeal of, 3
  limitations of, 3

Open-type formulas, 32
Optimum rule of integration, 122
Orthogonality, 33
Orthonormal polynomials, 34, 44
  separation property, 47
Oscillatory integrands, 66, 99
  integration of, 59

Panels, 20
Peano's kernel, 109
Peano's theorem, 108
Periodic functions, integration of, 53
Poisson's formula, 57, 93
Polar coordinates, 13
Polynomials, 10
  fundamental, 13
  orthonormal, 34
Precision, 136
Primitive rules, 15, 91
Principal value, 7, 77–79
Proceeding to limit, 71, 90
Product rule, 130
  generalized, 133
Pseudorandom sequence, 143,148
P5, 196
$\mathcal{P}_n$, 10

Q-D algorithm, 48
QUAD, 199
Quadrature, approximate, 1

R[a, b], 10
Radau integration formula, 33, 39
Region, fully symmetric, 137
Remainder (see also Truncation error),
  compound rules, 26
  Filon's method, 64
  Gauss–Jacobi rules, 75
  Gauss rules, 36
  Laguerre and Hermite rules, 96
  Lobatto and Radau rules, 40
  Newton–Cotes rules, 30
  open-type rules, 32
  Riemann sums, 16, 129
  Simpson's rule, 19, 20
  trapezoidal rule, 17
RIEMAN, 197
Riemann, integral, 4, 7
  sums, 4, 6, 8, 15–18, 129
Romberg integration, 166
  singular integrands, 169
Roundoff error, 102
  fixed rule, 103
Rule, 1; see also Formula
  Boole's, 30
  compound, 20, 24, 141
  Gauss type, 33
  hypercube, 136–140
  midpoint, 15, 33, 162
  monomial, 135
  Newton–Cotes, 29, 30
  primitive, 15, 91
  product, 130, 133
  Simpson's, 19, 20
    three-eighths, 30
  trapezoidal, 15, 53
Runge–Kutta rules, 82

Saddle-point approximation, 184
Sampling, 142
Sequences
  equidistributed, 146, 150
  pseudorandom, 148
SIMP, 198
Simpson's rule, 19, 160, 164
  compound, 20
Simpson's three-eighths rule, 30
Singularity, 11
  elimination of, 72, 182
  ignoring the, 76

Speedup method, 99, 141
    oscillatory integrands, 66
Spherical coordinates, 13
Spline function, 112
Steffensen's formula, 32
Stirling's formula, 95
Stratified sampling, 148
SUM, 195

Three-point formula (open type), 32
Trapezoidal rule, 15, 53
    end correction, 53
Truncation error, 102
    Peano's theorem, 108

Truncation of interval, 72, 91
Tschebyscheff, coefficients, 86
    polynomials, 34, 84, 171
    second kind, 34
Two-point formula (open type), 32

Vandermonde matrix, 29
Variance, 144
    reduction, 146

Weight functions, 11
    Jacobi, 35
Weights, 1
    positive, 140